CAPTAIN COOK'S COMPUTER

THE LIFE OF WILLIAM WALES, F.R.S.

(1734-1798)

CAPTAIN COOK'S COMPUTER

THE LIFE OF WILLIAM WALES, F.R.S.

(1734-1798)

BY

WENDY WALES

© Wendy Wales, 2015

Published by Hame House

A CIP catalogue record for this book is available from the British Library.

ISBN 978-0-9933758-0-4

Book layout and cover design by Clare Brayshaw

Front Cover
Pastel portrait of William Wales by John Russell RA, 1794. Reproduced by kind permission of Christ's Hospital Foundation.

Book Cover back
Easter Island Statue, Author's own photo.

Prepared and printed by:

York Publishing Services Ltd
64 Hallfield Road
Layerthorpe
York YO31 7ZQ

Tel: 01904 431213

Website: www.yps-publishing.co.uk

For Paul

CONTENTS

FOREWORD

It is said that – A man is known by the company he keeps. If that saying is correct, then in the following pages you will come to know William Wales very well. Readers with a knowledge of the late 18th century will encounter many old friends, as figures from history step forth onto the pages of his biography. His life was so full of interest and adventure that it is worthy of several books, but the author has distilled down the essence of her extensive research to provide a feast of facts in this single volume.

If you have not come across William Wales before, then you are about to discover a many facetted character; a rare individual whose brain was equally at home whether composing mathematical puzzles or lines of verse. He was a writer whose pen accurately described the people and places that he encountered, from Hudson Bay in the North, to the frozen wastes of the Antarctic.

There are so many dimensions to this fascinating character that his biography will appeal to a wide range of readers. Through her meticulous research, the author has drawn together seemingly disparate threads to create a tapestry rich in historic narrative. No longer will historians be able to skip over Wales' humble beginnings, claiming that little is known of his early life. The author has now presented us with chapter and verse of his career, which he carefully crafted through his own diligence and hard work.

I know that this book is the culmination of many, many years of research by the author. I am pleased to say that the quality of this biography matches the achievements of William Wales. I am delighted to see the story finally in print – it has certainly been worth the wait.

Clifford E. Thornton

President

Captain Cook Society

INTRODUCTION

This biography is the result of research which was originally undertaken to satisfy the curiosity of both Jenny Elliston, who is the great-great-great-great grand-daughter of William Wales, and the writer. The information discovered, recorded, and shared as necessary with other researchers, has often been punctuated by requests to publish our findings as the biography of a fascinating character, whose life-story tells of the discovery, use, and teaching of science and mathematics during the 'Age of Enlightenment'.

One plea came from a lady who was writing a paper on the computers of the Nautical Almanac. She told that "William Wales was actually one of the better known computers and, compared to many others, there is much about him already in the public domain – but not nearly enough"

In the eighteenth century, computers were people who did calculations, laboriously working to produce tables which would assist astronomers, navigators, surveyors, and other scientists to do their work more quickly and efficiently. Britain being an island, it was essential that it should be able to trade overseas by means of efficient navigation, which was achieved by the practitioners of mathematics working in tandem with mathematical and navigational instrument makers.

The theory and practice of Mathematics was changing rapidly, and in England during the latter half of the seventeenth century Isaac Newton had produced his Laws of Motion, and published his *Principia*, also the Royal Observatory had been founded at Greenwich, and the Royal Society had been formed. Hatched from these events at the beginning of the eighteenth century was the Board of Longitude, which was set up to oversee a £20,000 prize offered by Parliament in 1714. William Wales was swept along in this surge of new learning, new thinking, and new working. When he was born the cartographers were struggling to imagine some of the land masses of the southern hemisphere, and they were marking these unknown territories *Terra Australis Incognita,* and *Terra Australis nondum Cognita.* By the time he was forty William Wales was not only visiting, but playing a leading role in putting these places firmly on the map, and on his return he spent the rest of his life educating, and calculating, and publishing, to ensure that our nation would have the skills to open the world to further exploration and trade.

As the personal life and career of William Wales unfolded, it became evident that his contemporaries from the area of his birth were also involved in like affairs in London. These facts were not I think purely by chance, it seems that there was a category of people with potential scientific and mathematical intellect from within the environs of Leeds and Wakefield in Yorkshire, which gradually drifted down to London to follow scientific careers, notably in astronomy, mathematics, and navigation.

The writer has relied heavily on the subject's own accounts, when describing his trip to Hudson's Bay and his voyage around the world with Captain James Cook. While reading these journals I have been fascinated by an author who was not only educated and knew his subject, but had that magical way of telling a good tale, and I have been constantly entertained by his phraseology in describing the various situations in which he found himself. This being the case, I must admit that to attempt to describe his work and travels from his writings into a different context was difficult, and I have often been tempted to abandon this work and merely leave the reader to the original Journals.

Of Wales' voyage with Captain Cook, I took a trip to Dusky Sound myself, and with me went the description of the place from his Journal. The entry into the Acheron Passage east of *Resolution Island* is a truly breathtaking experience, and for Wales to break into verse at this point can only be appreciated by one who has done the journey, it is fitting that the tall mountain on the island should now bear his name. A further bonus of this trip was to meet Jenny Elliston and her husband Viv at Melbourne, Australia, after researching together for some nine years it was good to meet the author of those many letters and e-mails.

I also had the Pacific experience, sailing to the islands of Easter, Tahiti and Cook, and was left with nothing but admiration for those early mariners. They tackled a vast ocean against all the odds, and were often isolated for days before encountering islands on which landing was often difficult, to face unknown indigenous people, fauna and flora. Easter Island remains one of the most remote inhabited places on earth.

To assist the reader, I have taken the liberty of changing some of Wales' original work to modern-day spelling, and Chapters 8, 9, and 10 are largely my attempt to condense his original prolific Journal written while on voyage with Captain James Cook, for this reason the endnotes within these chapters do not include references to his own journal. I hope this will encourage the reader to seek out the original version, which is largely contained in the second volume of J C Beaglehole's work on Cook's Journals, as *Appendix V*, and I have on purpose included Beaglehole's sub-headings in this biography.

On the vast subject of Cook's voyages, I have tried to write just of William Wales' role, that of his brother-in-law Charles Green, and enough I think to introduce the reader to the reason for a second voyage. Mindful that so much has been written already on Cook's voyages, I trust the reader will satisfy any further curiosity by referring to the many volumes available. It is I think pure co-incidence that Wales' worked so closely with the chronometers of John Harrison to help him to secure the Longitude prize, and that they both had roots springing so firmly from the same little village church in Yorkshire, far away from the London which shaped their eventual careers.

It is befitting that our subject should spend the latter part of his varied career instructing so many future sailors in his principal subjects of mathematics and navigation, at a time when the canal network was expanding. Our island nation so relied at that time on its maritime trade being supported by an efficient network of river and canal traffic.

To study a copy of the catalogue of William Wales' post mortem library sale was to discover a man of great learning, and with a great passion for books, for reading, for owning, and indeed writing them, a man who nonetheless kept his Yorkshire accent, and his Yorkshire sense of humour, as described by his pupils.

In conclusion, the last chapter is the author's attempt to instruct the reader on how the surviving family of our subject benefitted from his life, and how he laid a firm foundation for their future. The many dates of births, deaths and marriages in this chapter are not fully referenced, being taken from the many resources now open to us on the worldwide web.

Wendy Wales

ACKNOWLEDGEMENTS

My thanks are due first and foremost to Jenny Elliston, of Glen Waverley, Australia, who has remained a constant support during the research and writing of this work.

I am indebted to the Captain Cook Society members who have provided so much information and encouragement throughout the course of my task, noteably Bill Whelen of New Zealand, who has shared his prolific research into certainly the latter part of Wales' life, and also Cliff Thornton, Ian Boreham, Alwyn Peel, Margaret Morris, Brenda Paulding, Don Anderson and Ian Stubbs who have often added to my research, and helped me steer the right course for my writings.

My grateful thanks to Jan Shoulders, Rosemary Jackson Hunter and Patrick Wales-Smith, who not only supplied me with information which had been passed down through the family of William Wales' brother John, but also gave me their encouragement and support.

Other individuals to whom I owe my thanks and appreciation are James Holroyd of Chester, Dr Mary Croarken of Warwick University, Nigel Richardson of the Perse School, Cambridge, Richard H Wells of York University, John D Griffin of Rotherham, Yorkshire, Sir Patrick Moore of Selsey, Sussex, Ron Pullen and Eric S Whittle of Wakefield, Yorkshire, Dr Rosemary Arthur, of Wakefield Family History Society, John Collingwood of North Witham, Lincolnshire, K.E. Duffin, U.S.A., Jacqueline Cooper of Clavering, Essex, and René Vlug, of Culemborg, Holland.

Of the various London institutions which I have contacted and visited, I record my gratitude to the staff of the Guildhall Library, the Worshipful Company of Stationers and Newspaper Makers, the National Maritime Museum and the Royal Observatory, Christies, the National Portrait Gallery, the British Library, the Royal Society, and the Royal Archives at Windsor.

I thank the staff and pupils of Christ's Hospital School at Horsham in Sussex, who have not only offered information over the years, but were excellent hosts to myself and my husband Paul when we visited that establishment.

I must record my thanks to the Hudson's Bay Company of Canada, the Royal Astronomical Society of Canada, the Literary & Philosophical Society of Newcastle upon Tyne, and the Wakefield Family History Society, Yorkshire.

Finally, my thanks to Paul and our family for all their support.

ABBREVIATIONS

CH – Christ's Hospital

FRS – Fellow of the Royal Society

HBC – The Hudson's Bay Company

HEIC – Honourable East India Company

HM – His Majesty's

HMS – His Majesty's Ship

MRCS – Member of the Royal College of Surgeons

PRO – Public Record Office

RGO – Royal Greenwich Observatory

RMS – Royal Mathematical School in Christ's Hospital

LIST OF ILLUSTRATIONS on pages 277–284

10. William Wales' Teaching Chair, in the Museum, Christ's Hospital School, Horsham. Author's photo reproduced by kind permission of Christ's Hospital Foundation.

11. Portrait of William Arthur Trollope. Reproduced from a photograph by kind permission of Jenny Elliston.

12. Graveslab of John and Mary Wales, Kirkthorpe Churchyard, Yorkshire. Photo by Ron Pullan.

13. Sundial found at Fort Prince of Wales, Hudson's Bay , "Parks Canada – artefact number 2K1A10-14"

14. Memorial Plaque, Clavering Church, Essex, Photographed by Mrs Brenda Paulding.

15. Memorial Plaque at Christ's Hospital School, Horsham. Author's photo reproduced by kind permission of Christ's Hospital Foundation.

1

HUMBLE ORIGINS

"And one man in his time plays many parts..."[1]

Nostell Priory survives as one of those grand country houses of rural England, which rose from the ashes of the Dissolution of the Monasteries in 1540. The estate, at Wragby near Wakefield in Yorkshire, was eventually purchased by the Winn family in 1654. The family was already established in Lincolnshire, holding the estate and manor of Thornton Curtis, and the manor of Appleby just south of the Humber estuary. By the time the Winn family bought the Nostell estate, the old priory buildings had been converted into a dwelling house known as *Nostall Hall*.

The friars of Nostell had farmed the land and worked open-cast coal mines, so that the Priory stood in a landscape of chiefly farms and mine workings. At the end of the seventeenth century Nostell commanded a large staff, the estate carpenter and joiner was Henry Harrison who, as well as being responsible for the timber on the Winn's estate, also repaired the estate clocks. Henry and his wife lived at the neighbouring village of Foulby, and here in 1693 their eldest son John was born, he was baptized in the estate church at Wragby. John Harrison's formal education was meager, and he was never able to really express his ideas in writing, but working with his father, he inherited a love of working with clocks and wood which was to serve him well in his future life.[2]

Sir Edmund Winn of Nostell died in 1694, and was succeeded by Sir Roland, the third Baronet of Nostell. Sir Roland Winn began to build Thornton Hall at Thornton Curtis, on one of the Lincolnshire estates, the Hall was completed in 1700 and at this time Henry Harrison removed with his family from Foulby to Barrow-upon-Humber, near Thornton Curtis, and set up his own joinery business, taking an active part in the life of the church and the village. Young John Harrison worked alongside his father, and his interest in clocks grew, he started making them of wood – always in plentiful supply, if not grown locally then being imported from the Baltic, along the Humber estuary to Barrow.

The practical rural life of the Harrisons was seemingly a world away from that of the new sciences being forged in London, and yet from the dawn of Galileo and the work of Isaac Newton they now lived in a new mathematical age. Astrology had turned into the science of astronomy, and other sciences were taking the new mathematics on board. The world was changing, and nations were looking to push their boundaries to trade further abroad, but the maritime world did not have an accurate method of determining the longitude of a ship while at sea at the beginning of the eighteenth century, and navigation depended largely on the method of *dead reckoning*.[3]

In 1662 London the Royal Society had been founded, with the backing of the new monarch King Charles II. The Society's purpose was:

> To improve the knowledge of naturall things, and all useful Arts, manufactures, Mechanick practises, Engynes and Inventions by Experiments (not meddling with Divinity, Metaphysics, Moralls, Politicks, Grammar, Rhetorick, or Logick. In order to the compiling of a complete system of solid Philosopy

for explicating all Phenomena produced by Nature or Art, and recording a rationall account of the causes of things.[4]

By the efforts of Samuel Pepys the famous diarist, Charles II granted a charter in 1673 for a *Royal Mathematical School* within the Christ's Hospital School in Newgate Street, London, so that children could be educated in Mathematics for the practical purpose of navigation.

Two years later a new Observatory had been built at nearby Greenwich, its primary purpose was to help to solve the problems of navigation, and yet by the early 1700s despite the labours of many, the scientific world was still wrestling with the longitude problem. One solution which was first suggested way back in 1530 was by calculating the time difference between the ship at sea, and the time at the port of departure.

The problems of longitude came to the fore in October 1707 for the British Navy, after a disaster off the Isles of Scilly. Sir Cloudesley Shovell, Rear-Admiral of Great Britain, and Admiral Commander-in-Chief of the Fleet in the Mediterranean, was well qualified for his position when his fleet of ships was returning to Plymouth from Gibraltar, after conflict with the French forces during the War of Spanish Succession. Shovell had lots of experience sailing these waters, but for some reason this time he had difficulty confirming the fleet's position. The weather became hazy and stormy and gradually worsened as the ships headed north, and Admiral Shovell consulted with all the sailing masters of the ships of the fleet. Finally, thinking the fleet was further to the east than it was, Shovell ordered the ships to sail on up the channel, but despite being warned by lookouts from several of the ships who had spotted the lighthouse on St Agnes, the most southerly of the Isles of Scilly, the flagship *Association* struck the rocks of the *Gilstone Ledges,* and quickly sank. The ships *Romney* and *Eagle* also went down, with the loss of between 1600-2000 men – only the quartermaster of the *Romney* survived.

The loss of life shocked the whole world, Defoe recorded that:

> One can hardly mention the Bishop and his Clerks, as they are call'd, or the rocks of Scilly, without letting fall a tear to the memory of Sir Cloudesly Shovel, and all the gallant spirits that were with him at one blow, and without a moments warning dash'd into a state of immortality; the admiral with three men of war, and all their men (running upon these rocks, right afore the wind, and in a dark night) being lost there, and not a man sav'd. But all our annals and histories are full of this, so I need say no more.[5]

The body of Sir Cloudesley Shovell was washed up on the beach at Porth Hellick Cove on the largest of the Isles of Scilly, where a granite memorial was placed on the shore and he is still remembered with a degree of historic affection.

> "His body flung on the shoar and buried with others in the sands, but being soon taken up was plac'd under this monument"[6]

The Shovell incident had stunned the whole maritime world and petitions were made to the British Parliament, the need to find a solution became a matter of urgency. Mathematicians William Whiston and Humphrey Ditton came up with a possible solution in 1713, using shell fire and calculating the time gap between the flash and the sound from anchored ships along the main sea routes, but although this proved totally impractical it lead to consultations with Sir Isaac Newton, who mentioned the time-keeper theory as a solution.

The Astronomer Royal Dr Edmond Halley was called upon to guide the politicians through the problem, the solution of which would rely heavily on the complexities of astronomy and mathematics, Halley predicted that the method of lunar observation was the route to solving the problem.[7]

Parliament eventually passed the Longitude Act in 1714, it was defined as:

> Whereas it is well known by all that are acquainted with the Art of Navigation, That nothing is so much wanted and desired at Sea, as the Discovery of the Longitude, for the Safety and Quickness of Voyages, the Preservation of Ships and the Lives of Men:

> And whereas in the Judgment of Able Mathematicians and Navigators, several Methods have already been Discovered, true in Theory, though very Difficult in Practice, some of which (there is reason to expect) may be capable of Improvement, some already Discovered may be proposed to the Publick, and others may be Invented hereafter:

> And whereas such a Discovery would be of particular Advantage to the Trade of Great Britain, and very much for the Honour of this Kingdom;

> But besides the great Difficulty of the thing it self, partly want of some Publick Reward to be Settled as an Encouragement for so Useful and Beneficial a Work, and partly for want of Money for Trials and Experiments necessary thereunto, no such Inventions or Proposals, hitherto made, have been brought to Perfection;

> Be it therefore Enacted...

The above was the foundation for Parliament to draft a further Act for 'Providing a Publick Reward for such Person or Persons as shall Discover the Longitude at Sea',[8] which received the Royal Assent just twelve days before the death of Queen Anne. The Act appointed Commissioners for the Discovery of Longitude, and thus the *Board of Longitude* was established, with 22 members drawn from the elite of the worlds of science, politics, the navy and academia – the Astronomer Royal, the President of the Royal Society, the first lord of the Admiralty, the speaker of the House of Commons, members of Parliament, the first commissioner of the Navy and the Savilian, Lucasian, and Plumian professors of mathematics at Oxford and Cambridge Universities. The Board would offer incentives to persons who could find a way to accurately determine longitude while at sea, and they would act as adjudicators in this quest. They offered a reward of a maximum of £20,000 to the person who could determine longitude to an accuracy of half a degree, £15,000 to within two-thirds of a degree and £10,000 to within one degree. A degree represents 68 miles or 60 nautical miles, so not really accurate by today's standards, but in the 18th century such was the urgency to find a solution.

By 1720 word of the great *Longitude Prize* reached the attention of John Harrison, possibly via the local sea-going trade to Barrow on the Humber. John was confident that he could design and make a time piece which could be carried on board a vessel, and not be affected by changes in the earth's magnetic field, extremes of motion, humidity or temperature, so confident was he that he devoted virtually his whole life to this work, bravely taking on the might of the scientific world in his quest. He began work with his brother James to perfect the time pieces and produced two regulator clocks.[9]

To calculate longitude at sea it is necessary to refer to an accurate time-piece, set with the time at Greenwich or any other meridian line. Each 15 degrees of longitude corresponding to a difference in time of one hour, so comparing the local time, which is discovered when using the sun at its highest point to determine noon, with the time at a known meridian point, working from Greenwich time set at the zero meridian, it is thus possible to determine ones longitude.[10]

Two years after his father's death in 1730 John Harrison arranged to take drawings of his invention to London, where he had an appointment to see the then Astronomer Royal Dr Edmond Halley. This would have been a daunting journey for a humble country joiner, but it was a journey he had to make if he was to succeed in his quest for the Longitude prize. By now he had his own workshop in Barrow, and employed his younger brother James; he had family responsibilities, twice married, he had a young son John to his first wife,[11] his second son was born in May 1728. It was Halley who provided Harrison with the initial encouragement, and support to allow him to spend his life working on the production of an accurate time piece.

News of the Harrison family would no doubt still be mooted at Nostell, where one of John Harrison's long-case clocks still ticks away and has kept perfect time since it was made in 1717. The works are mostly of wood and it is claimed that one component made of mahogany is the earliest recorded use of mahogany in England.[12] In 1733 Nostell was in the hands of Sir Rowland Winn, 4th Baronet of Nostell, who had returned from the Grand Tour, married, and commissioned the building of a new house for himself and his wife to replace Nostall Hall. Sir Rowland had great plans for the estate, his architect moved into the village and work started on his grand design. Meanwhile on Christmas day in the estate church of Wragby in Nostell Park, where John Harrison had been christened forty years before, the wedding of John Wales and Sarah Cay was taking place.

The Wales family had lived on the banks of the old river Aire in Yorkshire for over a hundred years. John and his father John had been baptized at the parish church of Birkin, where the river wended its way from Leeds. The Leeds merchants had been pressing for a scheme to make the rivers Aire and Calder navigable, from the Ouse, past Birkin to Leeds, and on to Wakefield on the Calder.

Sarah Cay was probably of local stock, the parish registers of Wragby and Kirkthorpe list many entries of various spellings, Cay/Kay/Kaye/Key, making it difficult to pinpoint Sarah's origins.

Her age at death in 1786 was 88, so she would be born circa 1698.[13] One likely birthplace for Sarah Cay was Royston, near Barnsley, here a Sarah Kay was born in March 1697/8 the daughter of John Kay. Royston lies five miles south west of Wragby, where she had married.

John and Sarah were both in their mid 30s in 1733, and they settled at the village of Warmfield just three miles from Wragby. Warmfield was a small village in 1743, on the eastern bank of the river Calder which flowed from Wakefield three miles distant, its residents worked largely on the farms or worked the coal mines. The river had by this time been made navigable, as was the Aire, linking the textile towns of Wakefield and Leeds to the sea via the river Ouse, Humber, and the port of Hull.

William Wales was John and Sarah's first-born, he inherited the name of his great grandfather and was baptized at Kirkthorpe church on 1st March 1734/5.[14] Kirkthorpe is the parish church of Warmfield-cum-Heath and just across the field from the old river Calder. According to papers handed down through the family William was born on 19th June 1734,[15] and that William Wales was born prior to the end of December 1734

8

is further verified by the Board of Longitude's records.[16] In January 1736/7 another boy John was baptized and then a sister Sarah's baptism followed in February 1739/40.

The year of William Wales' birth coincided with the completion of John Harrison's first clock. Harrison had been advised by the Astronomer Royal Dr Halley to show his plans for a sea clock to George Graham, one of the leading London clockmakers, who had advised that Harrison return to Lincolnshire and construct the timepiece. Halley advanced him the sum of £200, which he foresaw Harrison would need in order to support his growing family during the five or so years the clock would take to build.[17]

Harrison's first longitude timepiece, which was to be designated 'H1', was a huge machine measuring almost 3 feet in height, width, and depth, it weighed 75 pounds. It was made from wood and brass, and housed in a glass cabinet. The clock featured brass balances with a ball at each end, these were pivoted by balancing springs and wires used as frictionless gearing, to enable the balances to move together equal and opposite, which would compensate for any instability caused by the motion of the sea.[18] Harrison had built a gridiron pendulum for his timepiece H1 to compensate for any change in temperature. When he took it to London to show members of the Royal Society they were impressed and endorsed its usefulness, and when shown to the Board of Admiralty they requested sea trials.[19]

Harrison boarded *HMS Centurion* bound for Lisbon in 1736, taking with him his timepiece H1, however the Captain of the vessel was ill, and unfortunately died on reaching Lisbon. This state of affairs meant that the crew had no time to record the data accurately, and so Harrison and his timepiece returned on *HMS Orford*. The master was Roger Wills and despite again little data being recorded, Wills was impressed when the clock proved him wrong on nearing land, so impressed that in 1737 he gave Harrison a certificate stating that his timekeeper had accurately given their position.[20]

The Board of Longitude held its first meeting soon after Wills had furnished Harrison with the certificate, and Harrison was able to show this document with his clock to the Board, who were impressed. Harrison, on the contrary, and being a perfectionist, begged leave to build a second clock in order to correct certain defects which he had found in the first, and so his request was approved and the Board agreed, advancing him funds to progress. When the resulting clock was completed some three years later however, it still did not satisfy Harrison, and the Board were treated to a repeat performance, agreeing to fund the building of a third clock, which was to occupy Harrison – now living in London, for the next twenty years.[21]

William Wales' father's occupation was, according to his sister Sarah's entry of baptism in the parish registers, a *banksman*.[22] This was a mining occupation, a banksman was in charge at the surface of a coalmine and controlled the access of men to the cage, or chair. Below the surface, the bottom-man was in charge, and the owners of the mine relied on these two to control the colliers. The banksman, or his assistant, collected tallies from the men as they prepared to go down into the mine, the tallies were often in the form of round discs made of brass. He would then see them safely lowered into the mine, and as the colliers returned he would hand the tallies back to them, so that it was always known how many men were working at a given time. This was quite a responsible job, and from the parish registers just eight men from the village can be identified as banksmen between the years 1738 and 1795.[23]

Sarah Wales, wife of the above had received a good education, for she served the village school as a teacher for 52 years.[24]

This was probably the charity school for 26 children which was recorded in the Archbishop's Visitations of 1743.[25] If it was that Sarah started teaching at the village school after her marriage, then she must have continued there until her death.

When William Wales was eight years old, there were about 120 families in Warmfield, all of the established church, all duly catechized, and made to attend the church. There was a resident curate, but the vicar William Ridley was not resident, due his dwelling house being in need of repair.[26]

We are treated to a snippet of information about William Wales' childhood, when in later life he wrote that, 'many times when he was a child he was threatened with being eaten, by a man who he was sure would have been sick had he carried it out'.[27] This was probably his father.

The children of Warmfield and Heath villages had plenty of opportunity for both education and further education in the middle of the 18th century, it is undoubted that William Wales would receive a good schooling from his mother in his early years, his eventual career suggests that he had shown early promise in the field of certainly mathematics and astronomy, and from later events it is apparent that William's brother John had also received a decent education.

As early as 1591 an education charity was endowed in the will of John Freeston, a noted Elizabethan barrister of Gray's Inn, who was born in the nearby village of Altofts. A grammar school was founded for thirty scholars from Normanton and Warmfield to attend Normanton School, so that any boys showing aptitude in Warmfield would attend Normanton, where the school stood east of the church on Snydale Road. In 1743 the pupils at Normanton were taught only to read and write.[28] In the church there stands the tomb of John Freeston, here is also a window commemorating the death in 1594 of a famous navigator, born far removed from the sea at the nearby village of Altofts.

Admiral Sir Martin Frobisher was a seaman of note, he had amongst other things explored the possibility of finding a North-West Passage to India and China, he was born at Altofts in 1539, but his father died when Martin was only three, and so he was sent at an early age to London to live with his maternal grandfather. Frobisher was eventually sent to sea by his grandfather, but he did not forget his roots, and returned to build Frobisher Hall at Altofts, and asked that his funeral should be solemnized at Normanton Church. He was a contemporary of Freeston, two heroes of the local schoolchildren who had brought their villages to national recognition, and become role models for the local children of the 18th century.

When Frobisher returned to Altofts, the rural idyll of his birth, he purchased the Manor of Warmfield-cum-Heath with the money he had received as a share of the wealth from his adventures. The villagers venerated him, they believed he had found the North-West Passage, discovered King Solomon's gold mines, and single-handedly defeated the Spanish Armada, in this peaceful corner of England with its insular existence the myths of Frobisher were handed down from father to son. There is no doubt that when William Wales was growing up in nearby Warmfield the story of Frobisher still had its place in the local 'Hall of Heroes'.[29]

Dame Mary Bolles of Heath Old Hall had left £21 per annum for the Master of Heath School to teach ten free scholars, and had additionally specified that fee-paying boys of the parish could attend for £2 per annum plus some food for the schoolmaster in the form of poultry, corn or perhaps a small pig. These scholars were also expected to perform chores, whereas boys from other parishes at the school paid £4 and were excused chores. The school was originally intended for boys, but by the mid 18th century it had become co-educational and the estate had been taken over by the Smyth family. The local squire, John Smyth of Heath Hall, paid to have the building extended to accommodate the schoolmaster, who in 1731 had charge of 22 free scholars.[30]

Old Heath Hall stood immediately above the river Calder, and here the stone schoolhouse still stands.[31] In the eighteenth century a small cottage was built onto the end of the school for the master.

The universities of England were too closely associated with the church to take on board practical subjects in the eighteenth century, and so gradually in this Age of Enlightenment there was a rise in the opening of dissenting academies. These academies were founded and staffed as private institutions, they were alternatives to universities where boys of 15 to 17 years of age went to be taught practical subjects, mathematics, navigation, the sciences and geography, Latin was still on the curriculum, but also modern languages, rather than the purely classical subjects of the universities. Eventually these academies became public institutions, and had closed by the end of the century.

In 1740 Joseph Randall opened an Academy at Heath near Warmfield, and ten years later wrote an account of it, describing both his boarding school and the village. This establishment was happily removed from the temptations which boys were exposed to in towns, and he boasts that over the past ten years not one of his pupils had died there.[32]

Heath was described by Randall:

> The village is much taken notice of, for its healthful air, and the delightful eminence of its situation.

The gentlemen's seats and the other houses, form a square, a side thereof may be near three hundred yards. In the centre of this square is a handsome bowling green belonging to the gentlemen of the village.

On the west of the town, at the distance of about two hundred yards, in a park, stands an ancient and stately hall. The seat of the Baronet.

Below this glides a serpentine river, which makes its way over a pleasant valley, border'd with gently rising hills. To this river the young people resort in the fine season to bathe, under the care of one of the masters; but at other times they are not allow'd to go thither.

In this valley, or rather on the descent of a hill, about a quarter of a mile from the village, stands the Parish Church, which is very near being adorned with some good paintings and handsome monuments. Through an opening in the village, appears a dry heath, about a quarter of a mile in length, something better than half in breadth: and below that is a common about three times the area of the Heath[33]

The pupils were allowed to walk one mile from the Academy, provided their walk didn't take them through any other village.[34]

The building was modern and spacious in 1750, and stood on the side of the village square in front of a wood. Some 80 yards away was another building which housed the language schools where the classics were taught by three masters, and 40 yards from there stood a large school of mathematics. Music, dancing and fencing were taught in yet another building near the Academy, which doubled as the dining room. In the Academy building was the Public Library housing up to fifteen hundred books, and apparatus including a large astronomical orrery, so huge it answered all the purpose of a planetarium, and more. It was in this building that public lectures were delivered and the pupils did experiments in astronomy and philosophy. The airy handsome sleeping chambers were in yet another detached building, where the young gentlemen slept two to a bed, with further private rooms available to those willing to pay more. There were also spaces provided in their houses by several residents of the village who were prepared to take in boarders.[35]

Heath Academy had space for a maximum of 170 pupils, these were aged up to 17 years, and were taught by 10 qualified masters and assistants, their aim was to fit boys for the worlds of business, for the army and navy as officers, for university, and to be gentlemen. The pupils came from foreign parts as well as England, Scotland, and Wales, and the fees for pupils taking mathematics and philosophy were two guineas per annum, with half a guinea entrance fee. Pupils bound for the Army and Navy did a course of Mathematics and Philosophy, which covered geometry, trigonometry, geography, astronomy with navigation, and natural philosophy. Fees were five guineas per annum with one guinea entrance, and these fees also were the cost of the Gentleman's course which included classics and French, as well as many of the sciences.[36]

The fees of the academy at Heath may not have been within the budget of John and Sarah Wales for their family. It nevertheless must have been a part of village life, and would not have escaped the notice of the village children of Heath and neighbouring Warmfield. The following two of Joseph Randall's books appeared in Wales' personal library in 1799:[37]

Randall's Arithmetical Class–fellow. 1766. The young gentleman's geometrical class-fellow: or Commercial youth's perpetual lecturer. Being an extensive course of useful geometry...With eight copper-plates. Being the second part of ...An introduction to the arts and sciences. London.

Randall's System of Geography, 1744. Randall, Joseph. Exhibiting the Climate, Division, ancient Geography, Trade &c. of each Empire, Kingdom and State in the known World: With the Manners and Customs of their Inhabitants. To which is prefixed, an introduction to the Mathematics, viz. to the Theory of the principles of Arithmetic, Algebra, Geometry, Plain Trigonometry, Projection of the Sphere, spherical Trigonometry, and Astronomy. London.

One candidate who may have taken a part in the education of William Wales was John Arden, who, shortly after his marriage in 1751, began teaching at Heath Academy where he remained until its closure in 1755.[38] On 4th October 1752 an entry in the Kirkthorpe parish registers records the christening of James Arden, son of John Arden of Heath, mathematician, and three years later in 1755 the christening of a daughter of Mr Arden. In the early 1770s John Arden lectured on experimental science at Beverley in Yorkshire, these were attended by Mary Wollstonecraft, and he tutored her along with his daughter Jane on how to argue philosophical problems.[39] His son James went to Cambridge in 1774, when John is described as of Heath, county of York, gent. By 1776 John had moved to Bath where he was a local teacher, he taught science and astronomy from his house in Bath, and he is listed as a member of the Bath Philosophical Society at its inauguration in 1777, when he is further described as a roving populariser of science, always ready to give his public lectures on scientific topics.

John Arden was a product of the new scientific age, and although not listed as going to Oxford or Cambridge

Universities himself, his obvious enthusiasm was infectious, and sparked the imagination of his audiences and pupils. In 1782 his daughters opened an *Academy of Female Education* in Bath.[40]

From the evidence it was apparent that Heath was a centre of important scientific learning in the mid 18th century, one pupil of its Academy had been George Gargrave, who opened a mathematical school of his own in Wakefield in 1754, the year before the Heath Academy closed.[41]

In 1756 Joseph Lindley was born at Heath,[42] his father was an architect, and Joseph who had shown a flair for mathematics was sent to a London banking firm, which had in turn sent him to the Astronomer Royal Nevil Maskelyne. In 1781 Joseph secured a post as Maskelyne's assistant which he held for over five years. Here he developed his interest in surveying, and eventually, together with William Crosley, worked on the map of Surrey which was used by the Ordnance Survey at their foundation in the 1790s. [43]

Endnotes

1   William Shakespeare, (1564-1616). *As you Like It.*

2   Hobden, H & M, 1988. *John Harrison and the Problem of Longitude.* Lincoln, The Cosmic Elk.

3   When a log was placed in the water with a rope attached, which had knots spaced every 50 feet. As the knots went overboard they were counted, and the number of knots per half minute, timed by a sand glass, determined the vessel's speed, so that if 7 knots went overboard in the half minute the ship's speed was seven nautical miles per hour, this speed and the compass direction were then used to plot the position of the ship.

4   Smith, E, 1911. *The Life of Sir Joseph Banks.* London, Bodley Head.

5   Defoe, D, 1928 *A Tour through England and Wales*. London, Dent.

6   The imposing monument over his final resting place in the South Choir Aisle, Westminster Abbey, London, amidst *lesser monuments to William Dalrymple, Robert Blake and Clive of India.*

7   Johnson, Peter, 1989. *The Board of Longitude 1714-1828*. Journal of the British Astronomical Association, Vol. 99, No.2. pp 63-69.

8   Royal Greenwich Observatory papers, Cambridge University Library: 14/1, f.11.

9   Whittle, Eric S, 1984. *The Inventor of the Marine Chronometer: John Harrison of Foulby*. Wakefield. Wakefield Historical Publications.

10 Johnson, Peter, 1989. *The Board of Longitude 1714-1828*. Journal of the British Astronomical Association, Vol. 99, No.2. pp 63-69.

11 Widely recorded as 'Elizabeth Barrel', however the original marriage entry as illustrated in *The Inventor of the Marine Chronometer John Harrison of Foulby* by Eric S Whittle, published in 1984 by Wakefield Historical Publications shows this to be either 'Elizabeth Barret' or 'Elizabeth Barnet'.

12 National Trust, 1955. *Nostell Priory, Yorkshire*. London, Country Life Ltd.

13 A search of the Warmfield baptisms 1695-1702 was carried out by Dr Rosemary Arthur, Wakefield Family History Society, at the Wakefield Archives.

14 "1734/5 William the Son of Jno. Wales of Warmfield March the 1st" *St Peter's Parish Church Warmfield (Kirkthorpe) Baptisms, Marriages & Burials 1730-1757,* Published by the Wakefield Family History Society 2004.

    This baptism was according to the old Julian calendar when the year ended on 24th March. From 1752 the Gregorian calendar was adopted, when the year end date was moved to 31st December.

15 Personal contact, Jan Shoulders.

16 Board of Longitude Papers RGO 4/324 *Diary of Nautical Almanac Work.* Image 43, p.21r. Records that William Wales' died on 29th December 1798 aged 64.

17 Whittle, Eric S, 1984. *The Inventor of the Marine Chronometer: John Harrison of Foulby.* Wakefield, Wakefield Historical Society.

18 Quill, H, 1976. *John Harrison.* London, The Antiquarian Horological Society.

19 Whittle, Eric S, 1984. *The Inventor of the Marine Chronometer: John Harrison of Foulby.* Wakefield, Wakefield Historical Society.

20 ibid.

21 Sobel, Dava, 1996. *Longitude.* London, Fourth Estate Ltd.

22 *St Peter's Parish Church Warmfield (Kirkthorpe) Baptisms, Marriages & Burials1730-1757,* Published by the Wakefield Family History Society 2004.

23 A Valuation of Warmfield-cum-Heath of 1748 does not list John Wales, meaning he was not a tenant of any land there.

24 Mrs Mary Wales Fenton. *Memoir of Mrs Abigail Manners.* (by her daughter). Methodist New Connexion Magazine, October 1848.

25 Archbishop Herrings Visitations, 1743.

26 ibid.

27 Thomas, N, & Berghof, O (Ed)., 2000. A Voyage Round the World. by George Forster. Honolulu. University of Hawaii Press. p.738.

28 Archbishop Herrings Visitations, 1743.

29 McFee, William, 1928. *Sir Martin Frobisher.* London, John Lane the Bodley Head Ltd.

30 Various authors, 2000. *The Times of Our Lives in Heath.* Heath Residents Association.

31 This building was restored in 1975.

32   Randall, Joseph, 1750. *An account of the Academy at Heath, near Wakefield.* London.

33   ibid.

34   ibid

35   ibid.

36   ibid.

37   *A Catalogue of the valuable Mathematical library of the late William Wales F.R.S.* 1799. Leigh and Sotheby. Copy in the Graves Collection, University College of London Library. Lot numbers 239 and 726.

38   Turner, Anthony John, 1977. *Science and music in eighteenth century Bath.* Bath, Catalogue of an exhibition in the Holburne of Menstrie Museum, Bath. University of Bath.

39   Todd, Janet (Ed), 2003. *The Collected Letters of Mary Wollstonecraft.* New York, Columbia University Press.

40   Sotiropoulos, Carol Strauss, 2007. *Early feminists and education debates: England, France, Germany 1760-1810.* Fairleigh Dickinson University Press.

41   Taylor, E G R, 1966. *The Mathematical Practitioners of Hanoverian England 1714-1840.* Cambridge, Cambridge University Press. p.177.

42   *St Peter's Parish Church Warmfield (Kirkthorpe) Baptisms, Marriages & Burials1730-1757,* Published by the Wakefield Family History Society 2004.

43   Harley, J B, 1966. *English County Map-making in the Early Years of the Ordnanace Survey: The Map of Surrey by Joseph Lindley and William Crosley* The Geographical Journal, Vol.132, No 3 (Sept. 1966) pp. 372-378. Royal Geographical Society, Blackwell Publishing.

2

LONDON

"Hide not your talents
They for use were made,
What's a sundial in the shade."[1]

William Wales had shown an aptitude for learning, and like many other boys seeking a career at this time, he headed south. To quote one of Captain Cook's biographers, Wales was

> ...of parents of humble circumstances and is said to have walked to London with a Mr Holroyd".[2]

The year of Wales' and Holroyd's departure south is not known, but later events indicate the decade prior to 1762, and perhaps it was as early as 1754[3] that he left his home at Warmfield behind, his parents, his brother John, and his sister Sarah.

Walking, as a form of transport, was the norm in the mid eighteenth century. The canals had not arrived, nor the railways, so that all those who could not afford to hire a horse, pay a carrier, or ride in a coach, just walked. It would have been no hardship to the able-bodied to walk the 180 miles from Warmfield to London, probably sleeping outdoors en-route.

A memoir of one eighteen year old who had walked to London in 1765 from Leeds, reveals that it had taken him 34 days, and he had done almost the whole distance on foot at the total expense of one shilling and ten pence.[4] He was fellow Yorkshireman and son of a tenant farmer, Mr Reuben Burrow, who was born in Hoberley near Shadwell, Leeds, and was 12 years William Wales' junior. As a boy he also had shown early mathematical ability, and early in his career he opened a mathematical school in Portsmouth, tutoring boys in mathematics and navigation.[5]

Wales and Holroyd would probably have used a copy of Ogilby's road map *Britannia* to plan their route to London. This work, published in 1675, was illustrated with strip maps of roads, and detailed places and landmarks along the way.[6] William Wales' considerable library included a copy of John Ogilby's maps.[7]

The 'Mr Holroyd' mentioned by Cook's biographer was George Holroyd, a plumber born in 1738, he was the son of John Holroyd, a clockmaker of Wakefield. George married Eleanor Avarell, and they had a son John[8] who was apprenticed to his father in 1786.[9] They became plumbers to the royal family, and in 1785 payment was due to Mr Holroyd, plumber, of Scotland Yard, for work carried out at Carlton House in the City of London for the Prince of Wales.[10] The house had been improved for the Prince after its purchase from Lady Burlington. The plumbing trade included glazing, roofing, cisterns, and lead weights, and plumbers were a vital cog in the wheel of rebuilding the city after the Great Fire, there was plenty of work in the 18th century for skilled tradesmen.

In 1598, John Stow's *Survey of London* describes Scotland Yard before the Metropolitan Police had their first headquarters there in the 19th century as:

...the large plot of ground enclosed with brick, called Scotland, where great buildings have been for the receipt of the kings of Scotland.[11]

The Royal Archives hold a copy of a deposition by John Holroyd of Great Scotland Yard, Plumber to His Majesty', concerning the assassination attempt on King George III by James Hadfield in May 1800 – Holroyd had been sitting next to Hadfield in the theatre when the attempt took place.[12] Firing a pistol at the King who was sitting in the royal box at Drury Lane theatre, Hadfield apparently had received a head injury while in the army and was diagnosed as being mad, after his trial he was confined in Bedlam for the rest of his life.

By 1825 the Holroyds had expanded to another generation, when the firm of 'Holroyd & Son, Scotland Yard, plumbers' appeared in Pigot's Directory. For the Holroyds the streets of London appeared to be 'paved with gold', they worked on some of the best properties in the City. There is a tablet to the memory of George Holroyd 1738-1789 and his wife Eleanor 1750-1837 at Reigate Church, Surrey.[13] But what of William Wales, and what did he do when he arrived?

In reality the streets of London in the mid 1700s were a far cry from gold-paved. So bad were conditions that the nobility and gentleman classes of society were transported through the streets by coaches, or sedan chairs which were carried at speed along the pavements by chair-men, the occupants would never dream of even stepping foot onto the pavements. For the lower classes it was a different matter – this was the London as depicted by those graphically illustrated William Hogarth prints of gin-crazed inhabitants, barking dogs, and screaming children, living in streets of filth and squalor.

In Britain life expectancy in 1751 was estimated to be around 36 years, for London however this was more like 25 years, and half of the children were dead before they reached the age of 10. The adolescents, who crowded into London from other parts of the country looking for jobs, were not immune to the London germs, and many of them fell by the wayside.[14]

John Harrison, his wife Elizabeth, and their two remaining children had moved from Leather Lane, Clerkenwell, to Red Lion Square in London in 1739.[15] The majority of London's clock and instrument makers had their workshops in the Holborn and Clerkenwell areas at this time, and Harrison became well known to them. Besides George Graham, there was John Jeffreys who made Harrison a pocket watch in 1753, this proved to be a prototype in time pieces, and included a bi-metal strip, a component which was an important step in achieving a suitable timepiece to solve the problem of longitude. Jeffreys died the year after completing Harrison's watch, and it was his apprentice Larcum Kendall who was left to collaborate with Harrison in the production of the latter's future masterpieces.[16]

The Royal Society showed their approval of John Harrison's work in 1749, by awarding him the prestigious *Copley Medal* for his great contribution to science. By 1757 he had completed his third time-piece (H3), and although it was smaller than his first two sea-clocks, he was still not happy with its size, and now had it in mind to aim for a pocket watch which could do the same job, this was an obvious progression, especially after he saw Jeffreys' work of his own pocket watch. The resulting watch was completed by Harrison in 1759[17], it measured five inches in diameter and weighed only three pounds – now Harrison was at last happy, satisfied with his creation.[18]

First evidence of William Wales in London was in 1760 when he ventured into publishing, and produced a leaflet entitled *Ode to the Right Hon. William Pitt*,[19] priced at one shilling.[20] This work was inscribed to Pitt the Elder, the first Earl

Chatham, and his achievements during the *Seven Years War*. It indicates Wales' allegiance to the Whigs, and is a patriotic assurance that under Pitt's new government Britannia would rule the waves, despite the recent loss of Minorca by Britain to the French in 1756.

Set in almost classical Greek style, the *Ode to Pitt* opens with a melancholy Britannia posing on a rock looking out to sea, and lamenting her loss of Minorca, and then her guardian angel descends, and predicts that Pitt's new administration would bring peace to her Empire. After this lengthy preamble Britannia is consoled, and the Spirit duly re-ascends, leaving her to reflect on recent glorious achievements, of Robert Clive in India, and of Amherst, Boscawen, and Wolfe in North America. The *Ode* concludes with a modest discourse to the King, advising how his new native savage subjects had gained from conquering new lands, and should be tamed and instructed in the Christian way.

In 1763 William Wales contributed to the *Ladies' Diary*, under a pseudonym, this was an unlikely title for a publication which nurtured so many of the promising young mathematicians of the day. Founded in 1704 this women's almanac was published annually by the Stationers Company and included the calendar, school terms, moons phases, and enigmas. It covered improvements in the arts and sciences, and contained scientific queries, and mathematical questions. After about 20 years the number of ladies attempting the mathematical problems diminished, the posers became more and more complex, and solving them rapidly turned into a battle of wits between the male mathematical fraternity. According to Charles Hutton, Wales often used pseudonyms when contributing to the Almanac, using *G*, *Celti*, *Felix McCarthy* and others.[21]

To understand the course of Wales' future life and career, it is necessary to return to his native Yorkshire, and to a village fifteen miles south of Warmfield in the Dearne valley. Wentworth lies four miles from Rotherham in South Yorkshire, and here is Wentworth Woodhouse, home and estate of the Fitzwilliam family. Nearby is a hamlet called the *Barrow*, where the almshouses, which also housed a charity school, built by Thomas Watson-Wentworth in 1716 are still extant.

Barrow was home to the Green family, here father Joshua was a considerable farmer, a butcher, and in the 1734 Poll Book is listed as a 'freeholder of the county'. When he died in 1749, Joshua's wife Ann was the sole executrix of his will which had been written in 1735.[22] The will lists four sons and one daughter, yet the couple had a further two daughters after the will was written, Elizabeth, and then Mary who was the youngest, and only 8 years old when her father died, the eldest son John was destined for a career in the church, and education.

John Green, born about 1718, was in 1743 a church warden at Thurnscoe, a village some three miles north of Wath-on-Dearne, and in the same year Joshua Green was churchwarden at Swinton. The Archbishop's Visitation at this time also notes that there was neither a curate nor a school of any kind at Thurnscoe.[23] In 1741 the Poll Book records that Joshua Green had Freehold lands at Swinton, but his abode was at Wentworth. In 1745 John Green was licenced as curate of Thurnscoe[24] and was publishing books on theology, and had started teaching around 1740.[25]

It was John Wesley who first sent John Green to London to assist in rectifying what had been an oversight of Methodists in London.[26]

John and Charles Wesley, together with George Whitfield joined a Moravian style society of some 56 members in 1738, and they met for prayer and confession each week at a room in Fetter Lane, London. Early in 1739 John Wesley acquired the lease of a former royal arsenal at Moorfields, which he named *The Foundry,* and started preaching there in November of that year. Earlier in that year George Whitfield was preaching in the open spaces of Lower Moorfields, encouraging also the Wesley brothers to this open air preaching.[27]

In 1740 John Wesley withdrew from the Fetter Lane Society, establishing his own at *The Foundry.* The year following George Whitfield erected a temporary wooden building which he called *The Tabernacle.*[28]

According to *The Free Church of England* magazine edited by Thomas E Thoresby of 1867:

> ...The Rev John Green, in the early part of life, was Curate of Thurnscoe in Yorkshire, which he relinquished, and engaged in connexion with the Rev John and Charles Wesley, for whom he preached several years at the Foundry[29], and other places. On separating from them about the year 1746, he published a vindication of his conduct entitled "An Appeal to the Oracles of God".

John Green's 1746 publication was a pamphlet attacking the doctrine of Christian perfection of the Wesleys, he became antinomian in his views, and according to Wesley, proved unreliable,[30] preferring to follow the Calvanistic persuasion of George Whitfield.

It is difficult to establish the exact date of John Green's career move to London in the 1740s. He had married Sarah Slack at Sheffield Cathedral in 1740,[31] and at that time he was the vicar at Great Houghton, Yorkshire. In 1744 their daughter Catherine was baptized, followed two years later by their son Joseph, both baptisms were at Darfield in Yorkshire, the birthplace of their mother. In each case their father's occupation is recorded as *schoolmaster* at nearby Great Houghton.[32]

John Green then opened a school at Dudley Court, in Hog Lane[33] near Denmark Street in London. The building had been a Chapel, originally belonging to the Huguenots, the French Protestant Refugees.[34] This Chapel was drawn in 1738 by William Hogarth, described as where 'the faithful are coming out of the French Chapel in Hog Lane' in his work entitled *Noon*, which is from his series *The Four Times of the Day*. Hog Lane is now incorporated into Charing Cross Road.

John Green's establishment was a Dissenting Academy, akin to the one at Heath in Yorkshire. John Green's father Joshua could afford to pay for his children's education, and he could have paid to have his eldest son John educated – perhaps at Heath Academy.

It was usual for such schools to produce cards, to notify the public of their services. One school in London advertised fees of thirty pounds per annum, they were a 'sort of finishing school' where, as well as teaching Latin and book-keeping, navigation was taught to prepare boys for the sea. Boarding schools were for the children of the richer class above the tradesmen, those who assembled in coffee houses rather than taverns.[35]

Rev John Green's services were advertised on such a card, [36] and it revealed that he employed 'Proper' teaching Assistants. (see Illustration No 2)

At the end of Denmark Street stood the church of St Giles-in-the-Fields, which had recently been built. It stood on Holborn, which curved southwards by St Giles and then northwards to meet the newly formed Oxford Street, from this junction the turnpiked Tottenham Court Road went northwards. Along this road in 1756, George Whitfield built a second tabernacle, and John Green was a minister there, the chapel stood just up the road from Denmark Street.

John Wesley was the head of Methodism, and eventually he and Whitfield parted company. Wesley was a supporter of Arminianism, while Whitfield supported the Calvinistic Methodists. John Calvin, born in the 16th century, was a French protestant, and his beliefs lay in the reality of heaven and hell, and that people were destined for either salvation or damnation – one or the other. In 1769 Whitfield went to America, where he preached to huge crowds in the open air.

On the death of George Whitfield in 1770, John Wesley preached at the Tottenham Tabernacle, and in 1774 a plaque was placed here commemorating the death of Rev John Green. Wesley's base in London was at 32 Fetter Lane, and one of Rev John Green's publications is described as printed for the author, and sold at his Academy in Denmark-Street, and at his Chapel in Fetter-Lane in 1770. This was the Moravian Chapel, at Neville's Court in Fetter Lane, one of the earliest nonconformist meeting houses in London, which had been re-built after the Great Fire of 1666.[37]

There was a strong link with William Wales and the Green family. John's youngest brother was Charles Green, who was educated by his brother John, and who later took him on as an assistant teacher. Charles had gained a significant knowledge of astronomy,[38] and in 1760 at the age of 25, he became assistant to the Astronomer Royal James Bradley, at the Royal Observatory, Greenwich.[39]

That William Wales was a teacher at John Green's Academy is a distinct possibility, according to E.G.R. Taylor Wales was a teacher of practical mathematics in London as a young man.[40]

A contemporary of William Wales was Charles Hutton, they became great friends, their lives had followed much the same course, and we are treated to a peep into Wales' early life when Hutton wrote of him in 1815:

> ...by his natural talents and close application, rose from a low situation little connected with learning, to some of the first ranks in literary pursuits. We observe his early labours in the correspondence of the Ladies' Diary, that very useful little work, which has formed most of our eminent mathematicians. Here, and in some other periodical publications, for many years is observed the gradual improvement of Mr Wales in the various mathematical sciences...[41]

Members of the Green family were no strangers to London, the second eldest son Joshua, born 1720, had been working for Charles Brandling at Middleton, near Leeds in Yorkshire. Brandling had succeeded to the coal mine there, and working to improve transport from the mine into Leeds, sought permission to construct a wooden waggon-way, along which horses could pull coal wagons to a staithe on the river Aire at Leeds. It was Joshua Green who had travelled to London to put a private bill before Parliament for *An Act for Establishing Agreements made between Charles Brandling Esquire, and other Persons, Proprietors of Lands, for laying down a Waggon-Way, in order for the better supplying the town and Neighbourhood of Leeds, in the County of York, with Coals.* The bill had received the Royal Assent in June 1758.[42]

Endnotes

1   Benjamin Franklin (1706-1790).

2   Beaglehole, J C (Ed) 1955. *The Journals of Captain James Cook* Vol II, p 885.

3   Personal communication, Dr Mary Croarken.

4   *The Mechanics' Magazine, Museum Register, Journal and Gazette.* July 6th – Dec 28th 1850. Edited by J C Robertson, Vol 53. Pub London. Robertson & Co. Iron: An illustrated weekly journal for iron and steel manufacturers metallurgists, mine proprietors, engineers, shipbuilders, scientists, capitalists. Knight & Lacey.

5   Danson, E, 2005. *Weighing the World.* Oxford, Oxford University Press.

6   See *Appendix I.*

7   *A catalogue of the valuable Mathematical library of the late William Wales F.R.S.* 1799. Leigh and Sotheby. Copy in the Graves Collection, University College of London Library.

8   Personal communication, James Holroyd.

9   Webb, Cliff. 2000. *The Plumbers Company Book of London Apprentices 1571-1800.* London, Society of Genealogists.

10 Royal Archives, Windsor. Ref RA GEO/34987.

11 Bush, A, 1950. *Portrait of London.* London, Frederick Muller Ltd.

12 Royal Archives, Windsor. Ref RA GEO/9626.

13 Personal communication, James Holroyd.

14 Pickard, L, 2000. *Dr Johnson's London.* London, Phoenix Press.

15 Hobden, H & M, 1988. *John Harrison and the Problem of Longitude.* Lincoln, The Cosmic Elk.

16 Bonhams Catalogue, 20004. *Fine Watches and Wristwatches.* London.

17 Harrison watch, H4.

18 Sobel, Dava, 1996. *Longitude.* London, Fourth Estate Ltd.

19 Wales, William, 1760. *An ode, in two parts, humbly inscribed to the Rt Hon W Pitt.* London. Copy in the Cambridge University Library Rare Books room. http://copac.ac.uk

20 Watt,R, 1824. *Bibliotheca Britannica.* Edinburgh, Constable.

21 Hutton, Charles, 1815. *A Philosophical and mathematical Dictionary containing memoirs of the lives and writings of the most eminent authors.* London

22 Borthwick Institute of Historical Research, York. Probate records, Prerogative Court of York

23 Archbishop Herrings visitation records 1743.

24 Borthwick Institute, University of York. Inst. AB 13 (Act Book). Thomas Herring, York. Stipend £30.

25 Green, J, 1759. *A Short Grammar, or Rudiments, of the Latin Tongue by a Clergyman (J Green) who hath taught Grammar for twenty years past.* London.

26 The Works of John Wesley: Vol XXVI, Letters II. 1740-1755, Volume II. p.501 (footnote)

27 Website of the Wesley Historical Society: http://wesleyhistoricalsociety.org.uk.

28 ibid.

29 The Old Foundary School, near Moorfields, London.

30 The Works of John Wesley: Vol XXVI, Letters II. 1740-1755, Volume II. p.501 (footnote)

31 International Genealogical Index.

32 Parish Registers of Darfield, Yorkshire.

33 An ancient medieval thoroughfare, later renamed Crown Street, and then it became West Street before being incorporated into Charing Cross Road.

34 Wilson, W., 2001. *History and Antiquities of the Dissenting Churches.* Vol 4. The Baptist Standard Bearer, Inc.

35 Pickard, L, 2000. *Dr Johnson's London.* London, Phoenix Press.

36 British Library: Engraved Prospectus enclosed within Green, J.,1759. *A Short Grammar, or Rudiments of the Latin Tongue.*

By a Clergyman (J Green) who hath taught Grammar for twenty years past. London. British Library copy has 'C Burney' handwritten inside, probably Charles Burney (1757-1821) who kept a private school at Hammersmith, then Greenwich, brother of Frances Burney the diarist, and James Burney who sailed with Captain Cook.

37 Baker, T M M, 2000. *London, Rebuilding the City after the Great Fire.* London, Butler & Tanner Ltd.

38 Kippis,A, 1788. *The life of Captain James Cook.* London. pp176-8.

39 Information given by William Wales to Andrew Kippis, author of *The Life of Captain James Cook* published in London in 1788. footnote pp 176-178.

40 Taylor, E G R, 1966. *The Mathematical Practitioners of Hanoverian England 1714-1840.* Cambridge, Cambridge University Press. p.48.

41 Hutton, Charles, 1815. *A Philosophical and mathematical Dictionary containing memoirs of the lives and writings of the most eminent authors.* London.

42 Bushell, J, 1975. *The World's Oldest Railway.* Sheffield, Turntable Publications.

3

GREENWICH

"I saw Eternity the other night,
Like a great ring of pure and endless light,
All calm, as it was bright;
And round beneath it, Time in hours, days, years
Driv'n by the spheres
Like a vast shadow moved; in which all the world
And all her train were hurl'd."[1]

One of the methods which was thought could solve the
problem of calculating the longitude while at sea in the
mid eighteenth century, was known as the *Lunar Distance
Method*. This involved measuring the angle between the
moon and a particular star, and working out the resulting
longitude by referring to tables which could be made available
in almanacs. This had been first mooted in 1514, but the
problem in those days was that the available instruments
for measuring the angle were not very accurate, and it was
not until the eighteenth century that the development of the
sextant, quadrant, and octant by John Hadley produced more
accurate measurements. Despite the availability of better
instruments, it was still necessary to calculate local time by
observing the star's altitude above the horizon, and then
allowances had to be made for the observer's height above
sea level, and the angle of the moon's light entering the
atmosphere. The observer also needed to find the time at a
set meridian line in order to compare it with the local time,

all the resulting figures were then used for the calculation of longitude. It was so easy to make small errors by the *Lunar Distance Method*.

Precise angle measurements called for accurate lunar tables, and tables were being calculated by Tobias Mayer, a German astronomer and mathematician, employed in Nuremberg on the establishment of accurate coordinates for maps. His calculations were based on equations by Leonard Euler, and his work had given him an interest in mapping the moon, as well as producing accurate lunar tables. In 1754 Mayer submitted his work to the Board of Longitude, with a view that it would provide a solution to the longitude problem, and would thus qualify for its prize.[2]

One strong advocate of the *Lunar Distance Method* was Reverend Nevil Maskelyne who, although he had taken holy orders, was passionately interested in astronomy and his ultimate aim was to become an astronomer. In the eighteenth century ordination was a sort of 'inevitability', and was looked upon as a basic security on which to build a future career, the subject of which may have had nothing to do with the church. While a student, a Cambridge wrangler,[3] Maskelyne's hero was the third Astronomer Royal James Bradley, with whom he collaborated on the longitude problem. Bradley strongly supported the lunar distance theory, and worked laboriously on Mayer's tables in order to verify them, it is said he completed 1200 sets of calculations from observations taken at Greenwich between the years 1755 and 1760. Subsequently Maskelyne gained a position on an expedition to test Mayer's work, and to observe the transit of Venus in 1761.

Throughout the history of astronomy the *astronomical unit*, the basic distance from the Earth to the Sun, had been an enigma, yet it was crucial to the calculation of the actual distance of all the planets to the Sun, rather than just the ratio which had been determined. Edmond Halley had advised that to record the time taken for the planet Venus to appear to cross the surface of the sun from different parts of the Earth, would provide the information to enable the true distance to be calculated accurately. Halley knew that he would not witness the next transits during his lifetime, they occurred twice in every 112 years, and with just eight years between the two it had been calculated that the next transits would occur in 1761 and 1769. Halley was born in 1656 and advised that it was crucial to prepare for these two events in advance.[4]

Maskelyne sailed to St Helena in 1761, this was a significant year in astronomical observations, and many were sent out to different locations to observe the transit of Venus on 6th June. If observations failed then the transit in 1769 would be made all the more urgent, the next chance would not occur until 1874. Maskelyne stayed at St Helena, he had missed the end of the transit because of cloud cover, but he was also busy with experiments on gravity and astronomical observations, and on testing Mayer's tables, which proved to be most accurate and useful in determining longitude at sea, he determined the precise longitude of St Helena for the first time.

In 1762 Bradley died, also Mayer had passed away, and so it was Maskelyne who eventually published Mayer's tables as his own in his book *The British Mariner's Guide* in 1763. The next Astronomer Royal was Nathaniel Bliss who was in poor health when appointed, he died in 1764 after only two years in office. It was Nevil Maskelyne who was appointed the next Astronomer Royal, taking office in 1765.

Mayer was recognized for his work eventually – albeit posthumously, his tables were revised by Charles Mason, and published by order of the Commissioners of Longitude. In 1765 Mayer's widow received £3,000 from the Board of Longitude.

During Charles Green's career at the Observatory he assisted two consecutive Astronomers Royal, from 1760 Green was appointed assistant to Dr James Bradley, replacing Charles Mason, who left after being elected as an overseas observer of the forthcoming transit of Venus. In 1761 Green and Bradley observed the transit at Greenwich. On Bradley's death in 1762 Nathaniel Bliss became Astronomer Royal, and because of his poor health, during the following year most of the observing work at Greenwich fell to Charles Green.[5]

John Harrison's fourth timepiece[6] meanwhile was taken for its trials to Jamaica by his son William, his father being 68 years old by this time. Accompanying William Harrison was a representative of the Board of Longitude, who was able to confirm that the clock lost just five seconds after 81 days at sea. The chronometer's performance should have meant certain success at last for John Harrison, and the longitude prize was surely his – but there were members within the Board who were sceptical, and further trials were called for. Meanwhile Maskelyne continued to defend his lunar distance method of finding longitude.[7]

In August 1763 the Board of Longitude asked Maskelyne and Charles Green to go to Barbados, with Maskelyne officiating as ship's chaplain, and Green as purser, aboard the *Princess Louisa*. Their work there was to establish the longitude of Barbados, by comparing their observations of the eclipses of Jupiter's satellites there with comparable observations in England, this would assess the accuracy of John Harrison's fourth timekeeper,[8] a temporary assistant was appointed for Bliss during Green's absence. John Harrison's son William joined them with the timekeeper at Barbados in May 1764, and the necessary observations were carried out. Charles Green and William Harrison then travelled back together, leaving Maskelyne in Barbados to carry out further observations.

While in Barbados William Harrison had made it known that he did not agree with the Board of Longitude's decision to send Maskelyne to trial his father's timepiece, as Maskelyne was himself one of the contenders for the Longitude Prize with his 'lunar distance method'.

Green and Harrison reached London in July 1764, and Harrison was proud to report that his father's fourth timepiece[9] had performed with great accuracy. Green returned to his work at Greenwich, and when his master Bliss died on 2nd September that year, Charles Green was again in charge of the Royal Observatory, this important role would no doubt put heavy responsibility on Green's shoulders, a role which he held until eventually Nevil Maskelyne was appointed the next Astronomer Royal. Green's observations were completed on 9th March 1765, and Maskelyne officially commenced his post on 16th March 1765, when he appointed Joseph Dymond as his first assistant, on taking up residence.[10]

When Dymond joined Maskelyne from Lady Day on 25th March, Green left. It is recorded that Green and Maskelyne had disagreed at Barbados, and afterwards had not been on friendly terms.[11] Joseph Dymond was another Yorkshireman, born in 1746 at the village of Brierley, mid-way between Wentworth, the birthplace of Green, and Warmfield, the birthplace of Wales. Brierley is five miles from Thurnscoe, where John Green was the curate and also by this time a teacher. It is possible that Joseph Dymond was a pupil of John Green's London school, and had thus been taught by Charles Green – or even William Wales. Such was the concentration of mathematical and astronomical talent evident from that corner of Yorkshire.

James Bradley must have decided that the lodgings of the Astronomer Royal, and his assistant, were becoming somewhat cramped, and while in office he prompted the Board of Ordnance to build some new Observatory buildings, these were attached to the original building which was known as *Flamsteed House.* The new buildings included a transit room, assistant's sitting and calculating room with attached library – containing books sufficient only for his computations, and immediately above, the assistant's bedroom, complete with alarm to ensure his observations were carried out at the proper time. Here the assistant lead a lonely existence governed by the clock, his meticulous observations were made only to be followed by hours of tedious computations. His pay, as set by Charles II in 1675, was £26 per annum, and was not changed until 1765, when Maskelyne complained that he could not keep assistants due to their pay being so low. In 1765 the assistant's pay was raised to £86, net of tax of £10, his food and lodgings were free.

When Thomas Evans was Maskelyne's assistant from 1796 to 1798, he described the gloomy picture of his position. He likened his existence to a poor mouse which would creep from a hole in the wall to feed on crumbs, and be excluded from all society, spending lonely months working tediously on wearisome computations, and observing the heavens – frequently during the night – with only the owls hidden in the trees of Greenwich Park below for company.[12]

Candidates for the job of assistant were recommended to Maskelyne by friends and colleagues, during his 46 years in office he had 24 assistants.[13] They had to be able to write and understand Arithmetic, Geometry, Algebra, Plane and Spherical Trigonometry, and Logarithms. They had to be physically fit, in order to spend several hours per day laboriously observing and calculating, and it was advantageous if they had knowledge of astronomy and mechanics. They had to be sober and willing to give unreserved application to their work, to be able to stand the confinement of a hermit-like existence, and preferably be aged between 20 and 40 years of age.[14]

The trials of Harrison's H4 had been read to the Board of Longitude in the January of 1765, and although these proved Harrison was now well qualified for the Longitude Prize, the Board only approved that he receive half of the £20,000. They now insisted that John Harrison was to explain the workings of his timepiece to them, and he duly did this to their satisfaction.[15]

Meanwhile, the Board of Longitude took on as a practical expert Larcum Kendall, a notable clockmaker of London, who had been apprenticed to John Jeffreys, clockmaker, in 1735.[16] Other members of the Board at this time were Rev William Ludlam, Fellow of St John's College, Cambridge; Rev John Mitchell, Woodwardian Professor of Geology; Thomas Mudge and William Mathews, watchmakers of Fleet Street, London; John Bird, an instrument maker of the Strand, as well as Nevil Maskelyne. In August 1765 it was the members of this team who eventually signed a certificate declaring all details were to their satisfaction, on being shown the construction of Harrison's H4 timepiece.[17]

Back in Yorkshire in 1764, John, the brother of William Wales, had married Mary Eccles of Wakefield, both signed the entry in the parish register, indicating that each had received an education.[18] They were to produce three daughters and just one son – Mary born 1765, John born 1766, Sarah born 1768, and Abigail in 1769. Sarah's baptism entry gives her father's occupation as a *weaver*.

During the eighteenth century the West Riding of Yorkshire's output from the woollen cloth trade, of which weaving was just part of the process, grew eight-fold. Leeds was the heart of this local industry, and here the 1770's exports amounted to about one-third of the total for the whole country of this commodity.[19]

In Greenwich the following year John Wales' brother William was to experience a huge turning point in his career. From 13th June 1765 William was employed by Nevil Maskelyne – not as assistant to the Astronomer Royal – but to help compute Maskelyne's new *Nautical Almanac*, Wales comments many years later on this event, that Maskelyne was:

> ...a person to whom I owe very much indeed; one who took me by the hand when I was friendless, and never forsook me when I had occasion for his help...[20]

It seems an extraordinary reflection by Wales to describe himself as 'friendless', considering that less than 3 months later, on 5th September 1765, he married Mary Green, the youngest of the Green siblings, and sister to Charles. The wedding took place at St Alphege's Church, Greenwich by licence, which in those days could cost as much as 7s 6d, against 1s 6d for a marriage by banns – marriage by licence was considered a status symbol in those days. Mary's eldest brother Rev John Green officiated, and although a Methodist minister, he was still allowed to perform marriages in Greenwich church. Methodism began in 1738 as a movement to revitalize the Church of England, and did not officially break with the Church until 1795. Rev John had the degree of A.B. at this time (Bachelor of Arts), he is not listed in the Oxford nor Cambridge Alumni, and it is not clear where he obtained his degree. Reuben Burrow described him as John Green, A.M (Master of Arts), yet his Academy publicity document as Rev J Green, L.M. – the roots of which are uncertain. The marriage entry in the registers describe William Wales as a *gentleman*, witnesses at the marriage where John Naylor and Joseph Slack[21] – the latter almost certainly an elder brother of Sarah, wife of Rev John Green.[22]

St Alphege's church had been newly built fifty years earlier, after a second church on the site collapsed, it was here the first Astronomer Royal, John Flamsteed, had worshipped for over forty years up to 1719. There was no money to fund the large task of rebuilding then, as many of the residents were seamen or their widows, many were widowed due to the loss of Sir Cloudesley Shovell's fleet in 1707, and Parliament had to fund the new building which was of a bold classical design.[23] William and Mary Wales, both residents of Greenwich, would no doubt appreciate the beauty of this fine, new, English Baroque church.

After leaving the Observatory Charles Green was employed by a group of gentlemen, who had developed a system designed to supply London with sweet and wholesome water, from the River Coln, below Uxbridge, via a proposed canal, to Marylebone.[24] London had been experiencing many water supply problems in the 18th century, there were some bitterly cold winters, and open reservoirs froze, which caused real hardship.[25] Green carried out a survey, but concluded that the fall would be insufficient to be viable, the gentlemen had also received objections from owners of mills along the river, and the scheme was abandoned.[26] The proposed scheme was mentioned by Defoe in his *Tour* when he remarked that "the likely proposal of this work was equalled by the genius of the gentlemen who mooted it".[27]

John Green was a prolific author, and had published many works on religious and educational topics. He and William Wales had both been working on a dictionary of arts and sciences at this time, *Miscellanea Scientifica Curiosa* was published in London in 1766, by Periodical Publications. Reuben Burrow, had an excessive hatred of the pair, indeed he had many enemies through his attitude of intolerance to anyone who didn't agree with him, such was his insecurity.[28] Burrow wrote on the fly-leaf of his own copy:

Miscellanea Scientific Curiosa Or a Balderdash Miscellany of damn'd Stupid Raggamuffin Methodistical Nonsense and Stuability. By two of the most stupid and most dirty of all possible Fools Rogues and Scoundrels, viz: John Green A.M. Late Tubthumper and Soul driver in Hell and William Wales, _brusher at Christ's Hospital, not only the dirtiest Scoundrel that God ever made, but The dirtiest rascal that he Possibly could make. Amen."

and a further editorial note, also by Burrow:

This pimping, affected, dull, pert, contemptible, vile, fulsome, nauseous, villainous Note, the reading of which is enough to make a person spew their liver up, and to give the devil a vomit; was written by William Wales.[29]

The above indicates that John Green was a co-editor of the *Miscellanea Scientifica Curiosa,* according to Burrow he eventually attained the degree of Master of Arts, however it appears that Charles Green also had a hand in a similar work[30] when Wales wrote that Charles Green:

.....was engaged for a time, in concert with Doctor Scott the present Rector of Simonburn, Mr Falconer, the author of the Shipwreck, and some other persons in writing a dictionary of arts and sciences, but he did not continue his assistance through more than half the work...[31]

The Rev James Scott, also a Yorkshireman and born in Leeds, was resident in London from 1764.[32] Scott had written *Odes on Several Subjects* in 1761, the year after Wales published his *Ode to William Pitt*, this was also the year in which William Falconer the poet wrote *The Shipwreck,* and then went on to write a *Universal Dictionary Marine, or, a Copious Explanation of the Technical Terms and Phrases employed in the Construction...of a Ship* which was published in 1769.

All the above publications are evidence of the 'Grub Street' culture, which as James Boswell noted, was the name of a London street where book-sellers and writers of small histories, dictionaries and temporary poems dwelt.[33] In the eighteenth century this was Milton Street, in Moorfields, but in the nineteenth century became an epithet for Fleet Street.

By the mid eighteenth century periodicals appeared – the *Spectator, Tatler,* and *Gentleman's Magazine,* monthly and annual publications increasingly incorporated mathematical and scientific information. Between 1749 and 1753 there appeared Holliday's *Miscellana Curiosa Mathematica,* and in 1761 *Mathematical Magazine* was published by Thomas Moss and George Witchell. *Ladies' Diary* had appeared as early as 1704, between 1752 and 1760 the editor was Thomas Sompson. and then the *Gentleman's Diary* – or the *Mathematical Repository,* was founded in 1708.[34]

On the recommendation of the Board of Longitude, Charles Green was appointed a purser in the navy aboard the frigate *Aurora,* as a reward for his work in accompanying Maskelyne to Barbados for the chronometer trials.[35] The *Aurora* had been launched at Chatham Dockyard in 1766, Falconer's definition of a purser is:

> ...an officer appointed by the lords of the admiralty, to take charge of the provisions of a ship of war, and to see that they are carefully distributed to the officers and crew, according to the instructions which he has received from the commissioners of the navy for that purpose.

Charles Green vacated his post on *Aurora* in 1768, and his successor was William Falconer. On the 13th January 1769 *Aurora* sailed from the Cape of Good Hope to India, on board was Falconer, and three supervisors for the East India Company. *HMS Aurora* was never seen again, nor any of the crew, she had presumably been lost somewhere in the Indian Ocean by storm, or fire.

There is a strong possibility that William Wales had been in contact with the Green family for some years prior to his employment at Greenwich, certainly it was Charles Green who introduced him to Maskelyne,[36] and such was his destiny that, in 1765, he found himself married to Green's sister and in the employ of the Astronomer Royal, little knowing what was to follow.

Endnotes

1   Henry Vaughan, (1622-1695). *The World.*

2   Johnson, Peter, 1989. *The Board of Longitude 1714-1828.* Journal of the British Astronomical Association, Vol. 99, No.2. pp 63-69.

3   A Cambridge student who has completed the third year of the mathematical tripos with first-class honours.

4   Ronan, Colin A, 1967. *Their Majesties' Astronomers.* London, The Bodley Head.

5   Kippis, A, 1788. *The Life of Captain James Cook.* London. pp 176-178. (Is information given by William Wales F.R.S. on his brother-in-law Charles Green to A Kippis for this work).

6   Known as H4.

7   Sobel, Dava, 1996. *Longitude.* London, Fourth Estate Ltd.

8   Howse, D, 1989. *Nevil Maskelyne – the seaman's astronomer.* Cambridge University Press.

9   Known as H4.

10 Howse, D, 1989. *Nevil Maskelyne – the seaman's astronomer.*

Cambridge University Press.

11   Kippis, A, 1788. *The Life of Captain James Cook*. London. pp 176-178. (Is information given by William Wales F.R.S. on his Brother-in-Law Charles Green to A Kippis for this work).

12   Croarken, Mary *Astronomical Labourers: Maskelyne's Assistants at the Royal Observatory, Greenwich 1765-1811.* (2003) Royal Society.

13   ibid.

14   N Maskelyne, *Memorandum Books*. Wiltshire Record Office.

15   Whittle, Eric S, 1984. *The Inventor of the Marine hronometer: John Harrison of Foulby*. Wakefield, Wakefield Historical Society.

16   *Duties paid for Appricntice's Indentures*. The National Archives, Kew, Surrey.

17   Bonhams Catalogue, 2004. *Fine Watches and Wristwatches*. London.

18   Parish Records of All Saints, Wakefield, Marriage Registers.

19   Burt, S & Grady, K, 1987. *The Merchants' Golden Age. Leeds 1700-1790*. Leeds.

20   Wales, W (Ed), 1777. *The Original Astronomical Observations, Made in the Course of a Voyage Towards the South Pole, and Round the World, in His Majesty's Ships the Resolution and Adventure, in the Years MDCCLXXII, MDCCLXXIII, MDCCLXXIV, AND MDCCLXXV, by William Wales and Mr. William Bayly.* J Nourse, J Mount & T Page.

21   Parish Registers of St Alfege, Greenwich.

22   Parish registers of Darfield, Yorkshire.

23   Howard, John Philpot, *The Parish Church of St Alfege, Greenwich*. A Guide Book.

24   Kippis,A, 1788. *The life of Captain James Cook*. London. pp 176-8.

25   Pickard, L, 2000. *Dr Johnson's London*. London, Phoenix Press.

26   Kippis,A, 1788. *The life of Captain James Cook*. London. pp

176-8.

27   Defoe, D, 1928. *A Tour through England and Wales*. London, Dent. Vol I.

28   Danson, E, 2005. *Weighing the World*. Oxford, Oxford University Press.

29   A de Morgan. *Notes & Queries* Vol 12 (304) Aug 25 1855, p 143.

30   Scott, James, 1765-66. *A General Dictionary of Arts and Sciences: or a complete system of literature ... Poetry ... and Theology by James Scott...the mathematical branches by Mr Charles Green...Naval Affairs by William Falconer. ... Botany ... and Gardening by Mr James Meader ... And the other branches of literature by a society of Gentlemen*. London, Crowder.

31   Kippis,A, 1788. *The life of Captain James Cook*. London. pp 176-8.

The work *A Dictionary of Arts and Sciences* was published in 1766 by Crowder, it was a 3 volume work, edited by Rev J. Scott, Trinity College, Cambridge, Charles Green of the Royal Observatory, Greenwich, Mr James Meader, and William Falconer.

32   Matthew, H C G & Harrison, B, (Eds), 2004. *Oxford Dictionary of National Biography*. Oxford, Oxford University Press.

33   Boswell, James, 1930. *Life of Samuel Johnson*. London, G Bell & Sons Ltd.

34   Honeybone, M, 1998. *The communication of science by popular books 1700-60*. Open University.

35   Beaglehole, J C, 1974. *The Life of Captain James Cook*. London. A & C Black.

36   Croarken, Dr M. *Providing Longitude for all: the eighteenth century computers of the Nautical Almanac*. (Sept 2002) Journal of Maritime Research.

4

THE COMPUTER

"To apply himself with the utmost care and diligence to the rectifying of the tables of the motions of the heavens, and the places of the fixed stars, so as to find out the so much-desired longitude of places for the perfecting of the art of navigation ..." [1]

When Nevil Maskelyne became the fifth Astronomer Royal he was a bachelor, and was to remain so until in 1784, when he married at the age of 52. One of his brothers was Capt Edmund Maskelyne of the East India Company, who had been widowed in 1762. His sister Margaret had married Robert, Baron Clive of Plassey, who had left for India in 1764 to become Governor of Bengal, taking with him his brother-in-law Edmund as ADC.[2]

The next year Nevil Maskelyne moved into Flamsteed House at the Greenwich Observatory with his manservant and a housekeeper, while his assistant, Joseph Dymond, moved into rooms in the new Observatory across the courtyard.[3]

One of Maskelyne's first tasks as the new Astronomer Royal was to attend a meeting of the Board of Longitude. At this meeting awards were recommended for John Harrison, and Maskelyne was also on the agenda – here he first set down his proposals to publish a *Nautical Almanac with Astronomical Ephemeris* annually, together with his accompanying *Tables Requisite to be used with the Astronomical and Nautical*

Ephemeris, to be published occasionally. This *Almanac* was to become his most important contribution to both astronomy, and more significant at this time, navigation, – particularly to simplify determination of longitude while at sea.

Harrison's work was not the practical solution for all mariners at this time. Chronometers were costly to produce, and Maskelyne's tables would provide a faster method of calculating longitude by the lunar distance method. The *Tables Requisite* contained calculations which did not change year on year, so that although they were necessary for use with the *Nautical Almanac*, their publication was not required on a strictly annual basis. In 1767, when the first edition was published, 10,000 copies were printed.

The Board of Longitude accepted Maskelyne's proposal, and by May 1765 Parliament had approved the Board's publishing of the Almanac which would be funded by the Admiralty. Nevil Maskelyne was to be the editor, he had just one assistant to help him at the Royal Observatory at any one time, however work on the Almanac tables was to command a whole army of computers – starting with forty individuals.[4]

In July the Board considered a *marine-table*, which had been invented by George Witchell for the finding of longitude while at sea by the lunar method, and he was awarded one thousand pounds for further advancement of his invention. The Board also appointed computers Israel Lyons junior, William Wales of Greenwich, and Mr Mapson, to work on a nautical ephemeris, also Richard Dunthorne, who would compare the calculations and prepare them for publication.[5]

In August the Ipswich Journal announced:[6]

The Right Hon. the commissioners of Longitude have been pleased to appoint Mr. George Witchell, of Fleet Street; Mr Israel Lyons, jun. of Cambridge; Mr William Wales, of Greenwich; and Mr Mapson, Computers of a Nautical Ephemeris, for the Use of Navigation and Astronomy; and Mr. Richard Dunthorne of Cambridge, to compare and correct the Press for the same. At the same time Mr. George Witchell undertook to compute a Table for correcting the Effect of Refraction and Parallax in the Moon's Distance for a Star, and to furnish 1000 copies of the same for 1000 l.

In 1766 Maskelyne wrote in a letter to his brother Edmund, telling him that:

........The board of longitude have engaged persons to compute a very complete nautical & astronomical ephemeris which will come out next Septr. for the year 1767 : and be continued annually. There will be 12 pages in every month. All the lunar calculations for finding the longitude at sea by that method will be ready performed: & other useful & new tables added to facilitate the whole calculation; so that the sailors will have little more to do than to observe carefully the moon's distance from the sun or a proper star; which are also set down in the ephemeris, in order to find their longitudes .....[7]

Maskelyne had previously worked tables for his 1763 publication *British Mariner's Guide,* when he claimed accuracy of 1°, saving the user a calculation time of four hours,[8] and experience for this led him to devising the system for accurately computing the *Nautical Almanac.* For the *Almanac* he needed tables of lunar distances for each three hours of Greenwich time, and kept the method as simple as possible, incorporating checking systems to ensure absolute accuracy – which was imperative – any error, however minor, could result in the miscalculation of a ship's position, and cause major disaster at sea.

A sort of 'cottage industry' was established, with the most important calculations worked by two human 'computers' working independently from home. Accuracy was of prime importance, and at a certain stage in the calculations, which had been determined by Maskelyne, the resulting tables were to be posted to the 'comparer', who would check one against the other, to find any errors before the computers were allowed to move onto the next stage of calculation. When a discrepancy was found it was the job of the comparer to determine whose calculations were wrong.

The system of computing was such, that the comparer was able to pinpoint any charlatan computers. On one occasion computers Keech and Robbins were found to be guilty of copying figures from each other, resulting in instant dismissal, they were further asked to reimburse the Board for the resulting extra work they had created for the comparer.

On 13th June 1765 the first four computers were employed, Israel Lyons the younger and George Witchell were to work on the calculations for January to June 1767, while William Wales and John Mapson were to calculate the latter half of 1767.[9] Their pay was £70 for each twelve month's calculations, to be paid by instalments as progress proved satisfactory. They were each given the necessary books and tables to assist their work, which was tedious and involved spending hours on repetitive calculations and, often by necessity, aided by just candlelight.

Israel Lyons was the son of a Cambridge watchmaker, he was a self-taught mathematician who also had botanical skills. He had been prevented from going to Cambridge University because of his Jewish roots, but despite this he lectured at Oxford to Joseph Banks, after Banks had demanded to be taught botany and there was no one there to lecture in the subject. Lyons remained a friend of Banks throughout the rest of his life, and in 1773 went as astronomer towards the North Pole on Capt Phipps' expedition. Lyons died in 1775 at the early age of 36, after a remarkable career.[10]

George Witchell, had been publisher of the *Mathematical Magazine*. His work as one of Maskelyne's computers was followed by his headmastership of Portsmouth Academy, he was elected a Fellow of the Royal Society, and throughout his life had close association with William Wales who, along with Witchell's son, was appointed Executor of his will.

Of Wales' fellow-computer Mapson not much is known, but the pair apparently worked well and with good progress to such an extent, that when Witchell and Lyons failed to keep up with their calculating schedule for the first half of 1767, it was Wales and Mapson who were put to work on the calculations for the same period, to ensure they were finished on time.

The first comparer employed to check the calculations was Richard Dunthorne, he had published work on the lunar method of calculation to which Mayer had referred when working on his own tables. Dunthorne was from Cambridge, and his duties included overseeing the work of the computers and ensuring they worked to the accepted procedure and accuracy. He chose the stars from which the moon's distance was calculated, and was to gather all information of astronomical phenomena, tables, and explanations, for inclusion in the eventual *Nautical Almanac*.

The *Almanac* was to be divided into four sections, its structure as created by Maskelyne was to be:

The Preface – Giving the reasons for publishing the work and describing sources of data used.

Astronomical Data including a Key to symbols used and predicted eclipses for the year.

The Astronomical ephemeredes – Monthly for the year

Each month given in 12 pages as under:

Pg 1	Calendar of Holy days, notable dates, Oxford and Cambridge terms, moon phases and dates of various astronomical phenomena.
Pg 2	Sun's position data and means for converting apparent time to mean time for each day of the month.
Pg 3	Data on the sun's motion and a table of the eclipses of Jupiter's moons
Pg 4	Latitude and longitude of the planets.
Pgs 5 -7	Tables of the moon's place for noon and midnight for every day.
Pgs 8-11	Predicted lunar distance from the sun and stars for each day at 3 hourly intervals.
Pg 12	Chart of the positions of Jupiter's moons.

Explanation – What the tables contained, how they were to be used, and often with examples of calculation.[11]

Maskelyne had established the meridian at Greenwich, and had to keep changing the sources of data used by the computers as theoretical astronomy advanced, yet the clear and concise layout above remained basically unchanged for the remainder of his life-time. Eventually he had blank tables printed for the computers to complete with their own calculations, and once compared and found to be accurate, the neatest of the two sets was used by the printers when typesetting the *Almanac.*

William Wales and his three colleagues were supplied with explanatory notes, setting out precise instructions of the methods of computing, and tables with which to execute the work – solar tables, lunar tables, and logarithm tables accurate to 7 figures. In June 1765 the computers started work, with Wales and Mapson calculating for the latter half of 1767.

One of Maskelyne's official duties as Astronomer Royal was to supervise the testing of Harrison's H4 timepiece. John Harrison had complained to the Board of Longitude by letter in April 1766 that his timepiece H4 was being ignored at the Admiralty, and that he needed it himself as an aid when working on his timepieces. However the Board decided that they needed it at Greenwich for trials, and that Larcum Kendall be commissioned to make a copy of it. H4 was taken by barge to Greenwich and carried up to the Royal Observatory, Harrison's first three clocks were also handed over by him at his home in Red Lion Street, London, for transportation to the Observatory. The trials lasted nearly ten months until March 1767, the resulting report from Maskelyne was not good for Harrison, but in fact Maskelyne had made a mistake in the calculations, and eventually the Board of Longitude paid Kendall to make the duplicate of H4, thereby approving it.[12]

The first *Nautical Almanac and Astronomical Ephemeris* for 1767 appeared by January 1767, when one thousand copies were distributed around the United Kingdom, North America and Europe, at a cost of two shillings and sixpence each.[13] This publication cut the calculation time for navigators drastically from four hours to half an hour, and meant the seaways were now opened to more efficient trade. The next edition of the Almanac for 1768 was published later in 1767, assuring the Board of Longitude that Maskelyne's system was working well.

Authorization was then given for Maskelyne to enable the *Almanac* to be published up to three years ahead of time, so that copies were available to be used on long voyages, this had moved to up to five years ahead by the 1783 edition. The extra work load called for extra computers and comparers, and eventually computers were working from towns and villages all over England. Clergymen, schoolmasters, astronomers amongst them, all worked at different speeds, but their accuracy was always policed by the all-important comparers.

During his work on *the Nautical Almanac* as a computer William Wales completed calculations for 43 months, variously from the first 1767 publication to the 1797 almanac, and for the 1778 work he was employed as comparer for two of the month's calculations. The *Nautical Almanac* has been published every year since, and is currently produced by HM Stationery Office.

It is interesting to note that qualified teachers in London and Portsmouth were paid one guinea for each ship's master they trained in the use of the *Almanac*, a task which Wales' future career would no doubt encompass, adding to quite a lucrative income.

William's brother John Wales, and wife Mary, had celebrated the birth of their son John in the August of 1766 at Warmfield, and their daughter Mary the year before. It was sometime during the year to September 1767 that William and Mary's first child was born, a daughter who they named Sarah, no doubt after her paternal grandmother. The living expenses per annum for this time, for a gentleman with a wife and child in London, would have been about £250.[14]

William Wales and his family eventually moved to Fleet Street in London. The river Fleet had been covered in 1765 and the area paved, it had previously been 'stinking and noisome' according to one report, and Defoe had noticed its neglect, the warehouses on either side were unused, and the wharfs decayed. Fleet Street now buzzed with activity, there were buildings devoted to exhibitions of waxworks, freaks, and monstrosities, it was renowned for its taverns and its coffee houses, many booksellers and publishers had their businesses here, two trades which in the 18th century functioned as one. The street was thick with pedlars selling their wares, the noise of street criers, entertainers, and horses pulling metal wheels along cobblestones, a continuous hurly-burly.

The coffee houses had appeared in the mid seventeenth century, tea was being imported, brought by the Dutch East India Company ships, and coffee also, in small quantities. In this Age of Enlightenment coffee houses provided a sober alternative to the squalor of taverns, they became places to meet and discuss specific subjects, when science lectures were held in some of the houses they became known as *Penny Universities*. These establishments supplied publications which were laid on the tables for the benefit of their clients, people wrote articles in them, and had mail delivered to them, tea was sold in small amounts over their counters.

This was the London of Samuel Johnson, who had lived just off Fleet Street and where his famous dictionary had been completed. In 1759 he went to live in Inner Temple Lane to the south of Fleet Street. Boswell wrote that one evening in 1763 he and Johnson were walking in Greenwich Park when Johnson had remarked that this was very fine, but Boswell had then replied "Yes, Sir: but not equal to Fleet Street." to which Johnson had agreed – they both appreciated the hustle and bustle provided there, by busy individuals about their business.[15]

Many scribblers and pamphleteers eked out a living around Fleet Street at this time, among them was a young lad by the name of Samuel Hearne, who had just left the Royal Navy at the age of eighteen. Hearne's father had been managing engineer of the London Bridge Waterworks, but died when his son was just three years old, on leaving school at the age of eleven Samuel had joined the Navy and was servant to Captain Samuel Hood. In 1763 Hearne left the Navy and was seeking employment in London, it was this year that London experienced a very cold winter, the Thames froze, and the waterworks at London Bridge, which his father had been responsible for all those years ago, ceased working due to the severe frost. Unfortunately Hearne's literary skills weren't sufficient to exist among the coffee house clientele of booksellers, scholars, wits, and newspapermen, however it was in one of the coffee houses in 1766 that he learned of a position vacant with the Hudson's Bay Company in Canada, and applying, he secured the post at Prince of Wales Fort on the Bay.[16]

Meanwhile William Wales carried on his work as computer for Maskelyne, and in between continued setting posers for others to solve. Just like the *Ladies' Diary,* the *Gentleman's Magazine* of February 1768 was to include mathematical questions, in it there appeared:

A Society of gentlemen desire room in your Magazine for a monthly mathematical correspondence, they beg leave to premise that it will be necessary to have two months between the time of publishing the questions and the answers to them, in order to give their country friends an opportunity to consider them; they have therefore sent five questions to be inserted in your Magazine for February to which answers are requested on or before the 7th Day of April. The other five questions inclosed, are desired to be inserted in March, and the answers to them are requested to be sent on or before the 7th of May. In the mean time, such gentlemen as shall be pleased to favour the society with their correspondence, may depend on having their letters properly attended to, by directing them (post paid) to the Editor of the Gentleman's Magazine.

This Society of gentlemen included W Wales of Fleet Street, and the others who submitted the first five questions were Mr S Ogle of Rotherhithe, Mr R Mayo of London, Mr W Crakelt of the Charter-House, and Mr C Hutton of Newcastle.

W Crakelt was a classical scholar; he became master of Northfleet grammar school, he was ordained, and edited works on grammar and mathematics,[17] his career almost paralleled that of Rev John Green. Charles Hutton from Newcastle, had started his career in the coal pit, he was self educated and opened a mathematical school in 1760, he became a Doctor of philosophy, and was one of Maskelyne's *Almanac* comparers, he became professor at Woolwich Royal Military Academy and also edited the *Ladies' Diary* from 1773-1818. Hutton was a great friend of both Maskelyne and Wales.[18]

Of Stephen Ogle and Richard Mayo nothing is known, other than that the former was a mathematician. Certainly after the first five questions were published their authors were very soon joined by many others, not all based on astronomy, as were those submitted by William Wales.

Years later another member of the *Mathematical Group,* Isaac Dalby, wrote that they had a sort of club or society, frequently of the convivial kind, which met once a fortnight. The company was not always confined to mathematicians, but also included singers and poets. Certainly Dr Hutton was a member, as was Nevil Maskelyne, George Witchell, and John Bonnycastle, also John Landen who was Earl Fitzwilliam's agent attended, at least once a year.[19]

It was in June 1766 that the Royal Society started to consider preparations for the next occurrence of the transit of Venus three years hence, this was to be an extensive global effort, and there were decisions to be made, sites to be chosen around the world, and observers to appoint who could be trusted to take accurate readings and report back on their observations. At Greenwich Nevil Maskelyne was kept busy, he was a member of the Board of Longitude, and as Astronomer Royal he was responsible for preparing the scientific schemes of various voyages of exploration, he assessed Longitude proposals, and John Harrison's fourth timekeeper H4 was moved from the Admiralty to the Royal Observatory, so that he could personally test it daily for a period of ten months. His first assistant Joseph Dymond had stayed just 20 months, to be replaced by William Bayly in November 1766.

It was also in the November of 1766 that a special committee of seven, headed by Nevil Maskelyne, was set up by the Royal Society. Its task was to decide on the most suitable locations around the world for British expeditions to be sent to observe the forthcoming transit of Venus in June 1769. The success of these observations was vital, after the 1761 results had been rendered unsatisfactory, three sites were decided upon, and to each would be dispatched two observers. The Royal Society was however in no way able to afford to fund this work, resulting in a memo being dispatched to the King, in brief this laid down:

- That the passage of the planet Venus over the disc of the Sun, which will happen on 3rd June in the year 1769, is a phenomenon that must, if the same be accurately observed in proper places, contribute greatly to the improvement of Astronomy, on which Navigation so much depends.

- That several of the Great Powers in Europe, particularly the French, Spaniards, Danes and Swedes, are making the proper dispositions for the Observation thereof: and the Empress of Russia (Catherine the Great) has given directions for having the same observed in many different places of her extensive Dominions....

- That the like appearance after the 3rd of June 1769 will not happen for more than 100 years.

- That the British nation has been justly celebrated in the learned world for their knowledge of astronomy, in which they are inferior to no nation upon earth, ancient or modern; and it would cast dishonour upon them should they neglect to have correct observations made of this important phenomenon ....

- That the expense of having the observations properly made... would amount to about £4,000, exclusive of the expense of the ship.[20]

The request was approved, and the Committee's plans could go ahead. The three places chosen from which the observations would be made were North Cape, Hudson's Bay, and the Pacific Ocean.

In London the winter weather had been exceedingly cold during the 1760s, in January 1768 there had been severe frosts and deep snow. Charles Green, who had preceded Joseph Dymond as assistant at the Royal Observatory, returned from sea and married Elizabeth Long at the church of St Botolph Without, Aldersgate, London, at the beginning of March

1768.[21] In June 1768 the Board of Longitude paid Green £50, this was for his work at the Greenwich Observatory between the death of the Astronomer Royal Nathaniel Bliss in 1764 and Maskelyne's appointment the following year, the money was also for work done in conjunction with Dr Bradley.[22]

Meanwhile, there was a meeting of the full Council of the Royal Society at Crane Court on 5th May, which included Nevil Maskelyne among others. Charles Green had been summoned by the Council, and sat awaiting interview after the meeting, here he met James Cook, a fellow Yorkshireman and sailor, who had also been summoned. After interview Green was chosen as a candidate to go to the Pacific Ocean to observe the Transit of Venus. Maskelyne had previously suggested Alexander Dalrymple also be considered as co-observer. Dalrymple had distinguished himself as a skilled navigator in the East Indies, and had a passion for exploration and discovery, however when offered the post he accepted it only on condition that he would have full management of the ship chosen, and be given the rank of Captain. When told of this the Admiralty positively refused his request, despite Dalrymple's protests. So it was decided that James Cook be offered the post instead, with Charles Green.[23]

James Cook had greatly impressed the Secretary of the Admiralty Philip Stephens, by his recent survey work in Canada and Newfoundland, from where he had returned late in 1767. This was supported by Sir Hugh Palliser, who was governor and commander in chief at Newfoundland from 1762-6, and had directed the survey of its coasts.

Cook was called into the meeting, and it was agreed that he be appointed to the command of the vessel destined for the South Seas, and that he was a fit person to be one of the transit observers. Green accepted and agreed his allowance of £120 a year for victualling himself and the other observer, with a gratuity of 200 guineas for the voyage, and 100 guineas per year after two years should the voyage last that long.[24]

The Committee chose Jeremiah Dixon and William Bayly to go as observers to North Cape. Jeremiah Dixon was a surveyor from Cockfield in County Durham, and he was an amateur astronomer who had been chosen to go with Mason and Maskelyne to St Helena to observe the transit of Venus in 1761– Mason and Dixon were later engaged by the Crown to resolve a border dispute in America, resulting in the *Mason Dixon line.*

William Bayly was Maskelyne's assistant at the Royal Observatory, and on his departure to North Cape his position was temporarily filled by Rev Malachy Hitchins, who was working for Maskelyne already as *Nautical Almanac* comparer. The two observers Bayly and Dixon left in April 1769, having set off together, they split before reaching North Cape in Norway, just in case of cloud at North Cape. Dixon went to Hamerfast Island, while Bayly went on to North Cape 60 miles away, his eventual report describes his arrival:

> ...got the observatory and dwelling house built, and instruments on shore, set up transit instrument...etc[25]

The accommodation for each observer is described in a letter to Dr James Lind of Edinburgh, (who did not join the expedition), as a wooden observatory which had a moveable roof, large enough to house one observer, and a wooden dwelling hut of twelve square feet. The observer to be accompanied by five or six men from the ship.[26]

This left a voyage to Hudson's Bay at *Rupert's Land,* in what is now known as Canada, to arrange. The Royal Society had gone to some length to elect candidates from the famous astronomers of Oxford and Cambridge, but this had not proved fruitful. They not only refused to suffer the hardships of voyages to remote corners of the globe, but knowing of the inaccuracy of timepieces available, they did not wish to show themselves as incapable observers of such an important event. So after much deliberation, and despite indicating that he wished to be sent to somewhere with a warm climate, it was William Wales whom the Committee eventually persuaded to be prime observer at Prince of Wales Fort on the Churchill River in Hudson's Bay, and then only after the Royal Society had agreed to provide financial security to his family, should he suffer injury during the journey.[27]

Wales' assistant was to be Joseph Dymond, who had been Maskelyne's first assistant as Astronomer Royal. Dymond had left this post in November 1766 after only 20 months, being replaced by William Bayly. It is uncertain in what capacity Dymond was employed during the period from leaving Maskelyne's employ and starting out for Hudson's Bay eighteen months later, but it has been recorded that Maskelyne seized the chance to get rid of Dymond by nominating him to go to Hudson's Bay, as he was not a likeable person, and according to the factor at Fort Prince of Wales, Dymond was a 'difficult and unpleasant person.[28]

In order to observe the transit of Venus at Hudson's Bay in June 1769, Wales and Dymond would have to over-winter there and depart from London in 1768, this was due to pack ice which limited the shipping season to just two months of the year. The actual observing of the transit on the 3rd June 1769 took a mere 6 hours and 22 minutes, the time the two spent there in order to do the observation was 13 months.[29] The terms agreed for the Hudson's Bay work were, Wales £300 per annum and expenses, and Dymond would receive £250 per annum and expenses.[30]

The Hudson's Bay Company's Prince of Wales Fort at Churchill was to be the base for the scientist and his assistant during their stay. This was essentially a fur trading company, which had been founded some eight years after the establishment of the Royal Society. The HBC's head office was in London, and the two foundations had a mutual interest in both exploration and science, four of the adventures were Fellows of the Royal Society when the HBC received its charter. This being the case, it seems that William Wales and Joseph Dymond were to be the first scientists to over winter at Churchill.

On 7th August 1768, James Cook and Charles Green took a coach from London to Deal, from where they rowed out to join *Endeavour*. Charles Green was assigned his own cabin and, on discharging the pilot, they set sail for Plymouth, from where Cook was planning to depart on the voyage later that month. Bayly and Dixon were due to depart for Norway the following April.

During May of 1768 at Warmfield the brother of William Wales, John, and his wife Mary, had their third child, another girl whom they named Sarah, in her baptism record John is described as a *weaver*.[31]

When William Wales received instructions to prepare to sail for Hudson's Bay, his wife Mary, like her sister-in-law, was due to give birth to a second child, and with William due to depart on 29th May there were plans to be made. He arranged for his wife Mary, and possibly their daughter Sarah also, to travel to Yorkshire by coach.

It could be that Mary's sister, Elizabeth Taylor (née Green), also accompanied her to Yorkshire. Elizabeth also gave birth about this time to a son, William, at Greenwich.[32] Elizabeth had married Jonas Taylor, a clothier, at Calverley in Yorkshire ten years previously,[33] and had for some reason come down to Greenwich, again indicating that some of the Green family were living there, possibly with their mother Ann.

The first direct coach service between Leeds and London started in 1754, and by 1765 it was reported that the London and Leeds post coaches took two days to complete the journey, the vehicles were of an easy and genteel construction and had the new patent springs. The roads were well maintained by then and the journey would have been reasonably comfortable. Coaches started from Blossoms' Inn in London every Monday, Wednesday, and Friday, at two o'clock in the morning, arriving early Tuesday, Thursday, and Saturday evening, at the New King's Arms in Leeds. They carried six passengers, each paying two pounds and ten shillings for the journey to either Leeds or Wakefield. The coaches rested at Leicester both ways.

William Wales junior was born probably at one of the coaching inns on the Great North Road,[34] he was baptised at North Witham, which lies just about a hundred miles from London, on Friday 10th June 1768, the date of his birth. Mary perhaps left London on the coach on Wednesday morning the 8th, resting at Leicester on the next evening. It was a month later on 10th July 1768 that baby was again baptized, at Warmfield in Yorkshire.[35] The baptism records for North Witham gives baby's parents as "Willm and Mary his wife of Fleet Street, London", the registers at Warmfield curiously give just the father's name, and his abode as Warmfield.

It is not known how long Mary and little Sarah spent at Warmfield with baby William, but there is no doubt that they would be in good company. Her in-laws were now about 70 years old, and William's sister Sarah, aged 29, was still a spinster. William's brother John, now aged 32, and working as a weaver with his wife Mary, were living in the village with their young family, Mary aged 3, John aged 2, and baby

Sarah. William Wales' family at Warmfield must have been excited to hear of his new career, and his important work at Hudson's Bay, which in those days must have seemed a world away from the rural depths of Yorkshire.

Endnotes

1   Task entrusted to John Flamsteed, by Charles II in 1675.

2   Howse, D, 1989. *Nevil Maskelyne – the seaman's astronomer.* Cambridge, Cambridge University Press.

3   Today this is known as the Meridian Building.

4   Personal communication, Dr Mary Croarken, Sackler Research Fellow, National Maritime Museum.

5   Burke, Edmund, 1793. *The Annual Register, or a view of the History of Politics and Literature for the year 1765.* London

6   *The Ipswich Journal,* Saturday 3rd August 1765. p.2.

7   Nevil Maskelyne to Edmund Maskelyne, 15th May 1799 (National Maritime Museum manuscript PST/76).

8   Skelton, R A, F S A, 1954, *Captain James Cook as a Hydropgrapher.* The Mariner's Mirror. Vol 40, No.2. p 111.

9   Howse, D, 1989. *Nevil Maskelyne – the seaman's astronomer.* Cambridge, Cambridge University Press.

10 Cameron, H C, 1952. *Sir Joseph Banks K.B., PR.S.* London, Batchworth Press.

11 Maskelyne, Nevil, 1767. *Tables Requisite to be used with the Astronomical & Nautical Ephemeris.* London.

12 Howse, D, 1989. *Nevil Maskelyne – the seaman's astronomer.* Cambridge, Cambridge University Press.

13 Croarken, Dr M. *Providing Longitude for all: the eighteenth century computers of the Nautical Almanac.* (Sept 2002) Journal of Maritime Research. This amount equivalent to £12.16 in 2006.. Calculated by http://eh.net/hmit/ In 2006 the *Nautical Almanac* was published at £30.00 per copy.

14 Pickard, L, 2000. *Dr Johnson's London.* London, Phoenix Press.

15 Boswell, James, 1930. *Life of Samuel Johnson.* London, G Bell & Sons Ltd.

16 McGooghan, Ken, 2005. *Ancient Mariner.* Sydney/London, Bantam.

17 Lee, S, 1906. *Concise Dictionary of National Biography.* London, Oxford University Press.

18 Danson, E, 2005. *Weighing the World.* Oxford, Oxford University Press.

19 Leybourn, Thomas, 1830. *New Series of The Mathematical Repository.* Vol.5. London, W. Glendinning.

20 R S Council Minutes, 15 February 1768.

21 Authenticated by correspondence with the Royal Society, London.

22 Howse, Derek, November 1998. *Britain's Board of Longitude: The Finances, 1714-1828.* Mariner's Mirror, Vol. 84, No. 4. pp 400-417.

23 Weld, Charles Richard, 1848. *A History of the Royal Society with Memoirs of the Presidents.* London, J.W. Parker.

24 Hough, R, 1995. *Captain James Cook, a Biography.* London, Hodder & Stoughton.

25 Philosophical Transactions of the Royal Society Vol. 59, December 1769, p.262

26 Weld, Charles Richard, 1848. *A History of the Royal Society with Memoirs of the Presidents.* London, J.W. Parker.

27 McDowell, Linda & Green, Herman, 1995. *Tales from the Bay – Teacher's Guide.* Hudson's Bay Company.

28 ibid.

29 Houston, Stuart, Ball, Tim, and Houston, Mary, 2003. *Eighteenth-century naturalists of Hudson Bay.* Montreal. McGill, Queen's University Press.

30 Beaglehole, J C, 1974, *The Life of Captain James Cook.* London, A & C. Black.

31 *St Peter's Parish Church Warmfield (Kirkthorpe) Baptisms1758-1812,* published by the Wakefield Family History Society, 2004.

32   Obituary of William Taylor in *Annual Monitor* for 1854, New
     Series, or *Obituary of the Members of the Society of Friends in
     Great Britain and Ireland for the year 1853,* pp138-149.

33   Parish Registers of Calverley, Yorkshire. Marriages.

34   Personal communication: Local historian, Mr John
     Collingwood, advised "North Witham is next to The Great
     North Road now the A1. There is the old Black Bull Inn,
     formerly a coaching Inn on the road which was used as
     a staging place for coaches travelling between York and
     London" The Black Bull at Witham is listed in the *Tourist and
     traveller's guide to the roads of England and Wales and part of
     Scotland* by George Carrington Gray. Published in 1824.

35   '1768 Jul 10. William Wales, son of William Wales'. (no
     mother's name nor occupation of father given). *St Peter's
     Parish Church Warmfield. (Kirkthorpe) Baptisms1758-1812,*
     published by the Wakefield Family History Society 2004.

5

VOYAGE TO HUDSON'S BAY

They saw the icy foundlings of the sea,
White cliffs of silence, beautiful by day,
Or looming, sudden-perilous, at night
In monstrous hush; or sometimes in the dark
The waves broke ominous with paly gleams
Crushed by the prow in sparkles of cold fire.[1]

Nevil Maskelyne prepared for the 1769 transit of Venus with some urgency. He wrote formal instructions for each observer, and assembled the relevant instruments and equipment. Destined for Hudson's Bay were:

- Astronomical pendulum clock by John Ellicott, together with an apparatus for correcting the effects of heat and cold
- Astronomical clock by John Shelton
- Journeyman (or assistant) clock
- two Quadrants "of one foot radius" by John Bird and John Hadley
- two reflecting Telescopes "of two feet focus" by James Short, one with a Dolland double object- glass micrometer
- Heliometer by John Dolland
- Alarum clock.
- two Thermometers

- Barometer
- two Fahrenheit thermometers designed to read well below freezing
- a variation Compass
- two Stoves with accoutrements plus one Chaldron (36 bushels) of coal
- two observatories prefabricated of wood, designed by John Smeaton[2]

This was the height of the Enlightenment era, and great technological advances were being made in the production of scientific instruments. The clock by John Ellicott had been purchased by the Royal Society in 1760, and travelled with Mason and Dixon on an East India Company ship to the Cape of Good Hope for the transit of Venus observations in 1761, it then went with Nevil Maskelyne to St Helena during 1761/2, and had since been stored away in the Royal Society's house at Crane Court in London.[3]

The observations were to include thermometer and barometer readings, to enable refraction to be taken into account in the astronomical calculations. During the year the temperature at Hudson's Bay ranged between -45°F and 85°F, and as mercury freezes at -37.89°F, it was necessary to replace the mercury with spirits of wine which would not freeze.

The Royal Society negotiated with the Hudson's Bay Company the expenses to convey Wales and Dymond to Fort Churchill, their stay there and their eventual return. They paid £250 for food for the term, which would total about 18 months, and it was agreed that the two astronomers may be maintained by the Company, furnished with all they required, including clothing, which would be needed during their term on board and while at the Bay, and supplied with servants and materials to assist erection of the portable observatory which had been designed by John Smeaton, a civil engineer from Austhorpe in Yorkshire – just eight miles north of Warmfield. Smeaton had presented his design to the Royal Society in February 1768, and the observatory had then been constructed under the direction of Nevil Maskelyne, with James Cook.

The Company replied that it was:

> ....ready to convey the persons desired, with their baggage and instruments, to and from Fort Churchill, and to provide them with lodging and medicine while there, gratis, they to find their own bedding.

There were just two conditions imposed by the Company, that the observers should have no access to the business of the Company, and that they must attend Divine Service (although apparently Dymond did not show up for prayers which did nothing to endear himself to the Fort's chief factor).[4] Dymond refused to attend prayers even on Sundays, and so this being the case, the factor would not let him eat at his table, making him eat alone in the little stone hut which he and Wales called home.

The Company also wrote to Maskelyne asking for details of the observatory, in order that they could send lengths of timber for transporting it safely, they had recommended to the Royal Society that it be conveyed with all the necessary implements, and tools &c., which

> ....will be conveyed upon freight, the Royal Society likewise paying for any clothing that may be supplied the observers during their residence in Hudson's Bay.[5]

Wales' request to be sent to a warm climate was partly due to him reading of the fate of one Jean-Baptiste Chappe d'Auteroche, who was one of the observers for the 1761 transit of Venus. d'Auteroche had travelled to Tobolsk in Siberia by sled through the Siberian winter, but was accused by the townsfolk of interfering with the sun when an early thaw flooded the town, and had narrowly escaped a lynch mob.

The records show that the English winter of 1767/8 had also been particularly cold, with deep frosts lasting for weeks.[6]

Wales nevertheless was posted to a place where the climate necessitated his departure during the summer previous to the transit's occurrence. The Company's ships made annual supply voyages from London to the Hudson Bay posts, and Wales and Dymond were booked onto the 1768 voyage of the *Prince Rupert*.

The parting of William Wales from his wife and daughter at this time must have been traumatic, but when summoned by the Royal Society, at the Astronomer Royal's recommendation, to take part in an exercise of such national and world importance, then domestic affairs just had to take the lesser priority. Nevertheless it seems he had to clear his mind of these circumstances before he could embark on his voyage, when he starts his Journal with

> "1768. May 29th. Having settled all my affairs in London; about 22 hours I set off for Greenwich where I received my instructions from the Rev. Mr Maskelyne, his Majesty's Royal Astronomer."[7]

The journey to Greenwich, although supposedly by boat, was taken on a Sunday when restrictions on water transport had been imposed some centuries earlier, Thames watermen held the monopoly of river transport, and the best way to travel was by their water-taxis. However the date and times indicate that perhaps Wales travelled to Greenwich by coach to see Mr Maskelyne, and from here, caught a boat to Gravesend.

On boarding the *Prince Rupert* at Gravesend, under the command of Captain Richards, Wales immediately gave Maskelyne's instructions to Joseph Dymond for him to copy.[8] Dymond was Wales' assistant on this expedition, and the fact that Dymond had been Maskelyne's assistant, whereas Wales had worked as a computer for Maskelyne for the past three years, suggests that Wales had received more instruction on the practical use of astronomical instruments than had Dymond.

Joseph Dymond was born in December 1746 at Brierley in Yorkshire, and so was just 21 years old when he sailed for Hudson's Bay. He was the son of James Dymond, and a member of the prominent and well established Dymond family of Brierley, a village situated just six miles south of Warmfield, the birthplace of William Wales.[9]

The harsh climate that Wales and Dymond would face during the next winter necessitated warm clothing, and this was supplied by the Hudson's Bay Company in advance and duly packed in the luggage chests.

The *Prince Rupert,* accompanied by the *Seahorse* and the brig *Charlotte,*[10] arrived at Stromness in the Orkney Islands[11] on 12th June, here they anchored and took on water and supplies. It had been 191 years before, in June 1577, that Martin Frobisher had called at the Orkney Islands, also to take on fresh water, before voyaging to the north-west regions on a quest to discover a North-West Passage.

The HBC also used the Orkney Islanders as a source of new staff, and many of the labouring servants were engaged here by the ship's captains on route to the Bay. Between fifty and a hundred men annually were recruited as boatmen, tradesmen, and store keepers, each man signed a contract to serve for five years at a wage of £6 per year.[12] While the Company's trade and recruitment was good for Stromness and the Orkneys, these islands were often left with a surplus of females.

When the ship eventually departed on 23rd June having been delayed by thick, cold fog, Wales was eager to take bearings, first recording the latitude and longitude of Hoy Head, and once on course across the Atlantic, he was to check the accuracy of the watches, comparing Joseph Dymond's with that of Captain Richards. The results showed a discrepancy, which was to worry Wales for the rest of the trip, but meanwhile there was work to do, and on the 29th June the observations included the eclipse of the moon, which was duly recorded.

Thick fog was again experienced during the Atlantic crossing, and by 16th July they were sailing past islands of ice, which Wales described as being 'with spires and indented in the most romantic manner'. The sea was very rough, with large waves beating over the quarter deck, a rough crossing, until eventually on 23rd July they reached the entrance to Hudson's Straits, to the south lay the north Canadian coast leading to the entrance to Hudson's Bay, to the north was Baffin Land, at which point William Wales must have noted the entrance to Frobisher Bay, and been reminded again of his childhood home.

It was in 1610 that Henry Hudson, the English navigator, reached what was to become Hudson's Strait, and spent time in the bay beyond when attempting to find a North-West Passage through to the lucrative Spice Islands, following this the Bay named after him witnessed many other attempted voyages to discover the passage, many of which turned out to be disastrous.

The day after entering the Strait, Wales records that a boat appeared carrying several Eskimaux women and boys of the

Inuit people. He had been doing his research on the area and its social history, for he was to spend over a year at Fort Prince of Wales, and frequently refers in his Journal to the *History of Greenland* which had been written by a Morovian missionary David Crantz, and published just the year previously in 1767. He had read of the Eskimaux canoes, or kiacks, but was surprised that the party included neither men nor weapons, the boat's occupants just had clothes and home made toys to trade.

The Company ships hugged the northern coastline of the Straits when sailing to the Bay, this passage followed a strong westward current which usually became ice-free earlier than the rest of the Straits, the easterly currents to the south carried ice. This northern route took the ships close to Baffin Island and the Savage Islands, from where the local Inuit habitually appeared to trade with the Company ships.

The captains of the Hudson's Bay Company ships had for years been instructed specifically to make contact with the Inuit from the Upper and Middle Savage Islands, which lay to the south of Baffin Island, to treat them courteously, and to encourage them to trade goods.[13] The ships carried a variety of tools and hunting weapons, which were traded primarily for baleen – whalebone used in the clothing trade, especially as stiffening for ladies' corsets, but also for parasols. These flexible strips from the bowhead whale were a useful commodity prior to plastic.

During passage through Hudson Strait, Wales was in awe of the landscape. The islands and rocks rose out of the deep along the north shore of the Straits, some of ice, and with infinite bays and inlets. Wales' thirst for knowledge is well documented, his Journal describes:

...The north shore of these straits seems to be a chain of broken islands, or rather, large, bare rocks one rising, as it were, in perspective above another. But I cannot help observing, that from the accounts of authors, I expected to have found them entirely covered with ice and snow; whereas I found them entirely bare, except in some very deep vallies. I apprehend, however that this had not long been the case, as the water everywhere kept continually tumbling down the rocks in prodigious torrents.[14]

On 1st August, while carrying out his observations, Wales again records that the Eskimaux came alongside the *Prince Rupert,* trading toys, which again must have reminded him of home, and no doubt he obtained some of the toys for his daughter Sarah and the new baby which Mary was expecting when he left. He described in detail the dress of the natives, but not their boat, as this had already been covered by Mr Crantz in his *History.* The party this time included men who wore boots of seal skin, soled with the skin of the sea horse – which was another name for the walrus. They had knee breeches of seal or deer skin, and a shirt like the English shift, of one piece with a hood like that of a woman's cloak, over this they wore a jacket made of seal skin.

The women's dress was much the same as above, except their coats had long tails behind reaching down to their heels, and their boots came right up to their hips, where they were made very wide with a bow of whalebone for the purpose of holding the children. Wales described the race as small but broad built, and inclined to be fat, they had very small hands and very broad and flat faces, small mouths and noses, and their eyes were as black as jet, and eye-lids so encumbered with fat that they opened them with difficulty. Their hair was long, black, and straight, and despite their superfluity of flesh, they were remarkably brisk and active, he was very impressed with their character.

In the 18th century the Inuit were viewed as potentially dangerous by Europeans. who believed that it was they who had murdered the members of the James Knight expedition, which had sailed to Hudson's Bay in 1719 on a voyage to look for the North-West Passage, and mysteriously disappeared. Wales was quick to dispute this reputation when he entered in his Journal:

> ...never people less deserve the epithets of "treacherous, cruel fawning, and suspicious," the contrary of which is remarkably true in every particular. They are open, generous, and unsuspecting; addicted too much (it must be owned) to passion....

Crantz evidently made an error in his work regarding icebergs, when he described the ones of vitriol colour as consisting of salt water. Ever the scientist, Wales is quick to record that in fact from his experience he can state that they are certainly of frozen water which contains no salt, and therefore icebergs must be made from snow which broke away from the land. Research since has proved that they are formed from snow which has compressed to form glacial ice, which then flows into the sea.

This was the age of exploration, and most notably 'exploration for profit'. There had for some years been a race to find some route through the Hudson Strait and on to the Western Ocean beyond, but this labyrinth of ice and islands had time and time again been found impossible to penetrate. Wales was only too aware that he was now at the very point where these voyages had optimistically begun their quest, and in his Journal he recounts the attempt just 27 years before of Captain Christopher Middleton, one time commander of ships of the

Hudson's Bay Company, who had then been commissioned into the Navy, and in the vessel *Furnace* had attempted to chart a route through the North-West Passage. This voyage had proved most controversial, and was the subject of much debate and even a formal inquiry, eventually Middleton was cleared, but Wales was ever vigilant to the facts and records that in his opinion the ice islands he witnessed would melt far faster than Middleton had predicted.

To read the journal of Wales at this point, is to discover a man who is obviously in his element, for he is not only observing magnetic variations in the compass and recording them, but is also watching and recording the workings of the *Prince Rupert* and her diligent crew slowly inching a way between the ice. He and Dymond's astronomical observations were ongoing, sometimes recording them on deck until after midnight, these automatically prompted lengthy calculations, and there is no doubt that should Wales need to fill any spare time, he would busy himself with more of those eternal *Almanac* calculations for Maskelyne, and for himself. In 1794 Wales published a book which included *Tables of Equations to Equal Altitudes,* these were used in order to make it easier to determine local time. He admits these were:

> ....computed principally for amusement during the many dreary hours I passed on the coast of Hudson's Bay in 1768 and 1769.[15]

The Bay's commercial potential was recognized about 1660, and the idea of trading rich fur lands with the indigenous Indian population, for the European market, eventually culminated in 1670, when Prince Rupert, a cousin of Charles II, and seventeen other noblemen and gentlemen founded the *Governor and Company of Adventurers of England Trading into Hudson Bay*. The Company was granted a royal charter, and by 1768 was well established trading from its bay-side posts. The Company controlled the land around the Bay, its vast territory became known as *Rupert's Land*. They enforced the laws, erected forts, and maintained ships of war, and it was about 1702 that they started to recruit their workforce from Stromness in the Orkneys, their last port of call, where they took on stores before heading over the Atlantic.

One of the Company posts was at the mouth of the Churchill River on the Bay's west coast, where the Arctic tundra meets the boreal forest lands, this transitional forest area was exploited by the native American tribes, the *Inuit*, *Cree*, and the *Chipewyans*. Churchill was the Company's choice, it had potential for white whale fishing, as a port of departure for exploratory voyages to the north, and as an access point to investigate the fabled mineral wealth of the country. The post was named *Prince of Wales' Fort*, the building of which was begun in 1717, but such was the position of the Churchill river that eventually the Company decided that the fort should be a defensive structure for employees and possessions in case of war, and in 1731 work started on building a stone fort, four bastions with curtain walls holding 42 cannon. This was still under construction in 1768 and never was fully completed.

It was on 7th August that Wales' journal logs the sighting of Cape Churchill, but this was not reported by the observer at the top of the mast. The siting aroused the curious Wales to demonstrate his agility, and climb to the top of the main mast head himself, where he found it was indeed the case that the land had vanished before his eyes. He came down, and sure enough from the deck the land had appeared again, he had also observed this phenomenon during the voyage, with ice sheets which had appeared quite high from a distance, but on nearing them were hardly any higher than the water surface.

The sighting of the flag staff on the factory at Churchill heralded the end of the voyage, and the beginning of a time of new experiences for both Wales and Dymond, the *Prince Rupert's* signal was acknowledged from the Fort, and she made her way up the River Churchill to the appointed mooring. Wales and Dymond had arrived.

Endnotes

1   James Russell Lowell (1819-1891).

2   Broughton, P, *Historic Transits of Venus from a Canadian Perspective*. Website of the Royal Astronomical Society of Canada. www.rasc.ca/history/transit.pdf

3   Howse, F & Hutchinson, B, 1969. *The Clocks & Watches of Captain James Cook 1769-1969*. London, The Antiquarian Horology Society.

4   Griffin-Short, Rita. 2003. *The Transit of Venus* The Beaver, April/May. p10.

5   Willson, Beckles, 1900. *The Great Company (1667-1871)*. London, Smith, Elder & Co.

6   Website: http://www.hollinsclough.org.uk/weather.htm.

7   Wales, W, 1770. *Journal of a Voyage made by Order of the Royal Society, to River, on the North-west Coast of Hudson's Bay; of Thirteen Months Residence in that Country; and of the Voyage back to England; in the Years 1768 and 1769*. Phil. Trans.R.Soc., Vol 60, pp.100-136.

8   Maskelyne had written 40 pages of instructions for observing he transit in *The Nautical Almanac* for 1769 which had been published in 1767. It is clear from Wales' Journal that they been given just one copy of this between them.

9   Website of Brierley village and personal communication. www.brierley59.freeserve.co.uk

10   Griffin-Short, Rita. 2003. *The Transit of Venus* The Beaver, April/May.

11   In his Journal Wales calls Stromness in the Orkney Islands *Cairstown*, this is Carston Roads at Stromness which was the harbour where westward bound ships awaited favourable sailing conditions before setting sail across the Atlantic.

12 Willson, Beckles, 1900. *The Great Company (1667-1871)*. London, Smith, Elder & Co.

13 Barr, William, 1994. *The Eighteenth Century Trade between the Ships of the Hudson's Bay Company and the Hudson Strait Inuit.* Arctic Journal. Vol 47, No 3 (September 1994).

14 Wales, W, 1770 *Journal of a Voyage made by Order of the Royal Society, to Churchill River, on the North-west Coast of Hudson's Bay; of Thirteen Months Residence in that Country; and of the Voyage back to England; in the Years 1768 and 1769*. Phil.Trans.R.Soc. Vol 60 p.100-136.

15 Wales, W, 1794. *The method of finding the Longitude at Sea by Time-Keepers: to which are added, Tables of Equations to Equal Altitudes*. London.

6

CHURCHILL AND
THE TRANSIT OF VENUS

"... This sight, which is by far the noblest astronomy can afford, is denied to mortals for a whole century, by the strict laws of motion..."[1]

On the morning of the 10th August 1768 William Wales and Joseph Dymond stepped onto the beach at Churchill, and when Captain Richards took them up to the factory to meet the governor Moses Norton, he greeted them warmly.[2] The pair had been granted the privilege of eating at the captain's table while at sea, and now they were on land they dined at the factor's table. The Company officers at the fort were the governor and his deputy, the surgeon, sloop master, and clerk writer, among the skilled tradesmen were stone masons, carpenters, armourers, blacksmith, coopers, and tailors, the rest were labourers.

After breakfast the surgeon escorted them on a long walk to explore the countryside, this was probably at the request of Wales, whose writings always indicate a deep interest in the fauna and flora of the places he visited. Wales and Dymond had arrived at Churchill at the height of summer, they must have been apprehensive about winter conditions in this inhospitable environment, but for now Wales' journal describes ground of high rocks and gravel, through which poked small willows and birch. There were small gooseberry bushes creeping horizontally along the ground like bramble briars, there were strawberries, cranberries, ripe bilberries, and Wales could identify dandelion and yarrow, but other plants he was not familiar with.

Birds were always evident in Wales' journals, they were recorded with a passion, and often the subject of his attention. He had arrived at the height of the small bird season, and noted young ducks and curlews, plover and geese, he shot a few which he was told were known as the stone plover, but which he noted were similar to the woodcock, and he observed the whale-bird which he described as similar to a quail. Gulls were evident in great variety, and he identified linnets and larks. The bird he found most strange he described as

> .....called a man-of-war, and feeds on the excrements of other birds; its way of coming at its food is also a little extraordinary; he pursues the bird which he pitches on for his supply, until fear makes it void what he wants, and so soon as this happens, he catches the morsel in his mouth; after which he leaves that bird and pursues another.[3]

The creatures which were to become the bane of his life during his stay belonged to the insect world, and he identifies three in particular. The mosquito, or as Wales names it 'moschetto', he supposed he needed no description because its reputation was already well known. The sand flies he described as intolerably troublesome, and on hot calm days attacked his face and eyes in their millions, and finally an insect similar to the large flesh fly in England, but at least three times larger, which Wales described as having frequently seen and experienced, fixing its teeth on whatever part of his anatomy, and then carrying a piece away with it. Observations some thirty years previous described the swarms of sand flies, so dense they could choke a man who was foolish enough to open his mouth, and bites from the mosquitoes could swell a man's head to the size of a barrel.[4]

According to David Thompson in his writings of the 1780s, polar bear appeared about the beginning of October each year, though these creatures were never mentioned in Wales and Dymond's Journal.[5]

Wales had a problem with the variation compass. It had worked perfectly in London, when he had checked it after receiving it from Mr Robertson on behalf of the Royal Society, it had worked perfectly. But on unpacking it at Hudson's Bay, Wales and Dymond found that it had entirely lost its magnetic ability probably due to the intense cold, and despite this compass being kept in their living quarters and heated by a large fire and stove for the rest of their trip, this had had no effect. They eventually resorted to asking Captain Richards if he would send his azimuth compass on shore to enable them to make observations, the Captain obliged.[6]

The next week was spent getting the observatory and the scientific instruments on shore, but the observatory could not be built at this stage, so on the 16th August Wales went for a ten mile walk with Mr Fowler, who eventually was to take Governor Norton's place at the fort. They were hoping to find a piece of land on which to cultivate corn, but instead they found the ground marshy with long grass, and bordered by land covered with fir trees as high as twenty feet. Much of the bare rocky land was covered with low brush wood of birch and juniper, and many which were unlike any found in England, which Wales didn't even attempt to identify. He was no botanist, but nonetheless gathered some specimens for drying, and eventually taking home with him.

Originally built of wood some five miles up the Churchill River in 1718, Prince of Wales fort was designed to safeguard the Company's trading post, from both the French and the Indians. This original fort was replaced, and in the 1730s the foundations for a new more substantial structure were laid at the mouth of the river, with walls up to forty-two feet thick, and with a massive bastion on each of the corners, it was thought to be impregnable.[7]

In 1768 the building work of the Fort was still ongoing, the outpost was variously known as Churchill – the Factory – the Settlement – or the Fort, but officially it was Fort Prince of Wales and functioned as half citadel and half trading post. Manned by the Company which had been established for a hundred years trading with the indigenous people, who brought their furs to trade for the manufactured goods of Europe, yet still the Company knew little about the vast inland territory from which these people emerged.

During the second week Wales and Dymond were involved at last in starting to build their observatory, and laid the foundations some 50 feet above sea level on the south east bastion of Prince of Wales fort. Of the three transit of Venus expeditions sponsored by the Royal Society, all carried portable observatories of either wood or canvas.[8] The observatory was in two parts, a higher one, and a lower one, and after the walls were fixed a large oak plank was placed into the ground and supported with spars, to this the clock was secured by screws. Then a quarter ton stone was set, with a flat surface on which to place the clock case. A thermometer was hung inside the southern lower observatory away from the fire and next to the barometer, and outside on the northern side another thermometer was fixed. This pre-fabricated octagonal wooden observatory was likened to a large shower, with a circular brass rod and brass rings to hold up a tent, but the vital feature was a slotted roof which moved on rollers. Despite obvious painstaking care with the building and design however, it was ultimately described by the Fort's factor John Fowler as a flimsy affair for the climate[9]. The structure had in fact been designed by Nevil Maskelyne with the help of John Smeaton and Mr Ashworth, the carpenter at Greenwich.[10]

The rest of that week was spent writing letters to friends and family back home, these would be sent back to England with the ship when she sailed at the end of the month. One letter Wales wrote was to a friend Rev John Lawson, of Swanscombe in Kent, who it is apparent was of a like mind mathematically, dated 24th August 1768, Wales was obviously missing the mathematical challenge of geometric problems when he wrote:[11]

Churchill River, Hudson's Bay.

Reverend Sir-

To speak sincerely, I have no other motive for troubling you with this letter than the hope of obtaining one from you in answer to it by the return of the ship next season. I imagine you will think it a little extraordinary to give you one trouble in order to draw you into another; but I will, notwithstanding, flatter myself I shall be able to draw you into the snare, and that your good nature will excuse the liberty. If not, I am sure I have no excuses to offer for it. Had I any mathematical news to entertain you with, or were even in a country of which the description would contain anything curious it would be different; but I have seen nothing here yet but a few ignorant wretches, the sum of whose respective possessions are bare rocks and banks of sand. As for ourselves, we have yet had no opportunity or even inclination to study much. I have indeed thought a little about the question which you showed me when I last had the happiness of being with you, but I have not yet been able to construct it. You may remember you observed to me, it seemed to you somehow or other to be *double*............

the correspondence continues with the details of the geometric poser, and then ends with:

...Now, Sir, from this small morsel I flatter myself you will exercise your charity on behalf of a poor wretch who is deprived of conversing with thinking beings for so long a period. Return me all the mathematical occurrences that may come under your notice in my absence, such as 'Notes on the Diaries,' or anything in that way; for I shall have the 'Diaries' sent me by the ships; which, with your remarks, and those of my other kind friends who may think proper to send me a line or two, will make a feast for the greatest epicure in the universe. If you are so kind as to oblige me with a line, it must be directed to me here, and left at the Hudson's Bay House, in Fenchurch Street, London. Farewell. That health, which is the greatest happiness this world can give, may be your constant attendant, is the sincere wish and prayer of,

Dear Sir, your very obedient Servant, WILLIAM WALES.

During the following week the Company carpenters were occupied, first making beds for their visitors, who up to now had to sleep on the floor, and then they fixed a roof on each part of the observatory, the astronomers then finished off the building and set to work installing the clocks, the stove, and other instruments. By now it was September and snow had fallen on the plains, winter was setting in, and Wales wrote that he would now cease to keep his journal in its present form for a year, and while he was resolved to keeping weather observations during the winter, he would keep notes on the seasons in the form of short memorandums.

The observatory was not quite right, there were problems when the astronomers tried to calculate zenith differences of stars, the observatory needed to be moved further south, but as this was not practicable it was resolved by taking up the floor, and removing the piles on which the quadrant stood farther south instead, this was done with the assistance of the house carpenter entirely satisfactorily.

The Hudson's Bay Company had a history of hazards in exploration, especially in its expeditions which searched for a North-West Passage. The Company was so dependent on accurate navigation for its economic growth and survival, that the visit of William Wales was deemed a good opportunity by both the Royal Society and the Company, to make the most of his scientific abilities while at Churchill. It was Samuel Wegg, not only a Fellow and treasurer of the Royal Society in 1768, but also a committee member of the Company, who had been instrumental in arranging the visit of Wales and Dymond.[12]

Previous to the arrival of the two scientists in 1768, Indians trading at the fort had brought pieces of copper which they told were from a mine in the locality of the *Great River,* as they insisted in calling it. This had been brought to the attention of the Company by Governor Norton during his visit to London in 1768-9, and it was decided to send out a person by land to chart the area of the river, and find its latitude and longitude. The person chosen was Samuel Hearne, a mariner of the Company who was born in England in 1745, and had joined the navy at the age of 12. In 1766 he started working for the Hudson's Bay Company as part of a ship's crew, and at the age of 23 was mate on one of their brigs. Hearne spent winters at Fort Prince of Wales, and prior to starting out on his epic journey for the Company, he was to receive tuition from William Wales in navigation, surveying, and in determining latitude and longitude. Hearne was also detailed to note the nature of the soil, and should he consider any river to be useful to the Company, then he was to claim possession of it on behalf of the Company by recording his name and date on neighbouring rocks.

William Wales was to become a major influence on Hearne's life, and schooled him in the finer points of astronomical observation, geodetics, and navigation, on the instruction of Moses Norton before Norton's visit to London.

At the beginning of October all spare hands, both native and European, were occupied shooting geese which were eaten fresh, and from the start of the partridge season, groups of Englishmen went out in parties to shoot them. Wales often carried out observations to calculate the speed of the wild geese in flight, and found that in a steady gale this was 60 miles per hour, in which case, at a distance of 40 to 50 yards he would need to aim two to three inches before the beak when shooting with the wind, and at the end of the neck when shooting against the wind.[13]

One very windy day a fine rock cod was driven to the shore, and was enjoyed by Wales and Dymond, both had the honour of eating at the Governor's table at this time,[14] but this was later to be denied Dymond after his refusal to attend church services.

Winter was looming, and for Wales, Dymond, and those who stayed at the factory, they must prepare for the cold weather ahead. From descriptions of preparation for his work, there is no doubt that Wales was meticulous, and any event which hindered this groundwork displeased him intensely, this was expressed when he noted in his Journal that when the ship had entered the River, the Customs Officers had searched his chest and confiscated the very clothing that the Hudson's Bay Company had provided for his and Mr Dymond's protection from the cold during the winter months.[15] Despite protestation to the Commissioners of the Customs, they were adamant that the articles could not be returned.

The astronomers did not loose out however, they must have been furnished with another set of 'toggy' as Wales described their winter rigging. He reports that it was made out of beaver skins, and adds that no consultation was made of the person's shape for the fitting, it sufficed so long as it was wide enough and reached almost to his feet. The ensemble was completed with mittens and cap of beaver, and over the stockings sometimes broadcloth spatter dashes were added. On venturing outside of the factory a beaver skin cap is added, and a white fox skin cravat – on the feet, shoes of soft-tanned moose skin, and snow shoes.

By the beginning of November winter had taken its hold. The mile wide Churchill River was now completely frozen over, and it was possible to walk across its mouth. Wales noted that but for a solitary crow and the odd small bird, the birdlife had completely abandoned the factory, and the world was silent. It was so cold that in the observatory equipment was affected, and half a pint of brandy spirit was found to have frozen solid in a glass.

It was going to be a long winter ahead for the two astronomers who had undoubtedly experienced no such conditions before, but the food was plentiful, and weekly supplies of partridges, rabbits, and hares were brought by the indigenous hunters – these were supplemented by hogs which were left by the ship's captain with the Governor, and the joints hung frozen, to be consumed when needed throughout the winter.

The hunters lived in tents, and one week in December they were joined by William Wales, who was probably relieved by this opportunity to escape from the company of Dymond for a while, but by January he had returned to the small cabin which he and Dymond shared, it was less than nine feet square, and so cold that a fire had to be kept alight.

The walls were of stone, three feet thick, and lined inside with inch thick wooden boards which stood three inches from the stonework. The silence of the night was punctuated by noise, like artillery fire of rocks bursting in the cold outside, sending splinters flying through the air. Inside the house beams would crack and creak as the temperature dropped, and despite the house's wooden insulation, the bedding·was found frozen to the boards each morning. One particularly cold morning Wales' awoke to find his hair frozen to the wall, it had to be cut just so he could get out of bed.[16]

Christmas was celebrated at Churchill, the holiday stretched from 24th December to 1st January, and during this time little work was done, and the Chief Factor dispensed rum or brandy to make punch. The Company employees and Indians were great gamblers, and no doubt the Christmas holidays were spent playing games of skill, there is no doubt that the stakes were alcohol which was used almost as the currency of the Fort, even when the Company were rewarding its employees. Not only were the employees well paid and well fed, they enjoyed a range of recreational pursuits during their leisure time, they read, they fished, they kept pets, and tended gardens, they drank Labrador tea or *Wishapucka* which had medicinal qualities, and life for them was pleasantly civilized.[17]

Meanwhile at the observatory, on the south-east bastion, the spirits of wine were being used for the instruments, Wales recorded that in January he had carried half a pint of brandy into the open air, and in less that two minutes it had changed from a watery consistency to that of treacle. The effects of low temperatures on liquids fascinated him, and he was ever setting up experiments and recording the results. He also worked on the computation of tables of the equations to equal altitudes for fascilitating the determination of time, and was paid for six months calculations in 1768 and during 1769, for a further nine months.[18] Together with the hundreds of astronomical observations carried out during their stay, we learn that Wales and Dymond did not spend the long winter months merely awaiting the transit of Venus the following June.

It was the third week of March 1769 by the time the thaw started, as slowly the sun's rays warmed the land. In April it rained for the first time in over six months, and very gradually the Canadian winter melted into spring. From their winter partridge tents the hunters returned ready for the goose season, the results would keep the factory fed for a month with fresh meat, while further provisions were salted down to help to supplement rations for the rest of the year.

The geese were listed in Wales' journal as grey-goose, way-way, brant, and dunter, but he records that there were also several more species. His personal favourite was the dunter gander, which he described as one of the most beautifully feathered birds that he had ever seen.

The fish were also plentiful, and when the river ice eventually broke there was plenty of fine salmon to be caught, and the fishermen up-river provided pike, mathoy, and tittymegs. Later in July the kepling was to be found thrown onto the shore by the sea surf – there for the picking.

Heath and juniper berries were used for drinks, and in spring the gooseberry bushes were showing signs of life again, also Wales spotted that there was a luxuriant growth of dandelions which were to provide a salad most excellent to accompany that roasted goose. By July the radishes were ready, and turnip tops were used for greens, and then the lettuce followed, but Churchill was not the sort of place suitable for the production of a lot of arable crops, Wales had witnessed a trial of corn growing, but had not thought this a viable venture without a lot of proper culture over a long time. So although arable farming was not possible, sheep, hogs, cattle and horses were kept by some of the Company men.

Wales found the indigenous population of the country easy to talk to, and while they were not educated in the arts and sciences, he enjoyed conversation and banter with them on subjects they understood. He had broached the subject of religion with them, and discovered that they accepted two beings, one called Ukkemah, who was good, the other called Wittikah, who represented evil, he learned that Ukkemah made the first men and women from the earth – three of each – whiter than themselves from white earth, blacker than themselves from black earth, and the same as themselves. They acknowledged the story of the flood, but in their account the beaver replaced the dove.

These hunters are described in Wales' journal as rather tall and thin, with copper coloured skin, their thick lips and wide mouthed faces being framed by black hair, worn long and straight, while he described their eyes of black as the most beautiful he ever saw. They were a melancholic and good-natured people, friendly, honest, and hospitable to each other and the Europeans. Their lives were somewhat erratic, and if they suffered an injury, while they did not readily forget it, yet they sought no revenge, and having no laws their conduct was regulated by reasoning.

Wales managed to collect mineral specimens while at Churchill, adding geology to the subjects recorded in his journal, he was intent on taking back to the Royal Society as much scientific information as he could muster, that is other than the principal subject of his recordings – astronomy, and the observation of the transit of Venus

Whilst awaiting the transit, and as a further insurance against the accuracy of the time piece, which had been giving Wales some concern, he worked a massive sundial from a piece of limestone which he obtained from the coast of the Bay near the Owl River,[19] for this to be any use however the day of the transit would need to be sunny. In 1952, an octagonal stone pillar was discovered, together with a stand made of iron, and well-crafted.[20] This piece had been found amongst rubble from the south-east bastion of Prince of Wales Fort.[21] (see Illustration No 13) Due to the clock dial type markings on some of its 8 sides, each side of which has 5 faces plus the top, this has been described as a computer, and it was suggested that it was possibly the one which had been used by Wales and Dymond during their stay. Consultations were made with the National Maritime Museum at Greenwich, and although the dial had no gnomons affixed, there was no doubt its use had been for telling the time from the sun. [22]

Further examination of the Churchill stone sundial supported the above hypothesis, that this was the one carved by Wales, when it was found that the major face showed an error for the calculation of latitude – the same figure as recorded by Wales in his observations.

During their stay at Churchill the two astronomers had had to make hundreds of astronomical observations. They used Bird's quadrant to find their clock correction, as laid down in Maskelyne's instructions. and to take meridian altitudes to find their latitude, they had to use the thermometer and barometer readings in their calculations to compensate for refraction.

The aurora-borealis had been observed here, it appeared as a steady stream of light, narrow, and of the colour of pale straw, it had little or no motion, and Wales' records that it was nothing compared to the display he had seen in the north of England,. This was disappointing, as Churchill is probably the best place on the planet for viewing this phenomenon, it lies directly beneath the *Auroral Oval,* an area of high intensity and frequency for aurora activity, and conditions here are usually perfect for the viewing. It has been suggested that the conditions on this occasion were due to the sun-spot cycle, which at the time of Wales' visit was two years before its maximum, and the aurora appears in its greatest frequency a year or so after that maximum.[23]

One anomaly here which had been noted by Wales, was the haze which was always to be seen at the horizon, and this he concluded was the reason why two streams of red light always occurred before the sun's rising, this is an optical phenomenon, a parhelion which occurs when the sun is low in the sky.

Finally, after more than a year's wait and preparation, the 3rd June dawned with skies part cloudy and hazy, but mercifully with intermittent clear periods, the temperature was 45 degrees, and at precisely 56 minutes and 49 seconds after noon the transit of Venus began. Wales and Dymond were only too aware of the importance of the task before them, this event was rare, and a lot of time and money had been invested in the recording of its happening, the results were to be instrumental in the understanding of the universe for years ahead, and it was imperative that they should get them right.

The two astronomers carefully observed the passage of Venus, which appeared from earth as a black disk moving over the sun's solar face, to the best of their ability their task was to record the initial contact time, and the total transit time. The resulting time would provide an accurate means by which the distance between the earth and the sun could be calculated, a distance which was at this time still unknown.[24]

The time taken for Venus to cross the sun was 7 hours 19 minutes and 40 seconds, and although the initial contact times recorded by the two observers differed by 11 seconds – to the chagrin of Wales – they agreed on the actual transit time, and the time of the egress.[25] The main difficulty was that as Venus initially moved onto the sun's face the planet appeared to drag a black strip after it, and by the time the strip disappeared the transit was already in progress, and so the time of the start, or ingress, could not be determined accurately. This phenomenon was caused by the planet's dense atmosphere, and had caused problems to other observers around the world.

On the island of Otaheite[26] Wales' brother-in-law Charles Green, and Captain James Cook, performed the same observations at the northern end of the Island, at the place they had named *Point Venus*. (see Illustration No 6) They had set up three observing stations which were manned by the officers, most of whom had been tutored assiduously by Green during the voyage out. *Point Venus* was the main station, where a small fort had been erected, comprising a wooden palisade which enclosed the observatory, and which housed James Cook and Charles Green, with Daniel Solander who was one of Joseph Bank's colleagues, and Robert Molyneux, the master. The day of the observations was fine, so that the observers, while experiencing no apparent meteorological difficulties, did have difficulty in accurately determining the points of contact of Venus with the Sun, making the results from the different observers inconsistent.[27]

Further inaccuracy had been caused by damage to Green's quadrant, which had suffered rough treatment when it was stolen by the natives prior to the transit. They had witnessed the care in which the quadrant in its case had been treated when handled by the crew, and thought it must contain very precious goods, they subsequently stole it and subjected it to damage by their rough handling, a fact which had not been considered by Maskelyne when he later found cause to criticize some of Green's figures.[28]

It was on Monday 28th August that Wales and Dymond finally packed up their instruments, and stowed them on board the *Prince Rupert*[29] for their return home. Now that their main task had been completed, no doubt they were looking forward to returning to their families, and catching up with all the news. On the second of September they bade their farewells to the fort's governor and officers, and boarded the ship, only to be delayed by the unfavourable direction of the wind – but by the seventh of September the ship headed out of the river, with a brisk westerly breeze in her sails.

The work continued even after they left, on the day they sailed Wales recorded that he saw the great comet which had been observed in England that year, the tail spanned 60 degrees in the sky. Also recorded is an adjustment which had to be made to calculations of longitude, as there had occurred an immense difference between the latitude of the factory at Churchill, as calculated from observations made by Hadley's quadrant, and the latitude as calculated from observations made with their astronomical quadrant on shore. This was a problem which had occupied Wales' most serious attention for some time, and his only conclusion was that the refractive power of the local air was making the horizon appear to be higher than it actually was, this was causing the calculation of sun's altitude to be less than it otherwise would be, the consequence being the miscalculation of the latitude.

While becalmed again in the Hudson Strait, Wales reflected that the islands of ice had diminished quickly as he had predicted, although the passage home was rough, being again affected by easterly winds until they reached the waters of Ireland. They were held in the Straits for nine days, before sailing back to England with the great comet of 1769[30] visible in the night sky.

On the 10th October the Isles of Scilly lighthouse was spotted from the mast head. This was the light which none of Sir Cloudesley Shovell's fleet sighted on that fateful night of 1707, although when built in 1680 it was placed on the highest point of the most exposed island of the group,[31] still fuelled by coal as it was in Shovell's day, so not the brightest of lights, it was not until 1790 that the light was changed to a revolving type. The Governor of the Isles of Scilly did not support the project to build a lighthouse originally, the inhabitants were so reliant on the wrecks of vessels for their supplies that in the church of St Mary's they prayed:

> ...We pray thee, O Lord, not that wrecks should happen, but that if any wrecks should happen, Thou wilt guide them into the Scilly Isles for the benefit of the poor inhabitants.[32]

Shovell's fatality would be remembered by Wales as he recorded the Scilly light in his journal, as it must have been remembered by many a mariner for years after the event. Passing the *Lizard,* Wales and Dymond eventually sailed back into Plymouth on 14th October from freezing Hudson's Bay, just in time to experience what was to be an exceptionally cold British winter.

The ship berthed in *Hamoze* at Plymouth, but the easterly winds made early progress to London impossible, and so on the 16th of October 1769, Wales and Dymond took a stage coach to London. The two arrived three days later at nine in the evening, anxious to deliver their important report and calculations to the Royal Society, and no doubt even more anxious to return to their friends and families after enduring such a long, long journey.

Endnotes

1   Halley, Edmond, 1691. *Philosophical Transactions of the Royal Society.*

2   Wales, W, 1770. *Journal of a Voyage made by Order of the Royal Society, to Churchill River, on the North-west Coast of Hudson's Bay; of Thirteen Months Residence in that Country; and of the Voyage back to England; in the Years 1768 and 1769.* Phil.Trans.R.Soc. Vol 60 p.100-136.

3   ibid. p.117.

4   Williams, Glyn, 2003. *Voyages of Delusion.* London, Harper Collins.

5   Moreau, William E, 2008. *The Writings of David Thompson.* Montreal, McGill-Queen's University Press.

6   Wales, William, 1769. *Observations for determining the Magnetic Variations at Prince of Wales's Fort, on the N.W Coast of Hudson's Bay,* Phil. Trans. R. Soc. Vol.59, p.483.

7   Willson, Beckles, 1900. *The Great Company (1667-1871).* London, Smith Elder & Co.

8   Howse, D & Hutchinson, B, 1969. *The Clocks & Watches of Captain James Cook.* London, Antiquarian Horological Society.

9   Griffin-Short, Rita., April/May 2003. *The Transit of Venus.* The Beaver.

10 Forbes, Eric G, 1975. *Greenwich Observatory Origins and Early History.* Taylor & Francis.

11 T T Wilkinson, *Notae Mathematicae.* Mechanics Magazine, January 7th-June 24th 1854. by R.A. Brooman, vol LX London, 1854. Robertson, Brooman & Co. pp 436-7.

12 Houston S, Ball T, & Houston, M, 2003. *Eighteenth Century Naturalists at Hudson Bay.* McGill – Queens Press.

13 Moreau, William E, 2008. *The Writings of David Thompson*. Montreal, McGill-Queen's University Press.

14 Hearne, S, 1968. *Journey from Prince of Wales's Fort in Hudson's Bay to the Northern Ocean*. New York, De Capo Press.

15 There was a problem with the customs system at this time. The Canadian customs had been controlled from England, a practice which had been found impossible, and so in 1767 had been handed over to a newly formed American Board of Customs, controlled from Massachusetts. This Board was then dissolved some nine years later.

16 Portwood, John, 1995. *Tales from the Bay – The Transit of William Wales*. Canadian Geographic, Sept/Oct,1995 Vol. 115, Issue 5, p.76.

17 Payne, M, 1978-79. *The Healthiest Part in the Known World"*. Manitoba Historical Society Transactions Series 3, No.35.

18 Personal communication, Dr Mary Croarken.

19 McDowell, Linda & Green, Herman, 1995. *Tales from the Bay – Teacher's Guide*. Hudson's Bay Company.

20 ibid.

21 In 2003 this was on display in the Parks Canada office in Churchill according to Houston S., Ball T., & Houston, M., 2003. *Eighteenth Century Naturalists at Hudson Bay*. McGill – Queens Press

22 *Stone Sundial from Fort Prince of Wales* by Lester A Ross. Research Bulletin No. 193, June 1983. Published by authority of the Minister of the Environment, Minister of Supply and Services Canada, 1983.

23 Hogg, Helen Sawyer, 1948. *Out of Old Books* Journal of the Royal Astronomical Society of Canada Vol XLII.

24 For the official observations see *Appendix II*.

25 *Ingress,* is the start or point of contact and *Egress* is the point where the bodies lose contact.

26 Now known as *Tahiti.*

27 Robson, John, 2000. *Captain Cook's World.* Rochester, Chatham Publishing.

28 Taylor, E G R, 1966. *The Mathematical Practitioners of Hanoverian England 1714-1840.* Cambridge, Cambridge University Press. p.51..

29 Willson, Beckles, 1900. *The Great Company (1667-1871).* London, Smith, Elder & Co.

30 Comet C/1769 P1 Messier.

31 Isle of St. Agnes.

32 Harris, Simon, 2001. *Sir Cloudesley Shovell. Stuart Admiral.* Staplehurst, Spellmount.

7

BUSINESS IN LONDON

"Earth has not anything to show more fair:
Dull would he be of soul who could pass by
A sight so touching in its majesty:..."[1]

Having spent sixteen months away, there is no doubt that
William Wales would be pleased to be back home again in
London, and delighted to be reunited with his wife Mary, his
little daughter Sarah, now in her third year, and his new son
William of sixteen months, born the week after his father had
left for Hudson's Bay.

Mary, anxious to tell William about her travels to Yorkshire,
and her stay at Warmfield. How she would have been
welcomed there by William's brother John and his family,
and by William's parents, and his sister Sarah. Mary would
give William news of his two nieces, Sarah and Mary and
their brother John, and she would tell of brother John's wife
Mary due to give birth again in two months time to their
fourth child.

Back at Churchill, at the beginning of November, Samuel
Hearne was setting off on his expedition to find the Coppermine
River for the Hudson's Bay Company, his Journal begins:

> 1769. Having made every necessary arrangement for
> my departure on the sixth November, I took leave
> of the Governor, and my other friends, at Prince of

Wales's Fort, and began my journey, under the salute of seven cannon....[2].

To conclude his own journal, William Wales wrote of his apprehension in submitting such a personal document to such an erudite Society[3]:

> ....I flatter myself that no gentleman will think that I have laid the preceding remarks before this learned Society, under a presumption that they can, in any respect, merit their notice. There are many of them on subjects which I am but little acquainted with: these were made only for my own amusement, and are now submitted to the Royal Society, at their command, and under a thorough conviction that they will be read with those candid allowances, which, I am well convinced they stand much in need of. At the same time, I sincerely declare, that it would give me the highest satisfaction if they should be found to contain one useful hint, or be conductive of pleasure to any person whatsoever...[4]

One of the main documents submitted to the Royal Society by Wales with the Journal, was the report of the *Astronomical Observations* by Wales and Dymond. This was read to the Royal Society on 16th November 1769, but Wales was so distressed by the inaccuracy of their transit observations that he refused to submit them to the Society initially, however these would not be denied the members for long.[5] Another paper, this time of the Meteorological Observations, was published in 1770.[6]

William Wales was again contributing to periodicals. In November 1769 there appeared a letter from Wales to Mr Urban of the *Gentleman's Magazine,* explaining the method of configuring sun-dials, in reply to one which had appeared earlier in the magazine that year. He concludes:

… There is no need of a diagram to explain this to the intelligent reader.[7]

It was just two days before Christmas day of 1769 that Mary, the wife of William Wales' only brother John, gave birth to a baby girl Abigail, but sadly Mary died in labour, mercifully baby Abigail survived. On Christmas Eve they buried Mary in the churchyard at Kirkthorpe, Abigail was baptized the same day.

Mary's death hit the Wales family hard, especially John. A poem passed down through the family was reputedly written by John, who on hearing a robin sing on Mary's grave, was moved to reflect on her life, that she was good, and kind, not proud. He called her *Molly*.[8]

The members of the Wales family had been strict church people, but John, on questioning his faith, was advised by the vicar at Warmfield, the Rev Swiney, to go and listen to the *Methodists* who had come to Wakefield, and report back. The visit had resulted in John converting to Methodism. He introduced the Methodists into the village, his opinions commanded great respect amongst the villagers, and eventually the vicar converted and preached 'Christ and him crucified' until his death.[9]

Evidence of John Wales' career as a weaver indicates that he was perhaps more than a manual worker in the industry. With his daughters' conversions to Methodism, their eventual offspring were baptized in the chapels of that religion, when it was required to give the occupation of the mother's father. In 1797 and 1799 Mary recorded that her father had been a 'Gentleman'.[10] Abigail recorded that her father has been an 'Astronomer' when her daughter Ann was baptized in 1804.[11] These three entries were probably due to John Wales' work as a Calculator for the Board of Longitude, but then in 1806 Abigail recorded that her father had been a 'Tammy Manufacturer' when her son Thomas was baptized, tammy was a type of cloth.[12]

Baby Abigail Wales grew up to marry and have children of her own, and on her death, which occurred on her 78th birthday in 1847, her daughter Mary Wales Fenton, in a *Memorial* to her mother, told of Abigail describing her mother Mary's tragic death:

> ...My beloved mother, whose maiden name was Wales, was born at Warmfield, a small village about 3 miles from Wakefield, in the year 1769. My grandmother died in giving birth to my mother, and in her last moments gave her the name Abigail.......[13]

In the *Memorial* Mary Wales Fenton reveals that Abigail was raised by her grandmother, Sarah Wales. Sarah was then aged 71, and would no doubt also play a big part in bringing up Abigail's siblings Mary aged 4; John, 3; and Sarah, 1. Abigail's aunt Sarah Wales, then aged 30, would also be on hand no doubt to lend a hand.[14]

Abigail told her daughter that her grandmother Sarah refused to follow the faith of the *Methodists*, and when John was absent listening to their preaching, Sarah would often make Abigail kneel with her for 4 hours whilst she read prayers and prayed for her son John.[15]

It appears that William Wales, Mary, and the family, may not have been living in Fleet Street at this time. Mary soon became pregnant with their third child and was due to give birth in 1770, they named their new daughter Anne Hagley Wales[16] and it is evident from a later census that she was born in the Clerkenwell district of London.[17]

Mary Wales' brother, Rev John Green, was still operating his Academy in London, and working on his latest book which was published in 1771, *Grammatical spelling book...to which is added, Mnemonics memory'*

Of Joseph Dymond, his remaining career is a mystery. Two of his brothers were in partnership in Holborn, London, as *Surgeons, Apothecaries and Man midwives* in 1779.[18] Joseph headed back north and married Elizabeth Foster of Blyth in Nottinghamshire in 1777, here they had four children, Joseph, James, Elizabeth and Anne.[19]

The marine timekeeper made by John Harrison, and known as H4, was now the property of the Board of Longitude. Having had sea trials in 1761 and 1764, and tested at Greenwich in 1766, the next year H4 was placed in the capable hands of Larcum Kendall, who was commissioned to make a copy of it, meanwhile Harrison was busy working on a fifth timepiece, H5.[20] Kendall had been apprenticed to John Jeffreys who had died in 1754, and he had also worked for George Graham, Thomas Mudge, and William Dutton, in 1765 he had been appointed to the Board of Longitude as a 'practical' expert.. The copy of H4 had taken Kendall three years to make, and was finally handed over to the Board in January 1770, when it was subject to trials at Greenwich.[21]

William Wales' all consuming obsession with mathematics evidently covered all branches of the subject, his talent as a geometer was demonstrated many times in his contributions to the *Ladies' Diary,* and was further evident when, in 1772, there appeared in print *The two books of Apollonius Pergæus, concerning determinate section, as they have been restored by Willebrordus Smellius,* by the authors Apollonius (of Perga), Willebroardus Snellius, John Lawson and William Wales.[22]

In 1745 there had appeared *Algebra and the Elements of Geometry*, by Professor Thomas Simpson of Woolwich Royal Military Academy, who had incorporated into his work some of the principal hypotheses of the philosophers of the ancient world. This publication's content had caused the pages of the eighteenth century mathematical publications to show a remarkable increase in geometrical exercises, and after Simpson's death in 1761, it was Rev John Lawson, whom Wales had written to from Hudson's Bay on geometrical posers, who had taken the lead in delving further into the geometrical speculations of the ancient mathematicians and published works on his findings.[23]

The ancient geometrician Apollonius was of the time of Ptolemy c240 BC, and had written eight books on Conic Sections, of which only seven had been extant in the mid eighteenth century. The work had been translated, and restored, and published by various mathematicians, and it was William Wales' restoration of the work which his friend John Lawson had appended, with his own findings, on the subject in his publication of 1772.[24]

William's computing career continued, and on 8th and 15th March 1770 he finally presented his transit of Venus results to the Royal Society. He read the fifty page manuscript of his journal to the members, which included all the botanical, climatic, and scientific information. To his relief, his efforts were applauded on completion, and he returned home a happier man.

The minutes of the Secretary of the Royal Society, covering the reading of Wales' manuscript, state :

> ...A variety of new and useful matter; such as latitudes and longitudes of Harbours and Capes, and similar occasional investigations at Sea; Observations for

determining the variations of the needle in different latitudes and longitudes; Remarks upon the nature, formation, course, and Navigation of the numerous Islands of floating Ice; concerning the temperature; fossil vegetable and annual productions of the Country about Hudson's Bay; of the genius of the inhabitants and of the Eskimaux Indians &c.

The observations contributed to understanding the scale of our solar system and its place in the galaxy, the key lay in the precise timing to the second of the time which elapsed between Venus's entry and exit over the sun's face. The apparent simplicity of the exercise had potential problems, the weather, the exact latitude calculation of the observer, and the precision of the instruments and time-pieces used, could easily have threatened the whole exercise, astronomical clocks could prove temperamental when faced with extremes of temperature, and then there was the human element[25] – the transit of Venus would not occur again until 1874.

The observation data of the 1769 Transit of Venus totalled over 600 sets from observers around the world, this was eventually fed to the world's scientific establishments, and the results were analysed and computed. One of the most critical papers was eventually presented some two and a half years after the event to the Royal Society by Oxford University's Savilian Professor of Astronomy, Thomas Hornsby, who computed the results of five observations, from Lapland by Maximilian Hell, from the Kola Peninsula by Stepan Rumovsky, from Hudson's Bay by Joseph Dymond and William Wales, from California by Jean Chappe d'Auteroche, and from Tahiti by James Cook and Charles Green. Hornsby concluded from these five sets of data that the mean distance of the earth from the sun was 93,726,900 English miles. The current accepted distance by the International Astronomical Union is 92,958,329 English miles. After the 1769 transit the Earth and planets could take their place more accurately within the complexity of the solar system – not quite as accurately as today, but enough to push out the boundaries of 18th century astronomy.[26]

The astronomer Helen Sawyer Hogg, evaluated Wales' Journal as written in a scientific manner, with almost no comments on the discomforts he endured during the voyage, and while resident at Hudson's Bay. She wrote that his quaint and vivid phraseology makes it an enjoyable read, and that it remains a great rarity, being an important account of the only trip specifically for astronomical purposes in early days in Arctic Canada, and an important document of historical astronomy.[27]

Wales and Dymond certainly left their mark at Hudson's Bay, being the first scientists to winter there, their presence had certainly inspired the HBC into taking a more active role in the scientific world. The Company had been impressed by the work done by their guests, so much so that in the end they decided not to charge the Royal Society the £250 agreed formerly for the scientists' accommodation.[28]

When Wales left Churchill, Andrew Graham entrusted him with a collection of specimens to give to the Royal Society on his return – quadrupeds, birds and fishes were added to Wales' luggage. The collection's eventual presentation led to such excitement in London's scientific circles, that at the request of the Society, further specimens were conveyed annually from Hudson's Bay to London.[29]

Wales and Dymond had kept a complete record of the weather, and in 1770 the Royal Society requested that the Hudson's Bay Company send them natural history specimens, undoubtedly as a direct result of Wales' report. In the 1771-2 season Wales was asked to advise two of the HBC officers,

Andrew Graham and Thomas Hutchins, on the keeping of meteorological observations at the York Factory.[30]

Those first meteorological observations, started by William Wales in 1768, were continued at both Churchill and the York factories, and after 1852 they were recorded by the Royal Canadian Mounted Police, so that today the meteorological records for Central Canada go back almost 250 years.

The visit of Wales and Dymond inspired the HBC into unprecedented action. The Royal Society began to receive numerous boxes of natural history specimens after their stay, and Samuel Wegg was soon Deputy-Governor, and then Governor of the Company. In 1772 Wegg headed a special committee to preserve and catalogue the specimens.[31]

It was when Samuel Wegg eventually became governor of the HBC in 1782, that he made available the Company records to British scientists, and cartographers such as Aaron Arrowsmith.[32]

In this Age of Enlightenment the scientific knowledge of the North American Arctic had not been so far advanced as that of northern Europe, but commercial and mining interests of the Hudson's Bay Company and its status, meant that it was able to push expeditions into the interior of Canada and beyond, and scientific knowledge was taken on board as part of its explorations.

At the other side of the world, penetration into the Pacific and the South Seas region was not so advanced, the region was relatively uncharted by western explorers, with little or no contact between the indigenous people and the white man. In 1520 Magellan had named *Mar Pacifico,* and during the next 250 years the fringes had been visited by the Spaniards, Portuguese, and the Dutch.

The Seven Years' War had ended on 10th February 1763 with the signing of the Peace of Paris, when England had gained Canada, Nova Scotia, and a sizeable amount of the neighbouring islands, and with peace both Britain and France were looking to infiltrate the Pacific for trade, colonization, and the ever-growing scientific interest. In 1764 Britain sent Hon John Byron[33] out with two ships, he on the frigate *Dolphin*, and Captain Mouat on the sloop *Tamar*, with a brief to search for the Great Southern Continent, the fabled *Terra Australis Incognita*, tantalizingly mentioned in so many tales of the early explorers, to search for the North-West Passage, and to survey and thoroughly record positions of islands and other features, and to record sea, weather, and tidal conditions. Byron returned almost two years later having nothing new to report, he was not the best man for the job.

The British were determined to try again, and within a month the Government sent Samuel Wallis, also on *Dolphin*, with the same brief. Wallis had the necessary skill and experience to tackle the job better than Byron, he took with him the sloop *Swallow*, with Philip Carteret as its commander, Wallis looked after his men well, and had a desire to communicate with the natives. His voyage took him more south than Byron's route, and he had sighted a great land far in the distance, which he recorded as the Great Southern Continent, but as the weather closed in he had drifted towards a great island on which he spent six weeks, a beautiful land of plenty, and beautiful people, he claimed it for the King, and named it *King George's Land* – this was Tahiti.

In France Louis XV had sent Louis de Bougainville with the ships *La Boudeuse* and *L'Étoile* on a circumnavigation of the world. Bougainville was a mathematician, and in 1759, as a Captain in the French army, had been at the fall of Quebec during the Seven Years' War, where James Cook had also seen action, and carried out surveying work for the

British. Bougainville set sail on 15th November 1766, but the subsequent account failed to record any definitive information of his navigation during the course of this voyage, from which he returned in 1769.

By the time Wallis had returned from his voyage, the arrangement of voyages for the transit of Venus was a matter of urgency. Wallis had indicated that Port Royal Harbour, in King George's Land, would be a convenient place for observing the transit, and so Tahiti was chosen as one of the observation destinations under the command of Cook on *Endeavour*. Apart from the transit, a further reason for this voyage, would be to try and duplicate and then progress further the explorations of Wallis.

Cook's official sailing orders were:

> By the Commissioners for executing the Office of Lord High Admiral of he United Kingdom of Great Britain and Ireland, &c., &c.

> Whereas we have, in obedience to the King's commands, caused His Majesty's Bark, the *Endeavour*, whereof you are the commander, to be fitted out in a proper manner for receiving such persons as the Royal Society should think fit to appoint to observe the passage of the Planet Venus over the disk of the sun on the 3rd June, 1769, and for conveying them to such place to the south-ward of the Equinoctial Line as should be judged proper for observing that phenomenon, and whereas the Council of the Royal Society have acquainted us that they have appointed Mr. Charles Green, together with yourself, to be observers of the said phenomenon, and have desired that the observation may be made at Port Royal Harbour in King George the Third's Island lately discovered by Captain Wallis in His Majesty's

Ship the *Dolphin,* the place thereof being not only better ascertained than any other within the limits proper for observation, but also better situated, and in every other respect the most advantageous; you are hereby required and directed to receive the said Mr. Charles Green, with his servant, instruments and baggage, on board the said Bark, and proceed in her according to the following instructions.....[34]

The instructions went on meticulously describing where the observations were to take place, and what was expected of the observers, also that Mr Green was to have leisure in order to spend time adjusting and trying the instruments beforehand.

The methods of navigation at sea at this time were progressing well, Maskelyne had developed his lunar distance method for determining longitude, and the new *Nautical Almanac* had been published, both were to be used during Cook's voyage to prepare an accurate record for all who were to follow.

Cook's instructions were in two parts – the second, which was to be opened while at sea, detailed him that:

...Whereas there is reason to imagine that there is a Continent or Land of great extent, may be found to the southward of the Tract lately made by Captn Wallis or the Tract of any former Navigators in Pursuits of the like kind ...You are to proceed to the southward in order to make discovery of the Continent above mentioned...[35]

Cook was to take possession of this land with the consent of the natives, to explore as much coast as was practicable, and to note and collect samples of its natural products, both fauna and flora, his responsibilities for his ship, crew, and the scientists, added to the huge task of recording lands half a world away, and to include carrying out important astronomical observations. The magnitude of this eighteenth century voyage in a wooden ship can by today's standard only be left to the imagination.

When Charles Green boarded the *Endeavour* he was an energetic and capable man of 33 years, yet drastically untidy, he had a servant by the name of John Reynolds. His attempts to school some of the ship's company in navigation were not always successful, yet he was conscientious in his work as astronomer on the voyage[36].

Equipment and instruments taken on board for Green were meager, compared to that of another scientist who was to accompanying Cook on the voyage, this was Joseph Banks, the botanist whose family hailed from Lincolnshire. Banks was a wealthy gentleman, well versed in natural history, and his retinue comprised a further seven people, including Daniel Carl Solander[37] to assist him in his quest to record and gather botanical specimens from ports of call during the voyage. Elaborate preparations had to be made to *Endeavour* in order to accommodate Banks and his party.

After setting sail from Plymouth, and stopping at Madeira to take on board supplies, *Endeavour* sailed across the Atlantic stopping off at Staten Island where Cook and Green made a series of lunar observations, these had been the first ever made in this location. They then sailed around Cape Horne before entering the Pacific and on to Tahiti, this island was just a small dot on the map in a vast ocean covering some 400 square miles, but the tropical island paradise was the centre of Polynesian culture, and the inhabitants had welcomed these white-skinned curiously dressed sailors, who offered wonderful gifts and trinkets in exchange for items of their culture.

An observatory was sited on the northernmost part of the island, which was named Point Venus, tents were surrounded by a stockade, and thus Fort Venus was established. The magnitude of the investment in the forthcoming observations caused Cook to establish a further two observatories, just in case anything went wrong. At Point Venus would be Cook, Green, and Daniel Solander, each with his own telescope, making independent observations, while John Gore, Dr Monkhouse, and his brother went to a small island off Moorea to the west of Tahiti, and Messrs Hicks, Clerke, Pickersgill, and Saunders went to a small island off the east coast of Tahiti.

On completing the Transit observations, the second set of the Governments instructions were opened by Cook, and *Endeavour* headed south and west for the legendary southern continent.

Endeavour reached New Zealand, and Cook began exploring the coast of the North Island, during which he had been reminded by Green that a transit of the planet Mercury was due on 9th November 1769, and so a site was chosen at the place which is now called Mercury Bay, on the east coast and just west of the Purangi River. Here in the early morning Cook, Green, and Hicks took instruments onto the beach, and recorded their observations of the transit of Mercury in ideal conditions.

It was in March 1770, while Wales was reading his Hudson's Bay journal to the Royal Society in London, that his brother-in-law Charles Green, on board the *Endeavour* with Cook, found a bay while sailing around the coast of South Island of New Zealand. The bay looked most inviting, being a haven from the open sea and weather, and a safe anchoring place, but before it was possible to explore further darkness approached, and a fierce wind drove them north, Cook named the bay *Dusky*.

From New Zealand Cook pushed on to Botany Bay in Australia, and sailing north mapped the eastern coast. In October 1770 *Endeavour* dropped anchor in Batavia roads where Cook arranged for the ship to undergo necessary repairs. By chance a Dutch East Indiaman ship was leaving for England, and Cook took the chance to send to the Admiralty in London a copy of his Journal to date, and also all the Log Books and Journals he could muster of the Petty Officers and Seamen aboard.

Batavia was not a place to linger, malaria and dysentery were rife, and very soon the ship's company began to suffer from fever, seven of the ship's company died here, including John Reynolds – Green's servant. As soon as possible the ship set sail again across the Indian Ocean for Cape Town, on 31st January 1771 Charles Green died.

While on the voyage, it is evident that Green had a calm and collected disposition, this had been especially evident during times of danger. When, on one occasion on the Great Barrier Reef, *Endeavour* drifted precariously towards some breakers due to a particularly strong current, Green carried on taking observations with which to calculate their longitude. When visiting a new island, Green was usually amongst the party who went out on foot to explore the place.[38]

So it was that Green met his maker, he would never see England again. He had not apparently died of dysentery, a newspaper of the time reported that he had been suffering from an illness for some time, and his doctor had advised him to keep warm, but he had ignored this advice and stuck his legs out of one of the portholes one night, and this action had contributed to his death. Cook similarly reported that for some time he had been suffering ill health, and eventually the manner in which he ignored his illness had brought on the flux which was the cause of his untimely end.[39]

Green had apparently been a victim of his own self-indulgence, but he had been a considerable help to Cook with the tasks in hand, with the astronomical observations and the charting of thousands of miles of coastline – and Cook missed him.[40] Green was committed to the deep, possibly in the vicinity of the place where his previous vessel *Aurora* with Mr Falconer on board had been lost.[41] In all twenty four men died on the voyage.

Meanwhile back in London at the Board of Longitude's meeting in March 1771 it was resolved that 'William Wales be one of the persons to instruct the Masters of His Majesty's Ships in and about London in the use of the Nautical Almanac'.[42]

Cook arrived back in England after almost three years away, and anchored *Endeavour* at The Downs, off Deal in Kent, on 13th July, 1771. The Royal Society were highly satisfied with the way the Transit of Venus had been observed, and the relevant recordings made by Cook and Green were put into the capable hands of the Astronomer Royal, Mr Maskelyne, that he might deduce from them the important consequences to science resulting from the observation.[43]

All the observations were eventually passed to William Wales for his scrutiny and preparation for publication, when Maskelyne criticized some of Green's astronomical observations, Captain Cook sprang to his defence by reminding Maskelyne of the damaged quadrant, he went on:

> ...Mr M. should have considered before he took upon him to censure these observations, that he had put

into his hands the very original book in which they were written in pencil, only, the very moment they were taken and I appeal to Mr M. himself, if it is not highly probable that some of them might from various causes, as either to be wholly rejected or to be marked as dubious and which might have been done had Mr Green taken the trouble to enter them in the proper book. Mr M. should also have considered, that this was, perhaps, the only true original paper of the kind ever put into his hands; does Mr M. publish to the world all the observations he makes good and the bad or did he never make a bad observation in his life.[44]

Cook wrote in his journal in August 1770 of Green's persistent effort in making and recording his observations, and he had further instructed some of the petty officers in the same. Cook reflected that this was their only way of finding longitude, accurate to within half of one degree, which had proved sufficient for their needs. It was only by this means finding the longitude at sea could be brought into universal practice[45]

Whatever his critics said and wrote, there can be little doubt that Charles Green had played an important part in the mathematics and navigation of the mid eighteenth century, he had taught and practiced his skills, and worked hard to earn his place in the history of the British nation.

During the summer of 1771 at Warmfield in Yorkshire, John Wales the father of William Wales died on 14th May, and was buried two days later in the churchyard of Kirkthorpe, he was 73 years of age and described as a Labourer.[46] He would have been a proud father knowing of his eldest son's achievements at Hudson's Bay, he left a widow, Sarah Wales, and his three offspring William, John, now a widower, and the youngest Sarah, aged 31 and still a spinster.

James Cook was mindful of the huge contribution his crew had given, and set about making sure his crew-members achieved their deserved promotions. The voyage had been a great success, and he and his fellow travellers had brought back journals, detailed observations, many artifacts, and plant specimens from those far-off lands, as well as reporting to the Admiralty. He wrote to Green's family to tell them of the circumstances of Charles Green's death, tragic news for Charles' wife Elizabeth whom he had married just five months before he left on the voyage, and sad news for the rest of the family, some in London, and some in Yorkshire, Charles had been the youngest son of Joshua and Ann, and for his youngest sister Mary Wales the news came a year after the tragic death of her sister-in-law Mary Wales at Warmfield.

The public were naturally curious about the *Endeavour* voyage, but Cook was barely known in London Society at this time, and it was to the scientists that most of the attention was given on their return. Joseph Banks and Daniel Solander were heroes, celebrities whose lives would never be the same again. One of the first publications to print news of their return reported:

> ...On Saturday last an express arrived at the Admiralty with the agreeable news of the arrival at the Downs of the *Endeavour*, Captain Cook, from the East Indies. This ship sailed in August 1768 with Mr Banks, Dr Solander, Mr Green, and other ingenious Gentlemen on board, for the South Seas, to observe the Transit of Venus; they have since made a voyage round the world, and touched at every coast and island, where it was possible to get on shore to collect every species of plants and other rare productions in nature ...[47]

Cook's heroism was to be recognized, and the secretary to the Admiralty, Philip Stephens, was certainly impressed by Cook's achievement. First Lord of the Admiralty, Lord Sandwich, was a great friend of Joseph Banks, and the wheeling and dealing of the old boy network was soon in motion, Banks was negotiating plans for yet another voyage – his ambitions were huge, and he needed more people on the next voyage, with more room on board Banks had the money and now surely the celebrity to achieve this, he knew no boundaries at this time, and really convinced himself that the next voyage to the Pacific belonged to him.

Cook was included in Joseph Banks' plans of course, as captain and navigator of a proposed ship which would be larger than *Endeavour*. What Banks didn't know at this time was that Lord Sandwich had already promoted Cook to the rank of Captain, and discussion with Cook at the Admiralty had secured his position as leader of a second voyage to settle the existence of the Great Southern Continent, and claim it for King and country, this time two ships were to be sent.

The voyage preparations by Banks were punctuated by his visits to the grand houses of England and his lavish haunts in London, during which he assembled a potential staff of untold scientific expertise. Cook's more diligent approach was to carefully select two vessels, *Resolution* and *Adventure,* and leaving instructions for their fitting out for his next voyage, he still worked on his *Endeavour* journal while laying out his plans for the next voyage. James Cook nonetheless afforded himself, and his wife Elizabeth, time to travel to his native Yorkshire where he met with old friends and employers, as well as his family.

The Admiralty laid down plans for Cook's second voyage, to first head for Madeira to take on wine for the voyage of both vessels, and then immediately go to the Cape of Good Hope to take on provisions. To then search for *Cape Circumcision* as described by the Frenchman Jean-Baptiste-Charles Bouvet de Lozier in 1739, this was the prime object of the voyage. Bouvet had indicated that this was the route to finding a southern continent. Of the location of Cape Circumcision, Cook was to survey the land thoroughly, the position, the natural history, any minerals and mines, and any inhabitants, and determine whether the land was part of a southern continent or an island.[48]

Should the land described above prove to be an island, then Cook was instructed to head south from there, in search of a southern continent as near the South Pole as possible, and when the weather was such that exploration was no longer possible, then the vessels were to head back towards the north to refresh until conditions allowed further exploration near the Pole. Cook was to aim at circumnavigating the South Pole as near to it as possible, before returning to Cape Circumcision and then onto England. When he had the opportunity, he was instructed to seal and return to the Admiralty in England any journals, drawings, and maps completed during the voyage.[49]

On Cook's return to London after his family visit to Yorkshire in January 1772, he checked his vessels, agreed his route with Lord Sandwich, and Hugh Palliser the comptroller of the Navy Board, and hoped to set off in March – but the plans of Banks were huge and it was clear that *Resolution* could not cope with his plans. After many alterations to the structure to accommodate Banks and his entourage, the ship was taken on trials, but the vessel was proving to be unstable, and there was nothing left but to restore her to the original plans of Cook, resulting in the voyage being delayed by some four months. Eventually a devastated Banks was resigned to the fact that his plans were just too ambitious to accommodate a safe passage, and he reluctantly accepted that this time he was not to be the voyage's botanist.

Cook was to be joined on his second voyage by a German botanist Johann Reinhold Forster and his eldest son Georg, who had arrived in London on 4th October 1766 from St Petersburg. The elder Forster at the age of thirty seven, had been hoping to find a new life for his family in England, he had left his wife Justina behind with the rest of their children. He was a scholar and scientist of some note, his subjects covered natural history and sciences, and he was a master of some seventeen languages, he had associated and corresponded with some of the most noted scientists around the world, and was a favourite of Carl Linnaeus through his contribution to science.[50]

Like many other men of science of this age J R Forster had started his career as a theologian, reluctantly he took up the cloth, and it was only after twelve years that he managed to break free from his parsonage near Danzig to embark on a career in natural history, by now he had a wife and seven children. Forster was eventually called by the Russian government to travel to their new colonies and report on conditions there. His young son Georg, whom Johann was educating, went along with him. Georg had shown early scientific ability, and together they used the journey to work on establishing a scientific name for themselves.[51]

Events instigated by J R Forster's eventual reports back to the Russian government, culminated in Forster having to salvage what he could from what had been just verbal agreements. He had fully expected that his efforts would be justly rewarded on his return, with both monetary compensation and a promise of further promotion in the service of the Russian government, but this was not to be, and he was left to beg what introductory letters from his scientific friends he could, and head with these to England, where he hoped he could again try and carve out something of a scientific career.[52]

J R Forster and his now eleven year old son Georg had arrived in London with very little money, they lived in lodgings in Denmark Street and initially survived by selling some of the artifacts they had collected during their expedition, and producing and selling pamphlets on various scientific subjects – mineralogy and zoology, as well as botany. Eventually J R with the help of his friends, and through his experience and remaining artifacts retrieved from his Russian tour, somehow managed to become known in scientific circles, even to become a Fellow of the Royal Society.

In June 1767 J R Forster gained a position as tutor at the Dissenters' Academy in Warrington, Lancashire – replacing Joseph Priestley[53] at this increasingly prestigious learning establishment. He reluctantly decided to leave his son Georg in London, where he was to be apprenticed in a merchant's house. Johann was to stay in Warrington for three years, where he was among the first to publicly teach natural history in England, and it was during this time that his wife and the rest of their family joined him, before London called him back temptingly with a promise of a place on a voyage to the far east with Alexander Dalrymple, a voyage which failed to come to fruition. In March 1771 J R Forster was to again rely on his contacts to try and advance his career. The Forster family settled in London at No 2 Somerset Stable Yard in the Strand, and Johann worked on a translation from the French of Louis Antoine de Bougainville's *Voyage round the World,* which had taken place from 1766 to 1769, the work was published in London in 1772.[54]

The lawyer Daines Barrington, as vice-president of both the Society of Antiquaries and the Royal Society, at this time became acquainted with J R Forster through various papers Forster had been working on, and it was through this course of events that Barrington headed Forster's election to the Royal

Society. During the first half of 1772 the Royal Society had received the natural history specimens, sent by the Hudson's Bay Company as a direct result of William Wales' visit there, and these were given to Forster to work on, so that when it was obvious that Banks was no longer a contender as botanist on Cook's second voyage, Forster just happened to be in the right place at the right time, and doing the right task.[55]

To compensate for the loss of Banks' artists, who had been called upon on the *Endeavour* to record the people and lands visited on the voyage, William Hodges was chosen as official artist for the second voyage.

In October 1770 Nevil Maskelyne wrote to Lord Sandwich:

> ...representing that the intended expedition to the South Seas may be rendered more serviceable to the improvement of Geography & Navigation than it can otherwise be if the ship be furnished with such Astronomical Instruments as this Board hath the disposal of or can obtain the use of from the Royal Society also some of the Longitude Watches; and, above all, if a proper person could be sent out to make use of those Instruments & teach the Officers on board the ship the method of finding the Longitude.[56]

Maskelyne was mindful of Harrison's chronometer H4,[57] for although he was still an avid supporter of the lunar method of finding longitude, he had carried out trials on H4 on the Barbados voyage of 1764 with Charles Green, when the results were impressive, and he had carried out further trials at the Observatory for ten months during 1766-7. The actual timepiece had failed these trials, however Maskelyne was of the opinion that a more accurate copy of the timekeeper could be useful if used alongside his lunar distance method to find longitude. On these recommendations Kendall's copy of H4, known as K1, was completed in 1769, and was handed to the Board of Longitude in January 1770, when it was inspected by, among others, John Harrison's son William, who admitted it was even better made than his father's original,[58] but it needed testing at sea accurately if Harrison was to win that Longitude prize, a lot of money was at stake.

The forthcoming voyage was a golden chance to try Kendall's K1 timepiece, and the Board of Longitude agreed Maskelyne's suggestions at their meeting on 28th November, 1771. Each ship was to take two timepieces, and so three other timepieces were needed, these would be made by John Arnold whom the Board of Longitude had met at their meeting in May 1770. Arnold was a prolific chronometer maker, who had been greatly influenced by the publication *The Principles of Mr Harrison's Timekeeper,* which had been written by John Harrison and published by Maskelyne who had given him a copy.[59]

Banks" scientific staff, originally chosen for the second voyage, was to include Doctor James Lind of Edinburgh as doctor and astronomer. Reverend Joseph Priestley, now of Mill Hill Chapel in Leeds was also approached, but the choice of official astronomers for the voyage was the prerogative of the Admiralty, and it was Sir Nevil Maskelyne, as Astronomer Royal and leading consultant on astronomical matters for both the Board of Longitude and the Council of the Royal Society, who had already proposed two names to the Admiralty, and at this juncture he would not have had experience of the work of many. Charles Green, who had been with him at Barbados was now dead. On Maskelyne's appointment to the Royal Observatory, and Green's resignation, it was Joseph Dymond who was appointed as his first assistant. Dymond was then sent to Hudson's Bay with William Wales in 1768 to observe the transit of Venus, and Maskelyne had to appoint another assistant, William Bayly. Wales had proved to Maskelyne that he was not only a capable mathematician as a Nautical Almanac calculator, but also a capable astronomer, from the sterling work he had done at Hudson's Bay. It was William Wales and William Bayly who Maskelyne proposed as astronomers on Cook's second voyage.

It would seem that towards the end of his life, when recollecting events prior to Cook's voyage of 1772 to one Robert Brown, Joseph Banks sought to take credit for the selection of Wales and Bayly as astronomers of the voyage when he recounts that:

> ....besides nine servants, all practiced and taught by myself to collect and preserve such objects of Natural History as might occur; three of whom had already been with me on my last voyage. Besides this I had influence enough to prevail with the Board of Longitude to send with us Messrs. Bailey and Wales as astronomers[60]

The position of Joseph Priestley as astronomer was rejected by the Board of Longitude largely because of his religious principles, despite Joseph Banks objecting to their protestations on the subject.[61] Priestley, born in 1733/4 at Birstall near Leeds in Yorkshire to a deeply religious Calvanistic family, had been educated at a dissenting academy in preparation for the ministry. After a time ministering in Suffolk and Cheshire, he went on to teach at the Warrington Academy before moving to the Mill Hill Chapel in Leeds. Despite his early career he was essentially a scientist, and in 1766 he published *The History and Present State of Electricity*. Priestley had many friends in London, and was elected a Fellow of the Royal Society, he went on to be instrumental in the discovery of oxygen.[62]

The success of Cook's voyages was largely dependent on astronomy and navigation, the two were mutually inseparable and in fact this was *nautical astronomy*. Without the aid of good navigation instruments and capable astronomers on board, the expeditions could have ended in tragedy, and the astronomers were detailed not only to observe and record, but also to be responsible for instructing in advanced navigation techniques.[63]

It was on 14th December, 1771, after consultations with professors of astronomy at the universities, that, at a meeting of the Board of Longitude the Astronomer Royal Nevil Maskelyne, proposed William Wales as observer for the *Resolution*, with William Bayly as observer on the accompanying ship *Adventure*. William Wales, who attended, was then called into the meeting, and asked what terms he would be willing to receive for the service. He first asked for £350 per annum, exclusive of expenses which he would submit for consideration. Bayly, who did not attend, apparently expected £300 per annum exclusive of expenses, or one guinea a day inclusive of expenses, (equating to £383.5s per annum). Wales was asked if he would agree to this also, but he declined, saying he would not go for less than £400 including expenses per annum, this rate was then agreed for both.

Cook's biographer J C Beaglehole, considered Wales to be the astronomer to have done the more varied work of the two, and that he had the more civilized, wide, and incisive mind, Bayly he considers hardly compared, and although he knew his job, he was of a lesser order.[64] In a letter to D. J. McCulloch in 1970, J C Beaglehole tells of his great respect for William Wales.[65]

Wales was anxious that his wife and growing family would be well provided for during his absence on such a long voyage, and after agreeing his terms added that he desired his wife be paid part of his proposed allowance during his absence. Consequently it was agreed that Mrs Wales be paid £150 per annum, by 6-monthly payments, until her husband's return, or if he should die during the voyage, then until word of his death arrived in England.[66] Immediately, Wales and Bayly were given an imprest of £150 for fitting themselves out for the voyage.[67]

Whenever the ships stayed in any harbour for more than a few days the astronomers were to set up their portable observatories on shore, to protect the instruments from the weather and the native population, and they were to set the pendulum clocks going. They were to make frequent observations to determine geographical position – latitude by meridian altitude with the 1 foot Astronomical quadrant; longitude by lunar distance (as at sea), and by Jupiter's satellite eclipses if possible, all timed by the clock; and observations to measure the rate of the going of the clocks and chronometers. Maskelyne produced technical instructions for the observers.[68]

Meanwhile the timepiece K1 remained at Greenwich under trial, where there was a certain amount of panic when it stopped on 10th January 1772, try as he might Maskelyne just couldn't get it going again despite warming it by a fire and moving the balance. So back to Kendall it went, when it was carefully opened by the maker and witnessed by two watchmakers as well as Maskelyne. Much to Maskelyne's relief Kendall soon had it working again, but it was then stopped, and Kendall took it to pieces, checking all the parts for signs of injury or wear, whereon, entirely satisfied, he reassembled the mechanism and handed it back for recommencement of trials at Greenwich.[69]

At the end of January 1772 the Board of Longitude summoned Wales and Bayly to a meeting, and read an amended draft of their instructions to them. They requested that they be supplied with some other provisions while on board, including candles, and also that they may be issued each with a portable observatory, which Mr Bayly had been working on as a convenient method of housing the instruments away from the weather while being able to observe, this was granted, the cost of £25 per observatory being met by the Board.[70]

On 7th March 1772 Wales and Bayly were present at a further meeting of the Board of Longitude, when they each received their stationery requirements for the forthcoming voyage. Their instructions were signed and copies were to be sent to the Admiralty, who would be asked that they instruct the commanders of the relevant vessels to assist and support the astronomers on all occasions when needed, in order that they could carry out tasks as instructed.[71]

In May the Board of Longitude resolved the following management plan for the watch machines:

> That such boxes as Messrs. Kendal and Arnold shall judge most proper for the reception of their respective watch machines be immediately provided;
>
> That three good locks of different wards be also provided and affixed to each box;
>
> That the key of one of the locks of each box be kept by the commander of the sloop wherein such box may be; that the key of another of the said locks be kept by the 1st lieutenant of the said sloop or officer next in command to him; and that the key of the third lock be kept by such one of the above mentioned observers (Messrs. Wales and Bayly) as shall be on board: which three persons are daily to be present at the winding up of the said watch machine and comparing them with

each other whilst on board and with the astronomical clock whilst on shore and to see that the respective times shown at such comparisons be properly inserted and attested under their hands in the general observation book which the said observers are ordered to keep. But if it shall happen that the commanders, officers or observers or either of them cannot at any time through indisposition or absence upon other necessary duties conveniently attend, their key or keys are in such case to be delivered to such other officer or officers of the sloops as the commanders can best trust therewith, in order that such other officer or officers may attend at the winding up and comparing etc. of the above mentioned watch machines during such indisposition or absence.[72]

The Earl of Sandwich, anxious to ensure the safe custody of the watches, asked the Board to consider issuing some directions to Wales and Bayly regarding the proper management of the handling of the watches, and these were issued.[73]

So the career of William Wales, mathematical, astronomical, and nautical, was to continue apace with the important role to which he had just been appointed, he was to be part of a team, hand-picked by some of the most important people in his country, to voyage around the world. We can only imagine the reaction of his wife Mary to the news, for while she would no doubt be bursting with pride at her husband's achievements, she had lost her brother on Cook's first voyage, and her husband had now being chosen to join the second voyage. Mary had three children to care for, four year old Sarah, William, aged three, and baby Anne Hagley, her time would be well occupied caring for them, while her thoughts would frequently stray far across the seas.

Likewise James Cook's wife would no doubt have been apprehensive, yet proud. Elizabeth Cook was a year younger than Mary Wales, both had experienced their husband's absence at the transit of Venus, they both were left with young children to care for, and both were to suffer the loss of sons, both in childhood, and at Cambridge University. Both had set out on the long journey to Yorkshire when pregnant, both were to have their portraits painted for posterity, and despite their hard lives, both were to far outlive their husbands, dying well into old age.

Endnotes

1   William Wordsworth, (1770-1850). *Upon Westminster Bridge.*

2   Hearne, S, 1968. *Journey from Prince of Wales's Fort in Hudson's Bay to the Northern Ocean.* New York, De Capo Press.

3   The Royal Society.

4   Wales, W, 1770 *Journal of a Voyage made by Order of the Royal Society, to Churchill River, on the North-west Coast of Hudson's Bay; of Thirteen Months Residence in that Country; and of the Voyage back to England; in the Years 1768 and 1769.* Phil.Trans.R.Soc. Vol 60 pp.100-136.

5   Wales, W & Dymond, J, 1769. *Astronomical Observations made by Order of the Royal Society, at Prince of Wales's Fort on the north-west coast of Hudson's Bay.* Philosophical Transactions of the Royal Society lix,: pp.467-488.

6   Wales, W & Dymond, J. 1770. *Observations on the State of the Air, Winds, Weather, etc. made at the Prince of Wales's Fort, on the North-West Coast of Hudson's Bay, in the years 1768,and 1769.* Philosophical Transactions of the Royal Society, lx, pp137-78.

7   *Gentleman's Magazine*, November 1769, p.520.

8   Personal communication, Jan Shoulders.

9   Mrs Mary Wales Fenton. *Memoir of Mrs Abigail Manners.* (by her daughter). Methodist New Connexion Magazine, October 1848.

10 Baptism Registers of the Salem Chapel, King Street Methodist New Connexion, Dewsbury, Yorkshire, England.

11 England & Wales Non-Conformist and Non-Parochial Registers 1567-1970. New Connexion Chapel, Hull.

12 West Yorkshire Archive Service Ref NM/HSC/XVIII/1a Sheffield PNG Non Conformist Baptism.

13 Mrs Mary Wales Fenton. *Memoir of Mrs Abigail Manners.* (by her daughter). Methodist New Connexion Magazine, October 1848. p.437.

14 ibid.

15 ibid.

16 It is unclear why Ann was given the second name Hagley. There is evidence from the Wragby Parish Registers that a Thomas Wilson married an Ann Haglay (sic) in 1708, it could well be that Ann Haglay was some relation to the Green family. Another link with the name appears in Mary Wales' brother's will, when a Robert Hagley witnessed John Green's will in 1774.

17 The 1851 Census of England and Wales.

18 Will of Robert Dymond, PRO Probate Records. Ref PROB 11/1105.

19 Personal communication with descendants of the Dymond family, and the Parish Registers of Blyth, Nottinghamshire.

20 Howse & Hutchinson. 1969. *The Clocks and Watches of Captain James Cook 1769-1969.* London.

21 Messrs Bonhams, New Bond Street, London. Sale Catalogue *Fine Watches and Wristwatches.* 23.11.2004. p.26.

22 Printed by G Bigg, successor to D Leach, and sold by B White in Fleet Street; L David in Holborne; J Nourse, in the Strand; and T. Payne, near the Mews-Gate, 1772. 40 pages.

23 Wilkinson, T T, *Replies.* Notes and Queries. Vol. 2 (34) June 22, 1850, pp 57-59.

24 Hutton, Charles, 1815. *A Philosophical and mathematical Dictionary containing memoirs of the lives and writings of the most eminent authors.* London.

25 American astronomer David Rittenhouse is said to have fainted with excitement during the 1769 transit, and almost missed the time of initial contact.

26 Sellers, David, 2001. *The Transit of Venus.* Leeds, Maga Velda Press.

27 Hogg, Helen Sawyer, 1947. *Wales's Journal of a Voyage in 1768.* The Journal of The Royal Astronomical Society of Canada., Vol XLI., p 154.

28 Stearns, R P, *The Royal Society and the Company.* The Beaver magazine, June 1945.

29 1832, History Periodicals. *The Quarterly Review.* John Murray, p.361.

30 Williams, Glyndwr, 1979. *Dictionary of Canadian Biography.* Toronto, University of Toronto Press.

31 Stearns, R P, *The Royal Society and the Company.* The Beaver magazine, June 1945.

32 Lindsay, Debra (Ed), 1991. *The Modern Beginnings of Subarctic Ornithology: Correspondence with the Smithsonian Institute 1856-1868.* Manitoba Record Society Publications.

33 Hon John Byron was the grandfather of the poet, Lord George Gordon Byron 1788-1824.

34 Muir, John R, 1939. *Captain Cook.* London, Blackie & Son. Ltd.

35 ibid.

36 Cameron, R, 1965. *The Golden Haze.* London, Weidenfeld & Nicholson.

37 Dr Daniel Carl Solander 1736-1782, a Swedish botanist, a contemporary of Linnæus. Solander brought to England the Linnean system of plant classification.

38 Cameron, R, 1965. *The Golden Haze.* London, Weidenfeld & Nicholson.

39 ibid.

40 Beaglehole, J C,1974. *The Life of Captain James Cook.* London, A & C Black Ltd.

41 Kippis, A, 1788. *The Life of Captain James Cook*. London. pp 176-178. (Information given by William Wales F.R.S. on his Brother-in-Law Charles Green to A Kippis for this work).

42 Board of Longitude Papers, 14/5, 206.

43 Kippis, A, 1878. *Cooks Voyages and Life*. London, Bickers & Son.

44 British Museum Additional Manuscripts. 27888, fol.116v.

45 ibid. p.392.

46 *Burials 1758-1812, St Peter's Parish Church Warmfield (Kirkthorpe)* Published by Wakefield & District Family History Society. 2004.

47 *Bingley's Journal* Monday 15th July 1771.

48 Beaglehole, J C (Ed), 1969. *The Journals of Captain James Cook on His Voyages of Discovery. II. The Voyage of Resolution and Adventure 1772-1775,* Cambridge. Cambridge University Press.

49 ibid.

50 Hoare, Michael E, 1976. *The Tactless Philosopher*. Melbourne. Hawthorne Press.

51 ibid.

52 ibid.

53 Priestley had resigned being 'called to the pulpit' at Mill Hill Chapel in Leeds.

54 Hoare, Michael E, 1976. *The Tactless Philosopher*. Melbourne. Hawthorne Press.

55 ibid.

56 Board of Longitude Minutes. 28 November 1771, p.207.

57 H4 was completed, based on a watch that John Jeffreys, a London clockmaker had made for Harrison in 1753. His first three timepieces had been too cumbersome to go to sea, and he realized that the solution lay in watches rather than clocks. He got Jeffreys to make him a watch with a bi-metal strip, so that it would be not affected by temperature change, and he realized that he had to go for high frequency, high energy

oscillators, watches had high frequency oscillators, but they had internal disturbances which needed to be overcome by having high energy in the balance. Harrison was the first to realize this and he redesigned the swinging balance inside the watch, to give it a beat of five times a second, this was the solution to the problem. (This explanation by Jonathan Betts, Senior Horologist, Royal Observatory Greenwich. BBC Radio 4 *Making History* 25.11.2008.)

58 Dictionary of National Biography – Larcum Kendall (1719-1790)

59 Sobel, Dava & Andrewes, William J H, 1998. *The Illustrated Longitude.* London, Fourth Estate.

60 Smith, Edward, 1911. *The Life of Sir Joseph Banks.* London, Bodley Head. p.27n.

61 Smith, Edward, 1911. *The Life of Sir Joseph Banks.* London, Bodley Head.

62 Orange, A D, 1974. *Joseph Priestley.* Princes Risborough, Shire Publications Ltd.

63 Danson, E, 2005. *Weighing the World.* Oxford, Oxford University Press. p.99.

64 Beaglehole, J C, 1974. *The Life of Captain James Cook.* London, A & C Black. p.301.

65 Personal communication: Denis Joroyal McCulloch.

66 Beaglehole, J C, (Ed), 1969. *The Journals of Captain James Cook on His Voyages of Discovery. II. The Voyage of Resolution and Adventure 1772-1775*, Cambridge. Cambridge University Press. p.720.

67 ibid.

68 Howse, Derek, 1989. *Nevil Maskelyne, the Seaman's Astronomer.* Cambridge, Cambridge University Press. See Appendix IV of this volume for full Instructions given to Wales.

69 Howse & Hutchinson. 1969. *The Clocks and Watches of Captain James Cook 1769-1969.* London. p.192.

70 Beaglehole, J C (Ed), 1969. *The Journals of Captain James Cook on His Voyages of Discovery. II. The Voyage of Resolution and Adventure 1772-1775*, Cambridge. Cambridge University Press. p.722.

71 ibid. p.723.

72 University of Cambridge Digital Library. *Confirmed Minutes of the Board of Longitude, 1737-1779*. p.223.

73 See *Appendix III*.

8

VOYAGE TO NEW ZEALAND
WITH CAPTAIN COOK

A wet sheet and a flowing sea,
A wind that follows fast,
And fills the white and rustling sail
And bends the gallant mast—
And bends the gallant mast, my boys,
While, like the eagle free,
Away the good ship flies, and leaves
Old England on the lee.[1]

It was a Sunday morning on 21st June 1772 when William
Wales accompanied James Cook to Sheerness to board
Resolution, the weather was very hot, and each had just said
farewell to a wife and young family. Cook was six years Wales'
senior, but they had a lot in common, they each hailed from
Yorkshire, and from a humble hard working family. Both had
had the experience of observing the all important transit of
the planet Venus, Cook accompanied by Wales' brother-in-
law Charles Green, whom William Wales was now to replace
on this second voyage to the South Seas. Cook and Wales
were both able practitioners of mathematics, astronomy, and
navigation, and would have had so much to say on their way
to Sheerness, where they arrived that evening.[2]

HMS Resolution had been built at Fishburn's Yard at Whitby,
a 462 ton vessel with a maximum beam of 11 metres, keel

of 28.5 metres and draft of 4 metres. She was launched in 1770, and had started her career as the collier *Drake* carrying coal along the east coast, just the same as her now sister ship *Adventure*. Both vessels had been selected by Cook for his second voyage, the *Resolution* was fitted out for the voyage at Deptford with the most up-to-date equipment, 24 guns, the azimuth compass by Gregory, and anchors to cope with ice, and apparatus for distilling sea water to provide the sailors with fresh drinking water. *Resolution* had cost the Admiralty £4,151.[3] The *Adventure* meanwhile was fitted out at Woolwich, to a less sophisticated specification, she was a smaller vessel of some 340 ton.[4]

Wales was allocated a cabin of his own on board, and it was here he kept his instruments and time pieces, also his books and personal effects. The cabin was located in the gentlemen's accommodation at the aft end of the ship on the starboard side, and approximately in the same position as Charles Green had been accommodated on *Endeavour*.[5] Wales later wrote that his cabin was next to Mr Gilbert's,[6] while his servant, George Gilpin, would have been accommodated in the adjacent cabin, allocated as the servant's berth.

Wales and Gilpin's immediate task was to check and ensure the safe stowage of the instruments and timepieces entrusted to Wales. As well as an astronomical clock there was also a journeyman clock made by Jonathan Monk, and an alarum clock, there was of course the marine timekeeper made by Kendall, and one of John Arnold's' box chronometers, Wales also had a horizontal stop watch.[7] While unpacking the thermometers, it was found that one had been broken while the ship was undergoing alterations at Sheerness,[8] this was not a good start to the voyage, when part of Wales' job was to ensure the safe condition of his instruments in order that he could carry out his various tasks.

A particularly useful description of Monk's journeyman clock is given by Wales:

> ...The assistant clock had a simple pendulum, whose rod was of white deal, and was always adjusted so that it would beat with the Astronomical Clock without sensible deviation for several minutes together; it shewed only minutes and seconds, was wound up in the common way that 24 hour clocks generally are, by pulling at the string and constructed to give a very loud beat, and to strike with great exactness at the end of every minute, for the convenience of catching the second with more certainty in observing. The loudness of the beat is of great use when the wind is high; or when, on account of any other noise or disturbance, the Astronomical Clock cannot be heard; and was particularly useful to us, whose observations stood generally on the sea-shore where the roaring of the surf seldom permitted us to hear the Astronomical Clock all the time it was going.[9]

The astronomical clock, made by John Shelton, was one of five commissioned by the Royal Society for the 1761 and 1769 Transit of Venus Observations, and the one designated to go on *Resolution* had been used by William Bayly at the North Cape in 1769. It was then fitted with ruby pallets by John Arnold, before being lent to the Board of Longitude for Cook's second voyage, and called 'Clock B' in the voyage account.[10] These regulator clocks were made to enable the exact time to be read, by having separate dials for the minutes and seconds

In addition to the clocks, Wales was responsible for the astronomical instruments and equipment,[11] the instruments provided were of the very best technology that the leading makers of the day could provide. During the forthcoming voyage Cook reflected on the instruments and astronomers of the age, he applauded the astronomers who had worked to contribute to the accuracy of navigation through the publication of the Board of Longitude Tables, he wrote that due to the tables Sea officers now had no excuse for not availing themselves of these useful publications in order to carry out their essential duties. Cook added that these tables, now complimented by good instruments, made by makers such as Bird, Nairn and Ramsden, all contributed to make navigation so accurate.[12]

Cook weighed anchor on 25th June and sailed out to the Nore, *Resolution* handled well, and her figure-head, carved as a prancing horse, nosed easily through the fresh breeze, steering a course for Plymouth. On meeting the Admiralty yacht *Augusta,* which carried Lord Sandwich and Hugh Palliser returning from inspecting the Plymouth dock yards, the Captain was able to report that the *Resolution* now had so much in her favour, and described her as 'faultless'.

On docking at Plymouth on 3rd July, *Resolution* joined *Adventure* – the ship which was to accompany her. Efficient preparation was essential for the long voyage ahead, and while the ships were being stocked with necessary stores, William Wales, his servant George Gilpin, and James Cook, went to join William Bayly on Drake's Island off Plymouth. They camped in tents on the Island, and were employed setting up instruments in portable observatories to enable them to put in motion and set the various time pieces, and to carry out observations on the Island, which was the official starting point of the voyage, the whole exercise took about nine days.

The setting up here of the Astronomical clock which was to be taken on *Adventure,* is described as being fixed very firmly to a plank of oak, which was 11 inches broad and 2½ inches thick, this was positioned three feet into the ground and supported well on each side.[13]

John Arnold had travelled from London to start the three chronometers he had made, which performed with varying accuracy during the voyage.[14] The two captains, two astronomers, and other officers were present when K1 was set working by William Wales.[15] Eventually the tents, instruments, and time-pieces were packed up and stored back onboard the two ships, and Wales settled back into his cabin and spent time computing his observations, and writing letters. For the duration of the voyage he was to keep a journal, and a record of his observations, and was also to draw charts – all part of his contract with the Admiralty.

For the record, Wales and Cook used different times for recording the same events, differing again both when at sea, and in harbour.[16] Wales' Journal was kept in astronomical time, that is the day began and ended at noon, and was twenty four hours later than ship time. Wales remarked at the end of *Resolution's* Log that the time difference was troublesome, and caused confusion, particularly to the younger members of the crew, and especially when consulting the *Nautical Almanac.*[17]

J. R. Forster and his son Georg had left their London home and family on 26th June and travelled to Plymouth by post-chaise. They had stowed their luggage on board *Resolution* at Sheerness, but then stayed in London to complete purchasing their equipment. When they reached Plymouth they had boarded Lord Sandwich's yacht, when His Lordship ascertained they were satisfied with their appointment and conditions.[18]

On *Resolution's* arrival at Plymouth J. R. Forster discussed with Cook. and the carpenters and joiners. alterations to his cabin. which he required to be done before sailing. He and Georg then took the opportunity to travel on to Cornwall, visiting some of the copper and tin mines before returning to Plymouth on 8th July, and boarding the ship on 11th July.[19]

J R Forster found conditions on board ship, where the crew had just been paid, to be a scene of drunken confusion, and while he was able to arrange sleeping quarters well enough, stowing equipment, books, and other materials was hampered by the size of his accommodation. A cannon was taking up a lot of the space, and Forster was not well pleased. In the neighbouring cabin was Joseph Gilbert the ship's master, a proud professional, and an experienced navigator. In desperation J R Forster offered both Gilbert and Wales money to exchange cabins, a fact which caused much conversation among the ship's officers for the rest of the day. [20]

The Forster family's roots were in Yorkshire, and their patriarch George Forster had left England in the middle of the seventeenth century to settle in Danzig, these Yorkshire origins offered a good basis on which to build their relationships, with both William Wales, and Captain Cook, with whom they were to spend a lot of time during the forthcoming voyage. J R Forster at forty two was a year younger than Cook, and some four years older than William Wales, he was described by a friend as of strong physique with a firm gait, so evidently well suited for a voyage of discovery. [21]

The ships were ready to sail out of Plymouth Sound on 12th July en route for Madeira, when they would take on board fresh food for the first part of the voyage, and that all important wine. Before sailing Forster noticed the *Resolution* was apparently adrift from her moorings, and reported this to the master, causing alarm among the hands and officers on deck.[22] Despite these initial setbacks the observations continued, and the four time-pieces were checked, each watch had been placed in a box which had three locks, one key to each box was kept by William Wales, also Captain Cook had one key to each, and likewise Robert Palliser Cooper, the 1st Lieutenant, had three. It was a condition that for the timepieces to be checked, each key holder must be present.

Wales was becoming acquainted with the ship's company, people he was to spend the next few years with, and would rely on for help, support, and companionship. One hundred and twelve men were now heading south on *Resolution*, accompanied by eighty one on *Adventure*, all into the unknown, with their own tasks, and no doubt their own thoughts.

Resolution was a naval vessel, and thus was manned by commissioned officers, warrant and petty officers, able seamen, servants, and marines. Only the supernumeries were not naval personnel – artists, astronomers and other scientists, and their servants, and other members of their retinues.[23]

Cook, as Captain of *Resolution*, was supported immediately by his lieutenants. Robert Palliser Cooper was first lieutenant, a kinsman of Sir Hugh Palliser the comptroller of the Navy. Charles Clerke was second lieutenant, he had sailed on *Endeavour* with Cook as third lieutenant, and this time third lieutenant was Richard Pickersgill, a Yorkshireman from West Tanfield, who also sailed on *Endeavour*, and had sailed with Samuel Wallis on *Dolphin*.[24]

Charles Clerke was born in 1743, and had been on Byron's voyage in 1765 before joining Cook's first voyage, and when Charles Green died on that voyage, he had taken over most of the astronomical duties. On this second voyage, Clerke was described by Elliott as 'a Brave and good officer'. Clerke was described by Beaglehole as 'always cheerful, talkative, amusing....a generous spirit who made friends easily....He had enough mathematical ability to become a good navigator; with some interest in the scientific side of his profession'.[25] With his past experience, Clerke was often to accompany Wales in his duties during the voyage, and no doubt during their conversations, William Wales would learn more of the details of his brother-in-law Charles Green's life and death during the *Endeavour* voyage.

Richard Pickersgill had also worked quite closely with Charles Green on the first voyage, his particular skill was as a surveyor and maker of charts, but had also taken part in the transit of Venus observations.[26] He also must have often spoken of Green to Wales during the second voyage.

The surgeon on board *Resolution* was James Patten, he was well skilled, and would prove to be a real professional. He had a mate, William Anderson, who was also an amateur naturalist and had an ability to speak native languages. The ship's master was Joseph Gilbert, born at Kirton in Holland, near Boston in Lincolnshire[27], and Isaac Smith was master's mate, Smith was related to Mrs Cook and had been on the *Endeavour* voyage. William Dawson was purser. Of the young midshipmen on board was James Burney, aged 21, son of Dr Charles Burney, and brother of Fanny Burney, also three young midshipmen, John Elliott aged 15 from Helmsley in Yorkshire, Alexander Hood aged 14 a nephew of Admiral Lord Hood, and 15 year old George Vancouver, whose eventual survey of the west coast of Canada is well established in the annals of the history of that country. These three youngsters were to become firm friends during the voyage. [28]

Among the 'supernumeraries', apart from Wales and Gilpin, were listed the two Forsters, and William Hodges, an artist aged 28, whose work recording the people and places during the voyage skillfully complimented the work of the Journal writers.

We can only imagine the apprehension felt by the companies of *Resolution* and *Adventure* as they sailed out of Plymouth that summer day laden with victuals, tools and materials, instruments and charts – both man and beast sailed into the open sea.

One particularly calm day Cook sent William Wales out in one of the small boats to board *Adventure,* and compare the watch with that of Bayly's. Cook also took this opportunity to send Captain Furneaux of the *Adventure* orders, on what action he should take if the vessels should become separated – this was a constant worry especially in foggy weather, and plans always had to be made well in advance, just in case.[29]

In two weeks they reached Madeira, the first port of call on the voyage, an island which Cook called 'the place which was the recipient of nature's most liberal gifts'. On reaching Funchal, Cook saluted the Garrison with 11 guns, this was returned, and Cook immediately went on shore with Captain Furneaux, Johann Forster, and William Wales. The party were met by Mr Sells from the Vice Consul, and introduced to Mr Loughnan, a British merchant who supplied the King's ships with wine.[30] Permission was obtained to carry the instruments on shore, and it was agreed with Mr Loughnan that the astronomers should be accommodated in the upper apartment of his town house in Funchal. So the instruments were unloaded and set up on land – an exercise which was to be repeated many times in the months ahead.

Wales records his dealings with the Customs officials at Funchal, at the Custom house he had to wait until every box was opened and examined before moving his items, this must have reminded him of his dealings with the customs during his Hudson's Bay trip.

Once through customs, the astronomical clocks were stood on a brick floor at Mr Loughnan's house and firmly screwed to a large bookcase, which was crammed full with books, the bookcase was fastened firmly to the wall of the house.[31]

The two Forsters were to take lodgings in Mr Loughnan's country house, from where they would start out on many scientific excursions into the countryside of the island.[32]

Madeira really impressed Wales, this island was so green and lush, and so different to the landscape and climate of Hudson's Bay, he spent a lot of his free time ashore, visiting places, and learning of the island's culture. One day he went to visit the nunnery, he had probably learned of this place from John Elliott, who had visited it a year earlier with the son of one of his Uncle's correspondents, who had sisters there.[33] On leaving Madeira he could not resist recording the place, and proceeded to write in his Journal:

> ...So many persons have visited this Island that it may seem unnecessary for me to say anything concerning it: but as several circumstances occurred to me, which I have not met with in my reading, I cannot resist the temptation of committing them to paper. I could wish much to convey a tolerable idea of the appearance which it has when viewed from a ship in the offing which is shocking enough, but despair of doing it as it is subject much more suitable for the pencil than the pen.[34]

Wales continues to describe the geology, the climate, the flora and fauna, the surrounding islands, the defences, the churches, and buildings, public and domestic, the street paving, the transport, the local history – and so far as the currency is concerned, he is at pains to point out that:-

> ...English Guineas pay here to advantage as many of the monasteries will give 21 pistreens for them, and some of those which are out of town 22, and sometimes 23, I am told; but bills are best to pay for any thing you want here as a discount of 8 per cent is generally got on them, and the merchants are fonder of them, especially if drawn on the government, or any noted banker. If a person has to go from thence to the Cape of Good-Hope I would particularly recommend it to

them to take what money he may want there in English Guineas and change it here into pistreens.[35]

On 1st August the instruments again had to be taken down and packed up, this time in haste. Because of this, when they were carried back to the shore, the exercise was not carried out as smoothly as Wales would have liked, and apparently "several little accidents" occurred resulting in the Portuguese watermen taking advantage of Wales' predicament, and there followed a period of hard bargaining. Eventually Wales achieved a satisfactory quote from one of the boat men, but not before he had threatened him with complaining to the British Consul, Wales' had however to pay what he described as an 'exorbitant price' for conveying himself and his instruments safely back on board. At midnight *Resolution* was on her way once more.

As the voyage progressed south into the tropics the metal objects began to suffer from rust, and clothes and bedding cover with mould. Wales was naturally concerned for his instruments and watches, but Cook had the ship cleaned between decks and aired with a charcoal fire, he was determined that his ship should be clean, and his crew well fed. Cook ordered that the monkeys, which had been brought on board by a few of the crew, were to be sent overboard because of the stench from their droppings – Wales remarked that his Captain paid more attention to the health of his people than to the lives of a few monkeys.

William Wales was now settling into a routine of observations and calculations as the two vessels sailed into the Tropics. On 7th August the tropic of Cancer latitude was reached, and passing the Canaries to the Cape Verde Islands west of the African coast, they put into Port Praya on the Island of Sao Tiago. Here Wales spent some time on shore, and had the honour as 'one of his Britannic Majesty's learned

Astronomers' to be introduced to Don Joachim Salarna Soldanha de Lobos, the Governor General of all his most faithful Majesty's Dominions on the Coast of Africa. This was described by Wales as a 'very singular honour'.

It was while awaiting his introduction to the Governor General that Wales happened upon an elegantly bound book on the sofa beside him, which he recognized as a copy of *de la Lande's Astronomy,* this aroused his curiosity, and he couldn't understand how so modern a book on astronomy could be in this place, there must surely be someone amongst them who was tolerably proficient in the science. On enquiring as to the owner, he discovered it belonged to a gentleman in the next room who had arrived on one of the French ships, which carried out trials of Mr Le Roy's time keepers. The two astronomers on this expedition had had an observatory on the island and Wales would have liked to be introduced to the book's owner, but unfortunately this was not possible.[36]

On Sao Tiago Wales measured the island with the Gunter's Chain, and here it appears that Cook was his assistant, the resulting chart of Porto Praya was drawn by Wales, who also took tidal measurements, and observed the latitude.[37] Livestock was acquired by bartering with the natives for clothes and metal items, before the vessels continued on their way. It is evident from his writing that Wales wished to record more on the nature of the inhabitants of the island, but as his journal was subject to strict censorship, perhaps he felt constrained, and decided not to expand into the subject of slavery.

Cook now headed straight for Cape Town, the refitting of the ship after Joseph Banks had been eliminated from the voyage had delayed the start, and Cook was now anxious to reach, and have time to explore the high latitudes, before the ice would eventually force them to retreat.

At the end of August *Resolution* enjoyed the company of a swallow, which had hitched a ride during a period of particularly heavy rain. Unable to fly, it stayed on board several days, roosting in the rigging and surviving on flies, before regaining its freedom, only to return. Eventually it settled in William Wales' cabin for a while, before leaving to continue its journey on the wing and never to be seen again.[38]

On board were casks of beer brewed from essence of malt, some of these were showing evidence of fermentation in the now tropical heat and were nearly bursting, so had to be removed onto the deck for the pressure to be released. Very soon a loud explosion shook the ship, the sailors were horrified to witness their precious beer spilling out onto the deck, only to be consumed greedily by the ship's compliment of goats, who proceeded to stagger about in a drunken stupor. Rest assured however that enough of the precious liquor survived to celebrate the crossing of the Equator on 8th September.[39]

The weather was calm for the ceremony of the Equator's crossing, which was carried out amid much hilarity, mirth, and singing, as the liquor flowed – a break from the strict routine usually imposed by Cook. By sharp contrast Furneaux chose to allow no such hilarity and drinking on *Adventure*.[40]

On *Resolution*, around fifty of the men were subjected to the traditional ducking from the yardarm, while some were plastered with an indescribable mixture of grimy nastiness, and tar. The faint-hearted chose to pay to get out of these activities by forfeiting a gallon of rum, and a pound of sugar, the rum was eagerly consumed by the sailors.[41]

George Vancouver's biographer described the usual 'Crossing the Line' Ceremony which involved King Neptune, his queen and entourage, all climbing over the bows to demand payment of a penalty. This could take the form of enduring a shave with a menacing looking razor, taking a foul-tasting pill, or being thrown into a bath of sea water. All in all an entertaining event, and a chance for the ship's company to 'let off steam'.[42]

Wales was by now greatly impressed by the timepiece trials, and he remarked in his journal that he found Mr Kendall's watch infinitely more to be depended upon.

In October a large number of Pintado birds[43] were around the ship which were caught with hooks and lines, also albatrosses were shot, and these were used as food – fresh meat to sustain while the next landfall. It was at this point that an eclipse of the moon occurred, and observation of this event was a joint effort by Cook, Forster senior, Wales, Pickersgill, Gilbert, and Harvey, all recorded the time taken, and the average was duly recorded.[44] The eclipse observations were taken just three days prior to the ship crossing the Greenwich meridian, so the opportunity was taken also to calculate the longitude, albeit at sea. The scientific work continued when Gilbert, Wales, and Forster went out in a small boat to make observations of the ocean currents and temperatures.[45]

At the end of October land was sighted, Table Mountain, and Table Bay. Before anchoring the ship's company were occupied trying to identify mysterious creatures which were causing the sea to be illuminated, slimy particles were collected in buckets and found to be small jelly-like creatures, which Wales reports did not glow when placed on a piece of paper, but when disturbed gave off a bright glow. These organisms were identified as *Noctiluca*.[46]

Landing at Table Bay, *Resolution* now awaited essential supplies from the Dutch, and Wales and Bayly immediately took the opportunity to obtain permission to use a piece of ground for the setting up of their observatories, instruments, and clocks, they then spent the next few days taking observations. Kendall's watch was proving to be accurate beyond all expectation, gaining only around one second a day, while Mr Arnold's three were not performing with the same accuracy – in fact one of them had stopped.[47]

The town was at the base of Table Mountain, which tended to attract damp weather and thick clouds, but these were quickly dispersed by strong winds which bordered on violent gales at times.

Supplies for the ship, which were being delivered by the Dutch, were delayed, but Cook kept his men busy. Wales spent the next couple of days writing up his observations, computations, and writing letters which would be sent via the next available vessel that they would meet heading for England. The master of *Resolution* was Joseph Gilbert, who had worked as a surveyor with Palliser in Newfoundland at the same time as Cook, Gilbert was a year older than Wales. He and Wales spent time sounding and surveying the Bay, which he found to be an agreeable place, and Penguin Island. It was in 1750 that Murdoch Mackenzie from the Orkney Islands pioneered a method of preparing sea charts of the coast by measuring one length and two angles of a triangle, his charts were adopted by the Admiralty, and his method of surveying was now being used to provide charts which would make navigating the world much safer.

The Forsters busied themselves with their botanizing, the potential for collecting and studying the species at Cape Colony was overwhelming, luckily they met here another botanist Andreas Sparrman, a Swedish gentleman who had studied under the botanist Linneaus, and had only recently arrived. Johann Forster thought him a most useful assistant, and eventually Cook reluctantly agreed that Sparmann join the voyage to assist with the botanizing, he was to be accommodated in the steerage with the books.[48]

Recording the landscape of Table Bay was the voyage artist William Hodges, a blacksmith's son from London, who got on well with Wales throughout the voyage.

After two weeks the observatories, instruments, and clocks, were again packed up, and Cook sent boats for them to be transported back onto the ships. This was always an anxious operation for Wales, who positioned himself in the stern of one of the small boats with a watch at each side of him, on reaching *Resolution* the boat had struck the side of the ship, and the jolt may have caused harm to Arnold's watch, which was found to be stopped when Wales checked it once he was back on board.

When *Resolution* eventually weighed anchor on 22nd November, the ship's company began donning thicker clothes which had been especially supplied by the government, anticipating the icy conditions of the southern oceans, reminding Wales of his Hudson Bay experiences and his *toggy*. The ship was now heading south through the *roaring forties* where the prevailing westerly winds became exceptionally hazardous, there being no land to stop the blast. The weather was turning angry with squalls of wind and rain, and strong gales, the ship was labouring under the high and irregular waves, which hit one another from various directions. Wales spent some time setting up 'still' apparatus, which was used to try and turn the salty sea water into something drinkable.

Johann Forster, who had suffered sickness when setting off from Plymouth, was now feeling squeamish again and took to his medicine – a bottle of mulled port wine. Forster's condition wasn't helped when he was driven from his bed by water dripping through the seams onto his head, this he blamed on Gilbert, who had instructed a carpenter to caulk his own cabin which was situated next to the Forster's cabin, and the carpenter, while finishing off the work from the deck above, had not taken into account the position of the cabins below, causing Forster to become 'fairly soused'.[49]

The stormy conditions gave Wales a good opportunity to try Lind's wind gauge, he had an obvious interest in meteorology, as shown at Hudson's Bay, and his equipment included a portable wind gauge, developed by Dr James Lind, and made by Edward Nairne of London. The apparatus, scientifically known as a manometer, consisted of a U-shaped tube which was half filled with water. The wind was allowed to blow into one arm, and the wind pressure was read off on a scale, but an accurate reading was dependant on the equipment being held perpendicular, this proved rather difficult when the vessel was travelling through inclement weather conditions. Wales read a force of wind of 0.45 of an inch, and in his opinion the gauge could prove very useful, although it could be more accurate if furnished with a more extensive scale. William Bayly also attempted to get an accurate reading from the wind gauge, but found the results uncertain.

Wales' journal was punctuated by deeply philosophical remarks, he wrote that joy was all the greater when raised from fears, that the sun appeared more brightly after a storm, and after turbulent weather the more moderate conditions were all the more delightful.

There can be no doubt that besides being an accomplished scientist and mathematician, William Wales was also a gifted teacher. Throughout the voyage he was ever willing to school the company in whatever skills he was able, and midshipman George Vancouver was one Wales took in hand. He coached Vancouver on observing, surveying, and drawing, and Vancouver was to become a very proficient navigator. Wales was described by Raban as Vancouver's 'One man university'.[50]

By the beginning of December the more moderate conditions brought sightings of albatross – the wandering, sooty, and grey – also penguins, a whale, and islands of ice, like the ones Wales had seen in Hudson Straits in 1768, although these were smooth and straight, rather than rugged. They were huge, and on measuring one particular specimen by taking angles, he found it to be half a mile long. The various attempts at recording its height are interesting, for while Clerke believed it to be as high as the body of St Paul's in London, Masters mate John Burr estimated its height at 60 feet, while Wales passed it off as 'not very high'.[51]

Wales spent some time on *Adventure* at this point. Both vessels sailed further into the ice field, which caused the rigging to be covered with ice and made trimming very difficult.

The calm sea allowed William Wales and Johann Forster to leave *Resolution* in the small jolly boat to shoot sea birds, and to take readings of the current and temperature of the sea water, which was 32° on the surface, but on immersing the thermometer into the water a hundred fathoms deep, for twenty minutes, they found it to read 34°, which was just 2° above freezing.

What followed was an incident which was to haunt Forster for some time, Anders Sparrman described how they had found themselves in mortal danger as the fog got thicker until they could hardly see the end of the boat. Despite them shooting muskets and shouting into the fog, it could not be penetrated, and so they had to endure their plight without food, drink and navigation instruments – the only thing they had was a couple of oars. They feared that if the fog didn't clear soon, and a storm was to get up, they and their small boat would be consumed by the waves, and so they decided it would be wise to stop rowing. They spoke of darkness, and being adrift for ever, never to be reunited with the two mother-vessels, a dangerous situation which could have led to death by drowning, or even starvation. They could have brought at least a ship's biscuit, which would have kept them going for a while, but this was just a dream! Eventually to their relief they heard the welcome sound of the *Adventure's* dinner bell, and were able to guide themselves towards it with their minds no doubt on the meal it summoned. The incident had been a sharp reminder to the two of the dangers which could arise, even in the best of weather.[52]

It was Georg Forster and Anders Sparrman who wrote of the jolly boat's two hour adventure at length, but Wales merely mentions in his Journal, that while doing the experiments they could not find the ship when thick fog came, but then fortunately they found *Adventure*. Thus relatively undaunted by this recent adventure, Wales then turned his hand to electrical experimentation. He wanted to try and find out what the state of the air was with respect to electricity, and had brought with him apparatus which he explains in his journal:

> ...I got my Apparatus over the Tafferel of the Ship, and found the balls diverged about an Angle of 10°, but I do not see it as a fair Trial, on account of the Wind; which tho' but small was sufficient to hinder the excited wax from closing them again; it is therefore probable it might contribute to make them diverge.[53]

This apparatus, based on a little pocket electrometer of John Canton's, was described by Robert Symmer when he read his papers to the Royal Society in December 1759.[54] Symmer was curious when he noticed his silk stockings, on being removed from his legs, sometimes sparked and were attracted to each other, and his contrivance to measure this phenomenon consisted of two small pith balls suspended by fine linen threads, the upper ends of which were fastened inside a wooden box. The balls were attracted or repelled depending on the positive or negative state of the charge, which was produced by rubbing stockings together, these were later replaced by two glass rods, which were electrified by either rubbing the smooth tube with the hand for a positive charge, or a tube of rough glass rubbed by wax to produce a negative charge. The success of these experiments depended on the state of the weather, Symmer noticed electricity was produced better in winter and when dry, and a little frosty.

The electrometer was not included in the apparatus supplied to Wales by the Board of Longitude, and is thought to have been supplied by Joseph Banks, who had one made by Edward Nairne of London.[55]

Resolution and *Adventure* inched their way through this icy, still world, the silence being broken only by guns which were being fired to keep the two vessels together during the night. Islands of ice and the indigenous wild life were the only witnesses, islands which quickly disappeared when the thick fog closed in, only to loom again threateningly close-by, as the icy mist swirled past these vulnerable wooden vessels.

At this juncture, that scourge of all voyagers of the time, scurvy, began to rear its ugly head, and Wales records that he brewed some wort,[56] for some of the crew had begun to show symptoms – including himself. The fact that this was the Christmas season was not recorded in Wales' Journal, as the ships moved slightly north of east, all that was seen was ice, ice, and more ice. Ice which Cook was now eager to try and collect as the water on board was getting scarce.

The two ships now closed together in the company of many penguins, and inched their way close up to one of the ice islands, but the sea proved too rough, and inspection of the other sides of the island proved it to be covered either in penguins, or dung. The drinking water quest was abandoned for the time being, the vessels pushed on, and it was another ten days when the opportunity to collect ice came once more, the jolly boats were sent out to collect small pieces from a large island of ice, and these were handed onto the ships, and then the boats sent out again for another load. This ice was duly described by Wales as "of much more real value than Gold!"

Some of the crew suffered swollen glands on drinking the water, Sparrman wrote that this was because the water was iced, however Wales scoffed at this theory after his experiences at Hudson's Bay – they could not blame the icebergs, but rather it was more likely to be the low resistance of the crew to an infection, due to the cold and poor diet they were experiencing.[57]

Christmas celebrations were impending, and the cautious Captain ordered:

> ...the Sloops under a snug sail, seeing that the Crew were inclinable to celebrate the day in their own way, for which purpose they had been hording up liquor for some time past, I also made some addition to their allowance, had as many of the Officers and Petty Officers to dinner in the Cabbin as we [could] find room for, and the rest were entertain'd in the Gunroom, and mirth and good humor reigned throughout the whole Ship....[58]

Christmas and New Year were, according to Georg Forster, celebrated with cheerfulness among officers and passengers, whereas the sailors celebrated with savage noise, and drunkenness.[59] Anders Sparrman elaborated on the fighting games which the crew amused themselves with, and described them as being called boxing.[60]

Cook was now heading for his prime target of the voyage, the possible location of *Cape Circumcision*, the name given to a high rocky cape of land covered in snow, which the Frenchman Bouvet had reported as seeing thirty four years earlier. *Resolution* sailed west in pursuit, if Cook could only find the Cape and sail south from it, he must surely find land, but after a few days and no sighting in the area he gave up, and turned the ship around again eastwards, concluding that Bouvet had merely seen mountains of ice.[61]

The moon visible, Wales was able to fix their position for only the second time since leaving the Cape, and as the Antarctic weather closed in, strong gales, thick fog, sleet and snow, gripped the vessel and covered all the rigging with ice. But the crew, with an extra glass of brandy each morning, and dressed in large caps and 'fearnought' trousers and jackets, coped well.[62]

On 12th January, 1773, Wales optimistically recorded that a *Cape hen*[63] was sighted, and that these birds are seldom seen far from land. By the 17th they were clear of the Antarctic latitudes and experienced a heavy swell, all the while Wales was carrying out his readings, the marine barometer in particular seemed not to be performing accurately, and coupled with this, when he was out of his cabin at breakfast one morning, one of the midshipmen had broken his pocket watch.[64]

In February sea-weed was evident, and several diver birds and penguins. At this point a thick fog came down, and the *Adventure* disappeared from view.[65]

At Hudson's Bay Wales had been disappointed at the display of the northern lights,[66] especially as he had previously witnessed a much better show of these from the north of England, so that while in the southern hemisphere he was anxious to observe the southern polar lights.[67] The officers had been detailed to keep a look-out for these, and it was on 16th February that Mr Pickersgill reported to Wales that he had seen something like the Aurora Borealis. The next evening Wales reports on the spectacle which he had now witnessed for himself:

....a little towards the SE and about 10° high all round the horizon was a whitish haze through which Stars of the third magnitude were just discernable. All round the horizon was covered with a thick Cloud out of which arose Streams of Pale reddish light that ascended towards the zenith. These streams had not that motion they are sometimes seen to have in the northern parts of England, but were perfectly steady except that they had a small Irregular motion to the Eyes.[68]

Three days later Wales observed the aurora again, this time as a pillar of steady pale coloured light, almost the same as he had observed at Hudson's Bay, but this time the light was deflected into a kind of circular form which grew fainter as it ascended.

The sight of the aurora at this time was apparently a lucky occurrence, for when sighted on Cook's first voyage the sun was close to a sunspot maximum, resulting in solar flares which cause the dancing colours of the aurora. During the second voyage however, although the sun was just about at a sunspot minimum, the *aurora australis* was still able to give a spectacular display for the ship's company.[69]

Cook recorded in his journal, that while in the northern hemisphere the northern lights were often seen by voyagers, he could not recall any mention of them being seen in the southern hemisphere before.[70] This would indicate that William Wales was the first scientist in history to record observations of the lights from both the north and south hemispheres.[71]

Ice was becoming ever threatening, and as the ship pushed on through more inclement weather, Cook was aware that the surrounding ice made sailing during the dark nights a real hazard, and just as if they had been sailing amid rocks. Clerke and Wales describe one iceberg, which was four times as big as the ship, falling to pieces as the ship passed it, but that with the roar of the sea and the wind, nothing was heard of its demise. The next day Wales described a particularly beautiful ice island in the form of an old square ruined castle, with the Gothic arch of an old postern gateway – a better design would have puzzled an architect.

While Wales had experienced these harsh, icy conditions before at Hudson's Bay, such sights did not inspire the elder Forster to write of their beauty, they terrified him, and he described how he had to experience these hardships, an ordeal which should not be endured by mortal man.[72]

At the end of February there were whales and porpoises round the ship, and by the first of March *Resolution* sailed onwards through rough seas, between more islands of ice.

It was on the 24th March 1773 that land was finally seen, nine months after leaving London, they were now half way around the world and heading for the western shores of the south island of New Zealand, the Maori name for this island was *Te Waka a Maui*. The formidable shoreline of rocks hid safe entrances into the interior, and it would be another two days before *Resolution* carefully inched her way into the Sound which Cook had discovered briefly during the first voyage, and named *Dusky*.[73]

Endnotes

1   Allan Cunningham, (1784-1842).

2   Beaglehole, J C (Ed), 1969. *The Journals of Captain James Cook on His Voyages of Discovery. II. The Voyage of Resolution and Adventure 1772-1775.* Cambridge University Press for the Hakluyt Society. p.9.

3   Website: http://www.solarnavigator.net/history/hms_ resolution.htm

4   Hough, R, 1995. *Captain James Cook, a Biography.* London, Hodder & Stoughton.

5   Plan of Resolution's deck as displayed in the *Cook Memorial Museum,* Whitby, Yorkshire.

6   Thomas, N. & Berghof, O., (Ed), 2000. A Voyage Round the World. by George Forster. Honolulu, University of Hawaii Press. p.714.

7   Howse & Hutchinson, 1969. *The Clocks and Watches of Captain James Cook 1769-1969.* London.

8   Wales, William, *Journal on the Resolution, June 21, 1772 to October 17th, 1774.* Manuscript now in the Mitchell Library, Sydney, Australia.

9   Wales, W (Ed), 1777. *The Original Astronomical Observations, Made in the Course of a Voyage Towards the South Pole, and Round the World, in His Majesty's Ships the Resolution and Adventure, in the Years MDCCLXXII, MDCCLXXIII, MDCCLXXIV, AND MDCCLXXV, by William Wales and Mr. William Bayly.* J Nourse, J Mount & T Page.

10 Howse & Hutchinson, 1969. *The Clocks and Watches of Captain James Cook 1769-1969.* London. p.285.

11 See *Appendix IV.*

12 Beaglehole, J C (Ed), 1969. *The Journals of Captain James Cook on His Voyages of Discovery. II. The Voyage of Resolution and Adventure 1772-1775.* Cambridge University Press for the Hakluyt Society. pp.79.

13 Wales, W, & Bayly, W, 1777. *The original Astronomical Observations made in the Course of a Voyage Towards the South Pole, and round the World in His Majesty's Ships the Resolution and Adventure, in the years 1772, 1773, 1774, and 1775.* London, Strahan.

14 Howse & Hutchinson, 1969. *The Clocks and Watches of Captain James Cook 1769-1969.* London.

15 According to Professor Taylor, Larcum Kendall also attended at Drake's Island, although there is no mention of this in Beaglehole's edition of Cook's Journal. See ref. Taylor, E.G.R., 1966. *The Mathematical Practitioners of Hanoverian England 1714-1840.* Cambridge, Cambridge University Press. p.51.

16 Howse, Derek, 1997. *Greenwich Time and the Longitud.* London, Philip Wilson Publishers Ltd.

17 From this point most of Wales' Journal was published by JC Beaglehole in Beaglehole, J C (Ed), 1969. *The Journals of Captain James Cook on His Voyages of Discovery. II. The Voyage of Resolution and Adventure 1772-1775.* Cambridge University Press for the Hakluyt Society. p.cxli. n1

18 Hoare, Michael E, 1976. *The Tactless Philosopher.* Melbourne, Hawthorne Press.

19 ibid.

20 ibid.

21 ibid.

22 ibid.

23 Orchiston, Wayne, 1998. *Nautical Astronomy in New Zealand. The Voyages of Captain James Cook.* Wellington, Carter Observatory Board.

24 Aughton, P, 2004. *Resolution – Cook's Second Voyage.* London, Weidenfeld & Nicholson.

25 Orchiston, Wayne, 1998. *Nautical Astronomy in New Zealand. The Voyages of Captain James Cook.* Wellington, Carter Observatory Board.

26 ibid.

27 Parish Registers of Kirton in Holland, Lincolnshire, Baptisms.

28 Aughton, P, 2004. *Resolution – Cook's Second Voyage.*
    London, Weidenfeld & Nicholson.

29 Beaglehole, J C (Ed), 1969. *The Journals of Captain James
    Cook on His Voyages of Discovery. II. The Voyage of
    Resolution and Adventure 1772-1775.* Cambridge University
    Press for the Hakluyt Society. p.18.

30 ibid., p.21.

31 Wales, W. & Bayly, W., 1777. *The original Astronomical
    Observations made in the Course of a Voyage Towards the
    South Pole, and round the World in His Majesty's Ships the
    Resolution and Adventure, in the years 1772, 1773, 1774, and
    1775.* London, Strahan.

32 Hoare, Michael E, 1976. *The Tactless Philosopher.*
    Melbourne. Hawthorne Press.

33 Elliot, J & Pickersgill, R, 1984. *Captain Cook's Second
    Voyage.* London, Caliban Books.

34 Wales, William. *Journal on the Resolution, June 21, 1772 to
    October 17th, 1774.* Manuscript now in the Mitchell Library,
    Sydney, Australia.

35 ibid.

36 Probably Kerguelen's first expedition in the *Fortune* and *Gros
    Ventre.*

37 Beaglehole, J C (Ed), 1969. *The Journals of Captain James
    Cook on His Voyages of Discovery. II. The Voyage of
    Resolution and Adventure 1772-1775.* Cambridge University
    Press for the Hakluyt Society. pp 28-29

38 Aughton, Peter, 2004. *Resolution– Cook's Second Voyage.*
    London, Weidenfeld & Nicholson.

39 ibid.

40 ibid.

41 Salmond, Anne, 2004. *The Trial of the Cannibal Dog.*
    London, Penguin.

42 Coleman, E C, 2000. *Captain Vancouver north-west
    Navigator.* Whitby, Caedmon. p.8.

43 A kind of Petrel.

44 Beaglehole, J C (Ed), 1969. *The Journals of Captain James Cook on His Voyages of Discovery. II. The Voyage of Resolution and Adventure 1772-1775.* Cambridge University Press for the Hakluyt Society. p.42.

45 Hoare, Michael E, 1976. *The Tactless Philosopher.* Melbourne, Hawthorne Press.

46 Aughton, Peter, 2004. *Resolution – Cook's Second Voyage.* London, Weidenfeld & Nicholson. p.35.

47 Beaglehole, J C (Ed), 1969. *The Journals of Captain James Cook on His Voyages of Discovery. II. The Voyage of Resolution and Adventure 1772-1775.* Cambridge University Press for the Hakluyt Society. p.47.

48 Hoare, Michael E, 1976. *The Tactless Philosopher.* Melbourne, Hawthorne Press.

49 ibid.

50 Raban, Jonathan, 1999. *Passage to Juneau.* London, Picador. p.57.

51 Beaglehole, J C (Ed), 1969. *The Journals of Captain James Cook on His Voyages of Discovery. II. The Voyage of Resolution and Adventure 1772-1775.* Cambridge University Press for the Hakluyt Society. p.58n.

52 Sparrman, A, 1953. *A Voyage Round the World with Captain Cook.* London, Robert Hale.

53 Wales, William. *Journal on the Resolution, June 21, 1772 to October 17th, 1774.* Manuscript now in the Mitchell Library, Sydney, Australia. Entry 15th December 1772.

54 Symmer, R, 1759. *New Experiments and Observations concerning Electricity* Phil.Trans.R.Soc., Vol LI, p.340-347.

55 Beaglehole, J C (Ed), 1969. *The Journals of Captain James Cook on His Voyages of Discovery. II. The Voyage of Resolution and Adventure 1772-1775.* Cambridge University Press for the Hakluyt Society. p.60n.

56 Brewed from Malt. Beaglehole, J C (Ed), 1969. *The Journals of Captain James Cook on His Voyages of Discovery. II. The Voyage of Resolution and Adventure 1772-1775.* Cambridge University Press for the Hakluyt Society. p.64.

57   ibid., p75n.

58   Philo, Phil, 2007. *Christmas in the Eighteenth Century*.
     Middlesborough. The Captain Cook Birthplace Museum.

59   Thomas, N, & Berghof, O, (Ed.). 2000. *A Voyage Round the
     World. by George Forster*. Honolulu, University of Hawaii
     Press.

60   Sparrman, A, 1953. *A Voyage round the World with Captain
     James Cook in H.M.S. Resolution*. London, Robert Hale.

61   Beaglehole, J C (Ed), 1969. *The Journals of Captain James
     Cook on His Voyages of Discovery. II. The Voyage of
     Resolution and Adventure 1772-1775*. Cambridge University
     Press for the Hakluyt Society. p.71

62   ibid., p.74.

63   White-chinned petrel.

64   Beaglehole, J C (Ed), 1969. *The Journals of Captain James
     Cook on His Voyages of Discovery. II. The Voyage of
     Resolution and Adventure 1772-1775*. Cambridge University
     Press for the Hakluyt Society. p.853n

65   Instructions were in place should the two vessels separate to
     meet up again at a particular location in New Zealand.

66   Aurora borealis.

67   Southern lights or *Aurora Australis*.

68   Wales, William. *Journal on the Resolution, June 21, 1772 to
     October 17th, 1774*. Manuscript now in the Mitchell Library,
     Sydney, Australia. Entry 17th March 1773.

69   Lincoln, M (Ed), 1998. *Science and Exploration in the Pacific*.
     London, National Maritime Museum. p.64.

70   Beaglehole, J C (Ed), 1969. *The Journals of Captain James
     Cook on His Voyages of Discovery. II. The Voyage of
     Resolution and Adventure 1772-1775*. Cambridge University
     Press for the Hakluyt Society. p. 95.

71   Portwood, John, 1995. *Tales from the Bay – The Transit of
     William Wales*. Canadian Geographic, Sept/Oct,1995 Vol.
     115, Issue 5, p.76.

72 Hough, R, 1995. *Captain James Cook, a Biography*. London, Hodder & Stoughton.

73 From this point most of Wales' Journal was published by JC Beaglehole in Beaglehole, J C (Ed), 1969. *The Journals of Captain James Cook on His Voyages of Discovery. II. The Voyage of Resolution and Adventure 1772-1775*. Cambridge University Press for the Hakluyt Society. pp.776-869.

9

THE PACIFIC EXPERIENCE

"I do think that Dusky Bay, for a Set of Hungry fellows after a long passage at Sea, is as good as any place I've ever yet met with ..."[1]

Dusky Sound March-May 1773

A haven of shelter and peace from the storm opened up before the ship's company as Cook skillfully and silently manoeuvred *Resolution* to a safe anchoring place. In his journal William Wales recorded the scene:

> ...In this Inlet there are a prodigious number of small Islands most of them pretty high; and every one, though ever so small covered with Tree and herbage down to the water's edge; which it will readily be imagined must have a very beautiful appearance to us who had been out at sea between four and five Months, and most of that Time amongst dreary Islands of Ice most of which were larger and higher than those which now surrounded us: but our pleasures were not all merely Ideal; a boat which was sent to fish soon returned with as much fine Fish as the whole Ship's Company could eat. After Dinner I went with one of the Leiut[s] to examine the Bay and look for a better Anchoring Place & we were so fortunate as to find one complete as could be wished for. At daylight the boat was sent again to fish and I was entertained in bed with a serenade by the winged Inhabitants of the neighbouring Islands, far

superior to any ever enjoyed by a Spanish Lady in the like situation.[2]

This was half a world away from the scene at Churchill when William Wales had first stepped ashore on Hudson's Bay. Here the birds were singing more sweetly, but he had work to do, another landfall, another camp.

Resolution was eventually secured the next day at her new mooring, discovered by Pickersgill and Wales in a cove along the south side of the Sound. Wales went with Captain Cook to search for a suitable place to pitch the Observatory, but this was not an easy task for the undergrowth and trees grew prolific everywhere, and there were perhaps natives about. The instruments were Wales' first concern, and their protection was paramount, yet the observatory tent must be in the open to avail the telescope access to a view of the surrounding heavens – an area of ground would need to be cleared before the observatory could be set up and any of the instruments installed. The site of the observatory needed to be chosen carefully.

Curious natives soon appeared on the shores, and in their canoes. *Resolution* provided an uncommon site in this place, and the ship's company were ordered to stay below, but no matter what Cook did he could not entice the visitors to come any nearer, they kept their distance. After dinner Wales, the Captain, and some of the Officers, took a closer look at the encampment where they had first seen the natives – there was a net, a couple of deserted huts, and a canoe which was carved with the upper parts of a man, with eyes of limpet shells. The party left gifts – tokens indicating that they were of no threat – a hatchet, looking glass, and toys.

On first entering the Bay the weather had been dry with gentle breezes, but then the wind changed, followed by spells of heavy rain. Despite this, a place to set up the observatory was finally decided upon, not far from the ship, and away from the natives. Wales set to work clearing the ground, and he remarked that he cut down and destroyed more trees and herbage before dinner than would have sold in London for a hundred pounds.

The work involved was arduous, using axes in order to achieve a space, open to the sky in this wild forest which had not been disturbed since the beginning of time. Centuries of trees and foliage had fallen, rotted and re-grown, and achieved great height. This was not an easy place to tame.[3]

The clearing continued across the whole of the next day, and finally, assisted by a couple of the ship's company, Wales completed the job and erected the Observatory, despite strong gales and heavy rain.

The site chosen for the Observatory was given the name *Astronomer's Point.*[4] In 1863 this place was visited by Captain John Falconer who recorded in his log that in the clearing at the Point it was apparent that six to eight dozen trees had been cleared at the same time, the majority cut at waist height, the stumps were still standing, and of between 2 to 4 feet in diameter. A more recent report tells of the mossy stumps of the cleared trees still extant, and with close inspection they still reveal the axe marks.[5] The observatory stood amid the working of coopers, sailmakers, waterers, and a blacksmith's forge, while Cook brewed spruce beer to prevent scurvy from a tree which he had discovered resembling the *Americo Black Spruce.* Meanwhile some left the site to harvest the rich waters of fish, some worked to repair *Resolution,* all the company were well occupied.[6] In the clearing also stood a green hut for the woodcutters, and a pen for the sheep.[7]

The scene was captured by William Hodges, *Resolution* was anchored very near the shore where a convenient bough of a large tree had grown out over the water far enough to reach her. Hodges shows a figure on this 'gangplank', and beyond, a pool of light in the trees shows Wales' observatory tent, behind is a line strung with the ship's laundry.[8]

A week after entering Dusky Bay William Wales, and his able assistant George Gilpin, could finally set up the instruments, a precision job which was not easy in a howling gale, and on such unstable ground – evidence of this was found when, on the stamping of feet some 7 or 8 yards away, the instruments were still shown to shake. Soon the pair settled down to a regular regime of observing and recording, and Wales also made a machine for observing the tides, which had to be modified when it was found that the scale of the rise and fall of the tide had been drastically underestimated.

After a while the natives became more accustomed to the sight of a large wooden vessel in the bay and its inhabitants, they would sit for hours and watch. Wales also watched them, describing them as of pleasing open countenance, it is interesting that on one occasion he described them as 'Indians'. Cook was slowly able to build their confidence, and Wales described in detail, not only their dress, but the size and construction of their boats, made from tools of a green stone which was fashioned into chisels, axes and adzes.

One of the marines[9] was even bold enough to approach the father of one of the Maori girls, and ask for her hand in marriage – the father was completely shocked at this, and responded by asking that he be allowed time to consult his God before answering.[10]

Meanwhile the heavy rain continued, and on the 28th April Wales dismantled the observatory and got everything onto the ship. The Company were on the move once more, but they did not leave Dusky by the same route, rather they sailed deeper into the Sound, and then took the route northwards through a narrow passage between the mainland and what is now *Resolution Island*. The experience moved Wales to poetry, and in his Journal he quotes what was a corruption of *Summer* from *Seasons* by James Thomson, compared as under:

William Wales' version	James Thomson's version[11]
Smooth to the shelving brink a copious flood	Smooth to the shelving brink a copious flood
Roll'd fair, and placid; where collected all,	Rolls fair and placid; where, collected all,
In one impetuous torrent, down the Steep	In one impetuous torrent down the steep
It thundering shot, and shook the country round.	It thundering shoots, and shakes the country round.
At first, an azure sheet, it rushed broad;	At first an azure sheet it rushes broad;
Then whitening by degrees, as prone it fell,	Then whitening by degrees as prone it falls
And from the loud resounding Rocks below	And from the loud-resounding rocks below
Dash'd in a cloud of foam, it sent aloft	Dashed in a cloud of foam, it sends aloft
A hoary mist, in which Sol's lucid beams,	A hoary mist, and forms a ceaseless shower.
Refracted, form'd a triple coloured bow.	
Nor could the torture'd wave find here repose	Nor can the tortured wave here find repose,
But raging still amidst the shaggy Rocks,	But, raging still amid the shaggy rocks,

Now flashing o'er the scatter'd fragments, now	Now flashes o'er the scattered fragments, now
Aslant the hollow channel darting swift;	Aslant the hollowed channel rapid darts,
'Till falling oft from graduall slope to slope,	And, falling fast from gradual slope to slope
With wild infracted Course, and lessening roar,	With wild infracted course and lessened roar,
It gained a safer bed.	It gains a safer bed, and steals at last.

The version by Wales is immediately followed in his journal by a confession that he dare not ascribe it to Thomson, but that his corruption of it could not have been avoided. To commit at least part of it to memory was impressive as the whole of this work is some 5500 lines in length. Whatever was in Wales' memory, he had been inspired by this place enough to recall that very section which describes so well the dramatic features of this beautiful place, and it inspired him further to incorporate his own observations.

Despite the obvious attractions of Dusky, the ship's company had been busy, and Wales took a day off on 2nd May to go on a shooting trip with some of the Officers. He wrote in his journal that this had been the first day's amusement which he had been able to take since reaching Dusky, indeed since he had left England, but then he had to remember to go through the daily watch winding ceremony before he left. They returned soaking wet – the rain unrelenting, but with a good bag of duck, curlew, pigeons, etc etc – the supplies of fish and fowl from this place had not left them wanting.

Once more the experience had brought him thoughts of Thomson's poem, for they had been to a cove with a cascade even more beautiful than the one he described in his version of *Seasons,* this time Wales notes that Thomson's version would not have needed the slightest alteration.

With a slight breeze and frequent showers the ship headed north into the Passage, since named the *Acheron Passage,* this is a long and narrow waterway east of *Resolution Island,* where the steep hill sides drop straight down to the sea at each side. During the first night it thundered, and lightened, and hailed. The next morning snow was on the tops of the hills, and brisk gale force winds and snow showers accompanied the ship on its journey through the passage. One day Wales wrote of very thick whitish clouds skimming through the sky, but as these approached the hill summits they formed into a conical shape, and by the time they had dispersed, the hill tops were entirely covered in snow.

It transpired that Cook named one of the peaks on Resolution Island *Mount Wales,* (see Illustration No 8) and another *Mount Clerk,* while features to the east include Mount Patten, Mount Forster, and Mount Hodges.[12]

Cook was suffering, no doubt as a result of the shooting trip, he had a fever and groin pain which caused a swelling of the right foot. This made Johann Forster nervous, and fearing the worst he would not have been happy if command of the ship should fall to Cooper, whom he thought ill tempered, capricious, and whimsical 'without any principles'.[13]

Throughout this time William Wales experienced a severe cold and fever, probably brought on by the shooting trip, so that when they eventually reached the open sea again Wales thanked God they were now leaving this dirty and disagreeable place, it seems the weather was getting on top of him. Since experiencing the Hudson's Bay weather, and then that of Antarctica, he was looking forward to reaching warmer climes.

Wales now spent time reflecting on this past experience of Dusky, and wrote that he had had the greatest difficulty attending to his tasks, being almost all the time cold, and wet, and feverish. He had nevertheless waxed lyrical at the beauty of the place, and now felt that he must record for future venturers the best account of what they could expect to find there. He had described in detail the indigenous peoples and their dress while at Pickersgill harbour and now followed naturally with the weather, which at this time of year was certainly wet. The rain was probably due to the prodigious height of the hills, their steep sides covered with trees down to the water's edge, and the ground amongst them thick with moss and ferns in a soil of thick leaf mould. He goes on to describe the trees and other flora in minute detail, then onto the birds, always a favourite subject with him, and then the fish. He had met with no fossils, nor minerals.

The weather was improving as the ship headed north, but during the afternoon before reaching Queen Charlotte Sound, Wales records a weather phenomenon which he had not experienced before:

> ...The forenoon had been in general clear but subject to heavy squalls of wind, and thick flying clouds, which moved very swiftly from SW to NE (the direction of the wind). About 4 in the Afternoon it became calm; the heavens were almost covered with black Clouds, particularly towards the West & North-west, and presently after, we saw several Tail-like appearances descending from the Clouds in that quarter; these appendages were whiter than the clouds which they appertained to, and increased gradually in length until they extended as near as I could judge, about one-sixth part of the distance between the Cloud and the surface of the Sea. The water under them became violently

agitated, and soon after, to rise up into the Air in a sort of spiral form, directing its course towards the small part of the cloud which, at the beginning of its agitation had hung directly over it, but now, by a motion which they all had the contrary way to that the wind had been, was a little on the side. As the water rose, the end of the cloud descended, and in a few minutes, they joined in the middle; after which the water ascended out of the Sea into the cloud, with great Velocity. I think none continued entire more than 10 minutes; I saw four complete at one time; but there were several which began, but were dispersed (by what Cause I know not) before the Cloud and water joined. One, I was told came within 30 or 40 yards of the ship, but I was then below; when I got on deck it was about 100 fathoms from her. I am persuaded that if it had gone over her it would have torn away her sails & yards; perhaps her Masts and Rigging also.[14]

QUEEN CHARLOTTE SOUND MAY-JUNE 1773

Queen Charlotte Sound was a useful place for Cook to stop, with its protected anchorage it offered fresh water, timber, edible plants, fish, and birds, and the indigenous people were generally friendly and willing to trade. Cook could easily collect plants here to combat the dreaded scurvy, and nearby the setting was ideal for repairing casks and drying out any bread or ship's biscuits, which were perhaps beginning to decay due to the damp conditions on board.[15]

As *Resolution* approached Queen Charlotte Sound between the north and south island of New Zealand, she met with a signal from *Adventure* anchored at Ship Cove, where Cook had instructed Captain Furneaux to wait should they become separated while in the Antarctic waters. The Company were all well, and *Resolution* anchored alongside – this was a time to catch up, exchange stories, and discuss the next part of the voyage. Wales planned to get his shore observatory set up once more, but Cook had no plans to stay for long and did not think it worthwhile to move all the instruments and equipment onto the shore.

Adventure had arrived at this place some six weeks earlier, and the next morning Wales went on shore to visit Bayly who had set up his tent and instruments on Hippa Island. The ship's company had planted seeds, and Wales returned to his cabin with a large handkerchief full of the resulting salad, Cook returned to the ship with wild celery and other fresh herbage.

A particularly interesting experiment was carried out here by Wales and Bayly. In order to establish the difference in longitude between Ship Cove and Observatory Island, they fired guns at each site, noting the delay in time between the actual explosion and hearing the report. The resulting time differential was just ten seconds.[16]

Within a couple of days Wales learned that it would be some 3 or 4 days before the ships sailed again, so that at least some of his instruments now made it onto the shore near the ship, and though this was not ideal, some observations were made. All the time Wales needed to guard his possessions, as unlike their contemporaries at Dusky, the natives here were not adverse to stealing things at the least opportunity.

Cook was now anxious to set sail again, since arriving he had engaged both the ship's companies in gathering a lot of fresh herbage to combat scurvy, something which he felt the *Adventure* had not guarded against enough since the two sloops separated. He also had them planting seeds of vegetables and strawberries on one of the islands.

The Captain was worrying at this point that the longitude calculated for New Zealand, by both Wales and Bayly, did not compare favourably with the co-ordinates determined by himself and Charles Green during the first voyage on *Endeavour,* being over half of one degree further east. These calculations had been determined by the lunar method and he had every faith in Green, however with the help of the clocks on this voyage, the astronomers were better equipped to determine longitude more accurately. The discrepancy caused Cook a great deal of self doubt, he had by now experienced Wales' careful work, and held him in high regard. Blaming himself for the error in the earlier observations, Cook resolved that they must now be rectified.[17]

The 4th June was King George's birthday, and as was the custom this was a day of festivities on board, when Captain Furneaux and all the officers dined with Captain Cook, and all the seamen were granted double allowance.[18]

On 6th June 1773 the two sloops set sail again, leaving New Zealand and heading roughly in an easterly direction into the Pacific. It was recorded that Mr Arnold's Watch number 3 had to be left to run down as the key wouldn't turn, it had suffered some kind of accident, but meanwhile the other observations went on as usual. This was the second of Arnold's watches to fail – the other one on the *Adventure* had not worked since reaching the Cape of Good Hope.

Wales felt the urge to report in his journal on a subject which had been giving him some anxiety. The natives of New Zealand were generally thought to have been cannibalistic, and Wales had expected that he would witness this, and have to record it, however to his relief he had not seen the least signs of any such custom in reality, and was anxious to report his findings and thus entirely quit the subject. Nonetheless, it was a fact that ceremonial displays of weapon handling had indicated that after killing their enemy the natives cut off the head and limbs of their victims, and discarded the bowels, before proceeding to eat them. Furthermore, reports from *Endeavour* and *Adventure* had indicated that proof of cannibalism had been found.

The subject of 'food', and the illness he had experienced after leaving Dusky, still apparently weighed heavy on Wales' mind. Anders Sparrman reported that the meals were divided, and explained that on one table was the Captain, who invited two of the officers and one petty officer to share his table, and to the Officer's table a petty officer was invited each day. In this case the officers felt a need for fresh meat and soup, and had prepared a dog which had been particularly ugly, and had deserted them for a couple of weeks while at Dusky. Wales' diet on this occasion was rigidly tested. He disliked eating duck, or any seabird, due to their oily taste from consuming fish – nor could he face roast dog. So it was that on this day he left the table, preferring to eat with the other officers. Finally however he was tempted to try a small morsel, there being a need for him to overcome prejudices if he was to survive the voyage.[19]

The South Pacific ocean was reached at last, the two ships buffeted by gentle gales and choppy seas progressed without much hindrance until, on 16th June, the man at the wheel of *Resolution* had been carried clear over it by a sudden jerk on the tiller caused by the heavy sea swell. The Officer of the watch had caught the wheel, and placed a second man at it to assist, thus the wheel was double manned. After another ten minutes there was another jerk, and one of the men was again taken clean over the wheel, which then returned with such speed that the other man was taken over the wheel the opposite way. The Lieutenant had then caught the wheel, which was fortunate, as the man who had suffered the latter tumble by this time had his leg firmly wedged between a spoke of the wheel and the supporting standard, so that had the wheel not been firmly held by the Lieutenant at that stage the man's leg would have been shattered to pieces. Wales sums up the affair, which the reader assumes by now he must have witnessed, by penning his further observations:

> ...The care of Providence, in fitting the back to the Burthen, was never more conspicuous than in this circumstance. The man who went over to leeward, and of course had much the greater fall, resembled much a seal in substance and make, and accordingly his fall on the deck made the same squash that a Bag of Blubber would have done; on the contrary, the other was a poor raw-boned Lad, whose every bone rattled with the fall he got, and must have been broke to pieces had he gone over to Leeward ...[20]

The animals on board naturally suffered trauma during heavy swells, and needed extra care by the ship's company. A goat fell overboard and had to be picked out of the sea by lowering a small boat, but she soon died after being rescued.[21]

With *Adventure* now accompanying the main vessel, Cook took a course about ten degrees to the south of the one he had taken in *Endeavour,* taking the opportunity to take a wider sweep of the Pacific to look for land before heading north, and finally west, to Tahiti.

During this time the weather had been clear, and it was possible for Wales to occasionally visit Bayly on *Adventure* and compare and record the accuracy of the watches. By 7th August they were sailing with the trade winds when a thick haze appeared, but they were soon to reach their next landfall. A week later they were joined by a number of native boats loaded with fruits, which were anxiously traded for nails and beads, the fruit was enjoyed, and a change of diet welcomed.

Tahiti & the Society Islands August-September 1773

On 17th August, 1773 *Resolution* and *Adventure* anchored at Vaitepiha Bay on Otaheite,[22] after some hair-raising episodes on the surrounding reef had threatened to wreck both ships. The food and the climate were much better here, but again the natives were to be closely observed, Cook advised Wales not to take any instruments on shore, as it was not his intention to stay any length of time at this anchorage.

During the first day on Tahiti, Isaac Taylor, one of the marines, died on *Resolution* of dropsy, he was the first to be buried at sea since leaving England. Wales wrote in his journal that, at least if one is buried at sea, there is no danger coming back to life again, he could think of nothing worse for a man than being deposited in a vault only to come back to 'himself' again.

The natives were now coming on board frequently, bringing fruits to trade, the company had hoped to get fresh meat here – hogs and poultry had been received by former voyagers, but these were not forthcoming. After staying for almost a week Cook ventured on shore to seek out the King or *Aree* of this part of the Island, they had met before during the *Endeavour* voyage, and it was not long before Cook had secured three hogs.

On 25th August the boats moved to *Matavi Bay,* and at last Wales was able to get his Observatory set up, and his instruments on shore, guarded by a party of Marines from the ship's crews. This place had special significance for Wales, as it was on this very spot that his brother-in-law Charles Green had observed the transit of Venus in 1769. Bayly also set up his Observatory in this same place.[23]

The weather here was very hot, with light variable winds and in complete contrast to Dusky, so that William Wales enjoyed ideal conditions for his observations. He spent the next few days totally absorbed by his work, and in the few spare hours he had he was entertained by studying the behaviour and disposition of the four hundred or so natives who constantly stood around his encampment. They were kept back from the Observatory by just four guards, and a rope stretched from post to post some 60 yards away, and they behaved impeccably.

At the end of August the observatory and instruments were safely packed on board again. Wales had compared his brother-in-law's observations, and found his Latitude differed by less than two seconds, and his Longitude to be exactly the same. He also commented on Mr Bougainville's observations, a copy of whose journal he obviously had access to, perhaps even his own copy.

Wales was always anxious to record his assessment of the places he visited, and Tahiti was no exception, he had noticed that there seemed to be no boundaries, but that the properties seemed to belong to everyone, and any land which was not planted upon already could be taken over by anyone who wanted it.

After premature apologies for what he thought may be interpreted as 'lack of taste', there follows in Wales' journal a painstaking description of the Otahitean Ladies, small in stature with a complexion of light olive, then, on second thoughts, he added that this was rather a deadish yellow. Hair of glossy black and cut like the English country people in bowl-dish fashion.[24] The resulting coiffure, although of a simple nature, nevertheless inspired him to describe the effect as 'pretty, due to it complimenting the simplicity of dress'. Eyes exceedingly black, but too prominent for his liking – noses flat with wide nostrils, as also were their mouths – teeth close, white and even. Breasts of two kinds – round and beautiful before they have children, or the older women who have had children, drooped to their navels. He then decided that he was not going to describe the rest of their bodies when he explains:

> ...I have no occasion to call in the Aids of Imagination to describe every part of them, down to their very toes, as there were plenty of them who were not solicitous to hide any of their beauties from our Eyes; but it may be best to stop here, and proceed to say a little in defence of their Characters, which have, in my opinion, been as much depreciated as their beauties have been Magnifyed.[25]

Earlier voyages to these islands quickly gave them a reputation as a *Garden of Eden,* and resulting stories from returning sailors rendered them a popular destination with prospective ones, like tales that the Tahitians urged their naked women on unwary visiting sailors, who quickly discovered their pockets had been picked. Promiscuity was rife, and syphilis and other diseases were a problem. Marriage here was merely an agreement between two people, which was quickly reversed with little trouble, but most chose freedom rather than marriage.

Cook was a wiser man after the *Endeavour's* visit, and although he was aware of rather delicate situations when they first docked at Vaitepiha, he soon removed the company to Matavai, which somewhat eased the situation.

Wales had read of the reputation of the Otahitean ladies being eager to grant favours to any man who would pay for them, and was keen to observe their behaviour for himself. He found that in fact married women were not to be purchased, but on the whole were faithful and obedient to their husbands, and that the unmarried ladies could not be described as indiscriminately granting favours, but on the contrary were careful to whom they granted them. He did however note that there were prostitutes, as there were in London, and was in no doubt that such were those who had come aboard when they first docked here, but he concluded that the reputation afforded to the Tahitians by earlier voyagers was rather over-stated.

Native religion was always of interest to Wales, and in the short time he had been there he understood that the Tahitians believed in one supreme being, but he could not discover whether or not they paid any sort of adoration to this being. He had heard that they sometimes practiced the sacrifice of hogs, which may have been an offering to a supreme being, and that they marked burial places of their Chiefs, and raised piles of stones around which trees were planted, and fruits hung on these trees for the use of the departed. Bodies were not buried, but placed in sheds hung with cloths until the flesh had rotted, and then only the bones were buried.

On the whole Wales little understood the religion of the islands, but he did describe what he witnessed of religious practices, and further described his observations of the politics, the law, the crime, and punishment. He described bread-making, the manufacture of cloth – which was a very laborious process, and from his own experience practiced only by the old and the ugly.

It is evident from reading his journals that Wales developed a disciplined regime of observation, calculation, and recording, carried out no doubt with the help of his able assistant George Gilpin, whom he chose never to acknowledge in his journal. His work happily allowed him to observe also the environment and the indigenous people, whose hospitality he was always keen to experience. The first time he went on shore he found himself being invited into the homes of these people to eat fruit, and such was his delight at their friendliness, that at their request, he soon started handing out to them gifts which he had about him – beads, nails, a knife, and then went his handkerchief, coat, shirt etc – at the start he had been only too pleased to hand out small tokens for their hospitality, but soon he realized that things were disappearing which he had not offered. After a couple of days of this over generous behaviour, he had to change his conduct, with his stock greatly depleted he resolved that in future he would just barter and trade, this more satisfactory way of exchanging goods proved the best method, and after that Wales found himself on more friendly terms with the indigenous population.

One particular individual mentioned by Wales was *Ereti,* the chief of the district, whom he described as the friend of M. Bougainville. Ereti was sensible, and had impressed Wales by his questions, which showed a desire to learn more of the land of England, showing he was much more intelligent than the rest of his fellow countrymen. He was in the habit of visiting the astronomer's encampment at Point Venus, and he habitually took breakfast and dinner at their table, soon enjoying the taste of tea, biscuits, and butter – he took port with the others and toasted King George – not with relish at first, but after a few glasses he was drinking heartily with the rest of them.

Wales enjoyed his talks with Ereti, and listed the subjects of their conversations, from which he had gained more knowledge of this beautiful place, they had spoken of the animals and of the other voyagers who had visited, and traded hogs for axes, hogs were getting scarce because of this, as were fowls, but there were still plentiful small birds, and of course fruits as in all the tropical countries. Of the geology of the island, although this interested him, Wales saw none but a few pieces of pumice, he was obviously impressed with his visit, and felt he had gained much from it.

When September came they were moving again, Cook knew that unless they could find more supplies than Tahiti had to offer, they would not have enough to last them until they reached Queen Charlotte Sound again, so they headed for the Island of Huaheine,[26] one of the Leeward Society islands where they anchored in a harbour on the west coast. The chief of the island was called *Ori,* who welcomed his old friend Cook whom he called *Tute.* Here there were hogs in abundance for trading.[27]

Wales was fascinated by the native canoes, he had learned that these had a reputation for being the best and largest in the area, and made it his business to inspect one which belonged to the Chief of the island, a double canoe joined by cross beams, similar to the ones he had seen in New Zealand. His journal gives a full account of its construction, which was capable of carrying some one hundred and fifty rowers and steersmen, and in the margin of his journal, Wales drew a sketch of a cross-section of the body of the vessel.

After inspecting the canoe Wales went with Captain Cook to the King's house, where they found an old gaunt man, rather haggard, but much revered by his subjects. When *Endeavour* visited, Cook had given him gifts of metal coins and medals, telling him that if he showed them to visiting ships companies in the future, he would be assured of their friendship. The Chief accordingly greeted Cook by drawing these objects from a small bag, which were returned together with more, bearing the names of *Resolution* and *Adventure,* and accepted with much pleasure, the old man obviously treasured them.

Joseph Banks had arranged with the British Admiralty that 2000 brass gilt medals be minted after Cook's first voyage, to be distributed during the second voyage. The medals had King George III on the obverse, with *Resolution* and Adventure on the reverse, and were to be distributed to the natives of newly discovered countries, to commemorate them being the first discoveries.[28]

The next day Wales disembarked onto the surrounding reefs at low water, and took an afternoon walk of about half a mile. He found the reefs to be of firm stone – white like limestone, but harder, and almost covered with large bunches of white, and occasionally of brown, coral. Curiously the rock was covered with small holes, each one of which contained a shell with a live fish, he puzzled over these – for the most part the holes were smaller than the shells they contained, so that either the shell had grown within the hole, or the hole had grown over the shell, if only he were a naturalist – but for now he must return before the water rose above his middle.

Wales and Bayly went on shore to explore the Island one morning, heading through a delightful valley of fruit trees, and scattered with houses. Soon the population were greeting them in the manner of Tahitians – pocket picking while offering produce, hogs and cockerels. For some reason they didn't offer hens, despite appearing to have plenty, though fewer fruits.

Sparrman was not let off so lightly as the astronomers, he had taken himself off on a botanising walk and was stripped of all his clothes bar his trousers, he was hurt by this behaviour. Chief *Ori*, on recovering his clothes, assured him that the culprits would be punished.[29]

The stay at Huaheine had been successful, for the ships were well stocked with hogs when they sailed out of the bay, and onto Ulietea,[30] another of the Leeward Society Islands. It took just one day to reach this island, where Cook planned to stay for a while, and on the 8th September 1773 with the ships safely anchored, Wales and Pickersgill went on shore to look for a suitable place to erect the observatory once more. There was the end of an eclipse of the sun to observe on the 16th of the month, and Cook intended mounting a guard on the observatory while it was extant.

A suitable place was eventually found, and Wales and Pickersgill took the opportunity to explore some of the island by following a small river from the bay into the inner country, it was a hot day, and they walked quite a way before returning to ship.

Richard Pickersgill was 14 years Wales' junior, he was a fellow Yorkshireman and 23 when he joined the voyage. Though he was quite a heavy drinker, Pickersgill was reliable, and Cook often sent him out on survey work, and he often accompanied Wales on shore to find suitable observing sites and explore the terrain, they seemed to work well together.[31]

Wales and some of the ship's officers enjoyed the hospitality of one of the Chiefs, or *Arees,* of the island while here, they were entertained by music and dancing, which they called a *Heava.* Music from three drums of shark's skin, and described in detail by Wales, as were the two dancers, one of them being the daughter of the Chief, they danced under the direction of an old man, their tutor, who was also present. From Wales' journal we are treated to a full account of the dress of the dancers, their hair style, and their dance moves, some of which he finds not very amusing:

> ...the wriggling of their Hips, especially as set off with such a quantity of Furbeloes, is too Ludicrous to be pleasing, and the distortion of their mouths is really disagreeable, although it is for this the young Princess is chiefly admired. Her face is naturally one of the most beautiful on the Island; but in these performances she twists it in such a manner that a stranger would sometimes really question whether her right Eye, Mouth

and left Ear did not form one great Gash passing in an oblique direction across her face.[32]

After the girls had danced there followed theatrical pieces performed by half a dozen men, these were compared by Wales to those of Mr Garrick back in London.[33]

Cook often agreed to take on board an islander who was keen to travel to distant places, and whilst questioning the ethics of such undertakings, he did find that these natives were useful as interpreters, on the *Endeavour* voyage he had taken on *Tupia* who had become a good friend, and had proved to be very useful when communicating with the natives. At Tahiti *Porio* had joined the ship's company, but on sailing to Raiatea had fallen in love with one of the native girls there, and had been allowed to stay. *Porio* was quickly replaced by *Odiddy* who was a native of the island of Bolabola[34] in the Society Islands group, and now known as *Bora Bora*.

One day a shooting and botanizing party from the ship had headed northwards on Raiatea, these included ship's officers and Forster's party. Due to the illness of the Forster's servant, it had been necessary for Georg Forster to negotiate terms with a native to convey them back to the ship by canoe, whence a scuffle had occurred between Georg and the native. On witnessing this J R Forster had shot and slightly wounded the native. Later J R Cooper had informed Cook of the dispute, and Cook interrogated some of the witnesses from among his officers about the incident. Later reflection caused Cook to re-assert his position with Forster, but this caused tempers to flare between the two, causing consternation among the whole of the ship's company. Wales was not a witness to the dispute on the island, but had sensed the intensity of the resulting anger between Forster and Cook, filing the details for future reference.[35]

Wales had enjoyed Raiatea, between his astronomical observations he enjoyed the entertainment and the profuse dining on hog and all the riches of the place, despite the every present threat from the light fingers of some of the native people. The ships left on 18th September laden with hogs, sows, cocks and hens, dogs, yams, and breadfruit, sufficient to last the companies until they arrived back at New Zealand.[36]

Resolution was now replenished with food and interpreter and sailed for the Tonga Group of islands, which Cook planned to visit before heading south-west for Queen Charlotte Sound.

TONGA OCTOBER 1773

The Tongan group of islands had been sighted first by Tasman in 1642, the island which Tasman had named *Middleburg,* now named 'Eua, came into view on 1st October. It had a good anchorage and at first the island looked deserted, but then two natives were sighted, and within minutes more and more joined them. Canoes were steered out to the ships as they sailed past, and one came alongside *Resolution,* from where a rope was dropped over the side with a view to giving it a friendly tow, but without hesitation one of the natives ascended the rope and sat himself down unconcerned on the deck, obviously happy to start trading with the crew. Before long others joined him from other canoes, and it became obvious that one of them was the Chief, such was his authority. Cook was concerned that the Chief was suffering from the cold, and presented him with a large red cloth with which to cover himself, this seemed to please him.

Once anchored, Captain Cook went on shore with the Chief who led him to his house amidst a crowd of welcoming natives, once inside Cook enjoyed his generous hospitality, he was given drink and fruit, and shown the utmost respect.

The following day Wales went on shore with several of the ships' Officers and joined Cook and Furneaux at the Chief's house, where they were treated to singing and music from a variety of native instruments by the islanders. Afterwards Wales took the opportunity to explore the island, as was his usual practice in these places, unfortunately he didn't have time to walk right across the island but saw a sizeable amount, he described it as fruitful and pleasant, and noted the roads were as good as England's – his original walk to London had given him plenty of experience of those.

Back at the Chief's house fruits and yams were prepared for the two Captains to take back to their ships, and in the early evening the Chief and his family saw them back safely on board in this beautiful and agreeable location.

The next morning saw *Resolution & Discovery* weighing anchors and sailing on to explore more of this beautiful Island group, initial experience of which had again tempted Wales to put pen to paper and record his findings. He admitted that although his knowledge of the place and its people was only limited due to the short stay on 'Eua, he tried to see and observe as much as possible and commit it to paper. He goes on to describe once again in detail the inhabitants, their dress, their behaviour, and their hair which he notes of the women was all black, but of the men all colours – he had concluded that this was because of something they put on it.

The weapons were mentioned, but Wales was unable to establish why they were needed in such a friendly place, but then he was puzzled at the sight of many of the inhabitants having had parts of their hands mutilated, some had lost part fingers, some had lost whole fingers, both men and women, young and old. Before describing the fruits of the island he goes on to record the population of birds, one of his favourite subjects judging by his apparent knowledge of ornithology.[37]

Amid his studies of island life Wales recorded his observations, and when he gave the latitude and longitude of the ship at anchor, he stressed that although he had no opportunity of making more observations here, the one he did take may be depended upon. The longitude of course was that calculated by Mr Kendall's watch, with which he was increasingly impressed.

On 3rd October, 1773 the ships anchored just off shore on the west side of Tongatapu, when the natives greeted them in the usual Tongan manner and traded fruits, yams, hogs, and fowls for nails. Wales remarked that he supposed that Tasman, who as far as he knew was the only person to have visited the islands before, had introduced them to nails, these were the only articles they were familiar with – they were not interested in tools like knives and hatches.

As was his custom William Wales took himself off the next morning in the jolly boat to the landing place for a walk across the Island. Towards the shore the water became shallow and the boat was unable to reach terra firma, so he pulled off his shoes and paddled over to the crowd of four hundred or so natives who had gathered to watch. Once on dry land again he put down his shoes between his feet before attempting to put them back on, but they were immediately snatched by someone from behind him, and he could only stand there and watch the perpetrator disappear into the crowd, for to follow him barefoot would have been foolhardy and painful, the ground being composed of very sharp coral.

The companions who had accompanied him in the jolly boat were long disappeared, and left helpless Wales considering his next move when he saw Captain Cook with one of the Chiefs, beckoning them he spilled out his complaints, whereby the Chief immediately moved into the crowd and quickly retrieved his shoes which were amicably returned, this prompted Wales to reward the Chief with one large nail, to the satisfaction of both parties. Cook adds as a note in his journal that he found Mr Wales in a 'laughable and distressed situation', it must have been a situation which no one could ever imagine Wales getting himself into, for Cook to have expressed it in these terms.[38]

The eventual ramble over the Island was enjoyable. Wales and his two companions walked down a road between well planned and highly cultivated enclosed plantations, but there were also areas of open land planted with large trees. On reaching a small hill Wales noticed on the top was an area enclosed by a low wall with stone steps reaching up to it, he climbed to find a building which housed small images of wood, and on the floor, and around the building was brown gravel, the place was all very neat and tidy, and Wales supposed this to be a religious building, a shrine of some kind. He later was to question this theory when a similar image was set up as a target by the natives for Wales and his companions to practice their shooting skills.

The ramble continued for the rest of the day, the three circled the island, and despite meeting many large groups of natives they travelled unhindered, so that Wales had no use for the gun which he carried just in case.

It was the next day, after busying himself with observations both on the boat and on shore, that Wales again experienced a native's apparent effrontery. He was on the jolly boat returning to the ship when he saw one of the crew's jackets disappear over the side, on closer inspection he saw one of the natives running away from the boat underwater with the jacket in tow. When Wales alerted the rest of his company they fired a shot, the man was eventually stopped by an Officer on shore who, after shouting to the offender to give the jacket back and being ignored, had shot at the man. The jacket was recovered, and the offender walked away – but with small shot embedded in him.

What Wales found remarkable was, that although many natives had witnessed the shooting, they appeared unconcerned by the firing of guns, and he felt almost sorry that the thief was able to walk away from the scene without the incident setting an example. Had the man been seen to be injured or even killed by the incident, then the natives may not have continued to try and steal the clothes from their backs. What was even more remarkable was that the visitors were able to walk around the Island, even alone and unarmed without incident, incivilities only seemed to occur at the landing place on the Island.

The jacket incident over, the eventual return to the ship revealed even more audacity when a native was seen coming out of the Master's cabin with a pile of books, which included the Ship's Logs. When verbal threats proved no good, musket balls were fired in desperation through the waiting boat alongside, its crew followed their booty over the side, and the boat was committed to the deep. The books were recovered, and the time had come to prepare for the ships' departure. Cook was anxious to get back to Queen Charlotte Sound before heading out again into the Pacific for a much larger sweep of that giant ocean.

Queen Charlotte Sound November 1773

It was 2nd November 1773 when *Resolution* and *Adventure* reached New Zealand once again, but on reaching Cook Strait a great gale blew, and in testing conditions the ships lost site of each other, progress to Queen Charlotte Sound was hindered, so much that by the time Cook brought his ship to anchor in Ship's Cove *Adventure* was nowhere to be found.

The natives were soon alongside, and the ship's company recognized some of them from the previous visit. Cook recognized one in particular from when *Endeavour* had visited, he was a chief, and Cook learned from him that sadly the rest of his family had been victims of cannibalism.

It was decided that the tent observatory should be pitched in the same place as before, with crew members again stationed to guard it, and thus the instruments were set up, clocks and quadrant were installed, and again the wind blew up and brought rain. It was cold for the inhabitants of the tent – bitterly cold – only relieved by an oven, which was fixed up next to the tent in order to re-bake some bread which had been found onboard to be mouldy.

Wales certainly felt the cold again, especially after the weather experienced in the Pacific Islands. During the next morning it was discovered that some clothing had been stolen from the tent, so that it was even more imperative that Wales stayed in the tent, a watch was organized of two hours by six persons each night, and occupying two tents. He could not risk leaving his post, guarding instruments and the time keeper with his trusty gun, the rain outside continued, and the wind which he notes as 'all very disagreeable'.

After almost three weeks the instruments, observatory, and tents were back on board and ready for the next stage of the voyage, this was rather to Wales' relief, for he had long suspected from close observation and accounts of his fellows that the natives here were cannibals. Before leaving he went out with Cook and the elder Forster to Motu-Aro to check the garden they had planted, and to harvest some of the fresh greens for the next stage of the voyage.

On returning to the ship the scene on the quarterdeck was one of disbelief. There sat the severed head of a young Maori, this had been brought on board by Pickersgill who had apparently been on shore with other officers and witnessed a party of natives, their canoe decorated with a pierced human heart, while all about the scene of slaughter, bones and entrails, and a human head – the latter Pickersgill traded for two nails. On returning to the ship, the head had excited some natives there into taking a slice from it, and in front of a horrified cook had seared it on a gridiron in the galley, before devouring it greedily with much finger sucking.[39]

Captain Cook was so appalled on learning of the preceding hideous events, that what he did next was to perhaps shock the ship's company even more. Although horrified at the sight of the apparent practices of these cannibals, he realized that he had to witness these events first hand, and went on to order that a piece of flesh be broiled and placed on the deck, so that he could see one of the cannibals relish its taste. The resulting spectacle caused many of the crew to vomit.[40]

The whole question as to why the natives carried out the horrid practice of cannibalism was to become the subject of lengthy discussions in the stern cabin by Cook, Forster, Sparrman, and Wales, each writing extensive accounts of the episode in their respective Journals.

Before heading out once more into the Pacific, *Resolution* scoured the northern shore of the Sound, the fact that *Adventure* had not arrived, despite the winds having been favourable for entry into the Sound while they had been moored, made the crew uneasy. Cook left a note for them, with instructions, should they eventually make it back to Ship's Cove.

Endnotes

1   *Resolution: Log and Journal kept by C Clerke.* The National Archives, Kew, Surrey. ADM 55/124.

2   William Wales 1734-1798, *Journal on the Resolution 21 June 1772-17* October 1774. State Library of New South Wales. Manuscript Safe 1/84

3   Sparrman, A, 1953. *A Voyage Round the World With Captain James Cook in H.M.S. Resolution.* London, Robert Hale.

4   Erroneously recorded as *Observatory Point* in Beaglehole, J.B., 1974. *The Life of Captain James Cook.* London, A & C Black.

5   Begg, A, Charles & Begg, Neil C, 1966. *Dusky Bay.* Christchurch, Whitcombe & Tombs Ltd.

6   Beaglehole, J B, 1974. *The Life of Captain James Cook.* London, A & C Black.

7   Hoare, M E, 1982. *The Resolution Journal of Johann Reinhold Forster 1772-75.* London, Hakluyt Society.

8   Quilley, G & Bonehill, J, 2004. *William Hodges 1744-1797.* London, Yale University Press.

9   Possibly Samuel Gibson who could speak a little of the language.

10 Aughton, P, 2004. *Resolution.* London, Weidenfeld & Nicholson. p.62.

11 Internet site http://www.archive.org

12 Robson, John, 2000. *Captain Cook's World.* Rochester, Chatham Publishing.

13 Aughton, P, 2004. *Resolution.* London, Weidenfeld & Nicholson.

14 Wales, William. *Journal on the Resolution, June 21, 1772 to October 17th, 1774.* Manuscript now in the Mitchell Library, Sydney, Australia. Entry 17th May 1773.

15 Orchiston, Wayne, 1998. *Nautical Astronomy in New Zealand. The Voyages of James Cook.* Wellington, Carter Observatory Board.

16 Wales, W & Bayly, W, 1777. *The Original Astronomical Observations. Made in the Course of a Voyage Towards the South Pole, and Round the World.* London. Strahan.

17 Beaglehole, J C (Ed), 1969. *The Journals of Captain James Cook on His Voyages of Discovery. II. The Voyage of*

Resolution and Adventure 1772-1775. Cambridge University Press for the Hakluyt Society. p.174

18 Ibid. pg.172.

19 Sparrman, Anders, 1953. *A Voyage Round the World with Captain Cook*. London, Robert Hale.

20 Wales, William. *Journal on the Resolution, June 21, 1772 to October 17th, 1774*. Manuscript now in the Mitchell Library, Sydney, Australia. Entry 16th June 1773.

21 Hough, R, 1994. *Captain James Cook, a Biography*. London. Hodder & Stoughton

22 Named *King George III's Island* by Wallis in 1767. Modern name, *Tahiti*.

23 Beaglehole, J C (Ed), 1969. *The Journals of Captain James Cook on His Voyages of Discovery. II. The Voyage of Resolution and Adventure 1772-1775*. Cambridge University Press for the Hakluyt Society. p.206.

24 Referring to the common practice of putting a bowl on the head and cutting off all visible hair below it, usually the method used by people who couldn't afford to go to a proper barber or hair-dresser.

25 Wales, William. *Journal on the Resolution, June 21, 1772 to October 17th, 1774*. Manuscript now in the Mitchell Library, Sydney, Australia. Entry 31st August 1773.

26 Modern name, *Huahine*.

27 Hough, R, 1995. *Captain James Cook, a Biography*. London, Hodder & Stoughton.

28 Captain Cook display, Auckland Maritime Museum, New Zealand.

29 Hough, R, 1995. *Captain James Cook, a Biography*. London, Hodder & Stoughton.

30 Modern name, *Raiatea*.

31 Elliot, J & Pickersgill, R, 1984. *Captain Cook's Second Voyage*. London, Caliban Books.

32 William Wales 1734-1798, *Journal on the Resolution 21 June 1772-17 October 1774*. State Library of New South Wales. Manuscript Safe 1/84

33 William Wales had a love of drama, and his library contained many books of plays and the history of the theatre, as listed in the Catalogue of the Sale of his Books in 1799. Graves Collection, Library of University College, London.

34 Aughton, P, 2004. *Resolution*. London, Weidenfeld & Nicholson.

35 Hoare, Michael E, 1976. *The Tactless Philosopher*. Melbourne, Hawthorne Press.

36 Hough, R, 1995. *Captain James Cook, a Biography*. London, Hodder & Stoughton.

37 William Wales had in his library Benjamin Martin's *Natural History of England*. which had been printed and sold by W. Owen, of Temple-Bar, Fleet Street in London in 1759, and also by Martin who lived in Fleet Street. It is interesting to note that Benjamin Martin (1705-1782) was not only a teacher of mathematics, but also a maker of optical instruments, and thereby would perhaps be an acquaintance of Wales.

38 Beaglehole, J C (Ed), 1969. *The Journals of Captain James Cook on His Voyages of Discovery. II. The Voyage of Resolution and Adventure 1772-1775*. Cambridge University Press for the Hakluyt Society. Pg 253.

39 Gurney, Alan, 1998. *Below the Convergence*. London, Pimlico.

40 Beaglehole, J C (Ed), 1969. *The Journals of Captain James Cook on His Voyages of Discovery. II. The Voyage of Resolution and Adventure 1772-1775*. Cambridge University Press for the Hakluyt Society. p.293

10

SWEEPING THE PACIFIC

A mild wind sleeks the nap of waves
as clouds fly in bankrupt skies.
This is the zoo of the south.
Islands, like the backs of animals, rise,
and optic regiments drill the bay.[1]

At the end of November 1773 the lone *Resolution* headed out
into the Pacific once more in a brisk gale and fair weather,
and on December 6th she reached the point on the globe, the
antipode, directly opposite London. Home was in Wales'
mind as the ship sailed directly over the point, and he joined
the two Forsters to drink to their friends and the good people
of London, some eight thousand miles beneath, who could
now be sure that London had no land antipode, only the sea,
penguins, petrels, and seals.[2]

Islands of ice came into view again as the vessel headed south
to penetrate the Antarctic Circle once more in search of
that elusive southern continent. The rigging became heavily
frosted over as *Resolution* pushed deeper into the sea of ice,
by Christmas day Wales reported the greatest number of ice
islands he had ever witnessed, they were small and he likened
them to those which he had seen around the Churchill River
in the Spring of 1769, he wondered if they were nearing land,
but this was not so.

J R Forster was working on the differences between the Arctic and Antarctic frigid Zone, and this provided much stimulating discussion among the company in the great cabin, but then once again J R was taken to his bed just before Christmas with his painful rheumatism and toothache, and did not emerge again until well into the new year. In his journal Forster questioned the decision of Cook to take a vulnerable crew and ship into such latitudes, when it was obvious that there was no land to be discovered there, but Cook would not confide in anyone his reasons and intentions.

Cook had pushed the boundaries to achieve his ambition, and the achievement was recognized by George Vancouver, who climbed out onto the bowsprit when *Resolution* was at her furthermost point south, to become the first person who had ever been this close to the South Pole.[3]

As was customary the sailors celebrated Christmas by getting drunk, on rations which had been hoarded for months especially for the occasion. Cook tolerated their behaviour on this one day of the year, no doubt to help alleviate the stress of venturing into the unknown on such a long voyage. The Captain was joined by his officers, mates, and no doubt the supernumeries for dinner, after which of the lieutenant's entertained.[4]

Christmas Day and the passing of the entry into a New Year were not noted by Wales, he appears to have been far too engrossed in his work. In January he did record that one of the midshipmen had broken the cylinder pivot of his stop watch while he was at breakfast one morning and absent from his cabin, this would have made him really annoyed.

The *Resolution* had managed to reach 71°10′ south, before turning and heading north to continue this great circuit of the Pacific. Cook was now satisfied that there was no landmass to the south of his area of exploration, and next he intended to try and seek out the Easter Island,[5] as named by Roggeveen on his voyage some fifty years previous.

Wales busied himself with his observations, he saw another water spout, but found it remarkable that he had not once witnessed the southern lights here, what he did record was the size of the albatrosses which kept the ship company, one measuring a whole ten feet between wing tips.

After the miserable cold of the Antarctic the climate was warming again, and by March 1st the ship's company was suffering once more from the heat. Wales had been suffering a sickness, and had lost his appetite.

On 25th February, before reaching Easter Island, Cook was also taken ill, he developed a fever and suffered from bilious cholic, which confined him to bed. The ship was left in the charge of the first officer Mr Cooper, and the ship surgeon Mr Patten was in charge of Cook. There being no fresh meat on board J R Forster, so afraid his Captain would not survive the voyage, sacrificed his favourite dog, which he allowed to be killed to provide fresh meat for the Captain – the resulting broth nourished Cook so much that his health gradually started improving.[6]

EASTER ISLAND MARCH 1774

At last, on 10th March Easter Island came into view, much to the relief of all on board. The fabled statues, or obelisks, were seen, some standing to attention, and curious natives emerged to bring their offerings to the ship's company.

Jacob Roggeveen had arrived with three vessels on the day after Easter in 1722, and thus the island was named. Roggeveen was Dutch, and when one native who ventured on board was offered gifts, he was followed by many others, but unfortunately Roggeveen decided that there had been some thieving, and the whole experience ended in bloodshed when many of the islanders were killed by gunfire.[7]

Resolution dropped anchor, and immediately the Master went out in the cutter to find a suitable landing place. After two hours he returned with one of the natives who had swum out to him, a man of medium height, slim, and aged about fifty. He had a brisk and active manner, and had an obvious interest in all that was around him.

The *Resolution* was eventually moored more permanently in a small bay on the west side of the island, and a party of the Captain and other gentlemen, including Wales, went on shore to investigate. At the landing place the party was met by hundreds of natives who had gathered to watch and receive them. On embarking there was an exchange of roast potatoes and sugar cane for nails and trinkets, not really a fair exchange, as Wales noticed that when he received his food this was immediately begged back by other natives, or in one case, snatched from him immediately he had received it.

On shore was a stone wall which had appeared from the boat to be a defensive structure with possibly crenellations, but on examination Wales found that it had been constructed for housing two of the statues with very fine dry masonry, and was not defensive, but had merely appeared so by a missing stone which had fallen down and broken.

The party moved on to explore further, with the natives walking arm-in-arm with some of them, which Wales found most convivial – until he discovered his handkerchief and his achromatic spyglass telescope had been picked from his pocket.

The population of the island was about six hundred, the culture and language was very like that of Tahiti, with tattooing evident and the practice of pilfering. Their ancestors had apparently crossed the vast ocean centuries ago to reach the Island, but as they were now experiencing a poor quality of life, it was apparent that although they could plot a course to the nearby islands, they did not carry the navigation skills enough to return to their original homeland.[8]

Polynesia was inhabited from the west. The history of the Polynesian triangle, bordered by lines between Hawaii, Easter Island and New Zealand gives a settlement of Hawaii of 300-400 AD, and Easter Island of 300-1200 AD. The current population is circa five and a half thousand.[9]

The well which had persuaded the Captain to moor in this bay was located, but the water was not good. The island appeared barren, between the stones some potatoes had been planted, a few fowls were evident, but there appeared to be a curious surfeit of males in proportion to females. There were a few signs of recent European visitors from the dress and trinkets worn by the natives.

The next day back on shore, Wales recorded the tidal rise and fall with equipment installed previously, before setting out with William Hodges to walk across the Island. Soon the pair discovered however that they were so hampered by the behaviour of the natives, that they went back for a musket. They set out once more, but then one of the natives offered to carry the gun for them, his offer was politely declined, and after a great deal of grief the native eventually left them to their own devices – much to their relief.

When they eventually reached the other side of the island Wales and Hodges sat down to rest and take in the scenery, Hodges taking the opportunity to take a sketch of the Island.

After a while, on reaching for the musket to return, a passing Native snatched Hodges' hat, and Wales' immediate reaction was to cock the gun and point it at the thief, but then before pulling the trigger he quickly had second thoughts:

> ....but when I saw a fellow Creature within 20 Yards of its muzzle I began to think his life worth more than a hat, *and as to the Insult,* rot it! let him who next offends on the presumption of having gone clean this time punish it. As to the Owner of it He sat like Patience on a Monument Smiling at Grief.[10]

We varied our road in our return, for

> The Land was all before us where to chuse[11]

According to the journals of other visitors to Easter Island, hat snatching was a common occupation of the Islanders – Roggeveen, Gonzalez and La Pérouse had all experienced such behaviour.[12]

The pair walked back free from hindrance, except for the ground which was covered with large rough stones which Wales likened to the wasted matter from an iron furnace.[13] They saw no trees apart from one species which was no more than seven feet in height, and Wales described as like the common vetch[14] with pods. Being of a curious nature Wales tasted one and found it to be very bitter, the natives who witnessed this action bade him spit them out immediately, they were probably poisonous. On their journey back they passed plantations of sweet potatoes, the most important of crops which the natives called *kumara,* and plantains, but no fruit and no water – yet despite this, the island appeared to be able to sustain its population.

Wales and Hodges were invited into several of the houses on Easter Island, they found them to be constructed of upright sticks which had been stuck in the ground, and then bent to enable them to be tied at the top, forming a gothic-like arch. The houses were thatched with sugar cane leaves, which made the interiors low dark miserable places and which Wales concluded were used just for 'creeping into during rain'.

The following day the Captain organized a large party of marines and sailors to reconnoiter and find out what the Island produced. Pickersgill and John Edgecumbe, who was lieutenant of marines, headed the group, also in tow to carry out their own interests were Forster, Sparrman, Wales, and Hodges, making a party of twenty seven. This was an opportunity for Wales to assess the size and shape of the island, an estimated twenty five miles were covered in all over rough terrain, and in blistering summer heat.[15]

The party was followed by a great number of natives, which was not a comfortable experience for them. They had not proceeded far before one native appeared carrying a spear, and indicated to his fellow countrymen to distance themselves from the ship's company so that they may walk unhindered, he then moved to the front of the party and hoisted a white cloth onto his spear, which they assumed was a sign of peace. When they stopped, he did also, and each time they moved forward he would lead them with ensign aloft.

Across the island the party encountered three stone platforms, each of which had housed four statues, all now ruinous except for three statues, each of which had a large round cylinder of red stone on its head. Two of the three statues were broken and defaced, leaving one whole one which Wales measured and found to be fifteen feet in height, and six feet across the shoulders, and his Journal continues with a painstaking description of their construction, shape, and colour.

The *alus,* or platforms on which the images stood, had walls built parallel to the sea coast and measuring up to fifteen feet high, the longest being three hundred feet. The walls were reinforced and sloped to the landward side, each *alu* held two to fifteen statues facing landward. Originally each statue had on its head a top knot of red rock which was composed of compressed volcanic ash.[16] When measured, the height of each was found to be 52 inches, with a diameter of 66 inches.[17]

While continuing a circuit of the coast the party encountered natives who offered them water, which although brackish, salty, and stinking, was a welcome thirst quencher on such a day. Further on, roasted potatoes and sugar cane were offered to each of the party as they walked in single file along the narrow pathway. Wales was impressed, and thankful for their good services, but this soon turned to disappointment when there occurred more pilfering from the party, and when a bag was snatched containing all that they had brought with them, they had no alternative but to shoot the perpetrator in the back. The man fell, but amazingly recovered and walked off, and after a while the natives gathered and ran round the party chanting, but then when the party moved on, the man with the spear and white cloth appeared once again, and as before led them with little hindrance for all the rest of that day.

The spear carrier was still ahead when they encountered a small group amongst which was one who was a Chief. 'Spear man' presented him with the ensign, whereupon he immediately presented it to another, and this one then proceeded to lead the party, after they had presented the Chief with nails and some Otaheite cloth.

The party next encountered a well which, being above sea level, contained fresh water, but even before they drank from it they discovered it did not smell fresh because the natives had washed in it. Whatever the smell however the party found it palatable, and was therefore acceptable on such a hot day.

The gigantic statues were much in evidence at this side of the island, some were grouped on the platforms, some larger ones stood on their own directly on the soil. Wales measured one which had fallen over, and discovered it to be nearly 27 feet in length, and over 8 feet across the shoulders. The party dined in the shade of this one in the early afternoon sun.

The workmanship of the statues impressed Wales, he remarked that they were well sculpted, but he could not work out how the witnesses on Roggeveen's voyage could be certain that they had seen the natives idolizing them at sunrise, as they had not anchored within a mile of the island, and the company from *Resolution* had not seen any such idolizing of these colossal images. Wales came to the conclusion that they had been erected as memorials to past chiefs of the Island, and that because many human bones had been found among the fallen stones, they possibly marked burial places. The natives called the statues *Moi*, which he had thought meant burial place, but in fact means to sleep or die, and after the name of the chief the suffix *Areki* was added, which means 'chief'.

The placing and erecting of the statues was another puzzle, although the large red cylinders of stone which formed the top most hats of the idols could be rolled to the final building position, how they were placed on the heads, and how the idols could be raised to their standing positions, remained a mystery, especially as there was not sufficient wood on the island from which to build equipment with which to move or raise the giants. Small wonder the group had not come across any of these which had the appearance of being newly built, since the time, manpower, and effort needed to achieve the erection of just one of the statues was at the present time incomprehensible.

When Jacob Roggeveen recorded them in his Journal, he did not mention that any were fallen, he merely recorded their size, appearance, and the possible material of their construction. Sight of these huge images of some thirty feet high, caused Roggeveen to wonder how the native people had moved them – there was no evidence of large timbers or ropes for constructing machines with which to move them. Then he concluded, on examining them closer, that they were made from clay, or a sticky earth into which small stones had been incorporated, and that the images had been fashioned to show they wore long garments hung from their shoulders, and with carried stone basket on their heads.[18]

The giant brooding figures remain to this day with their backs to the sea, they stand from their carved hips, have small hands, and their long nosed faces with large ears frown over the landscape.[19] (see Illustration No 7).

The company had no alternative but to return to the well to get water for lunch, for by now they were suffering from real thirst. They climbed to the highest point of the Island, passing a place which Wales though must be the quarry for the cylindrical stone hats of the statues, and from where it would have been no problem for the stones to be rolled down the hill to their eventual resting places. In fact Wales had been correct about the quarry, there was a quarry of red tufa on *Punapau* hill on the island.[20]

On searching for the original well they passed another, but on inspection the water was covered with a thick green scum and tasted strongly of minerals, according to Wales the stench was worse than that to be found in his native Yorkshire at the spa town of Harrogate, from where no doubt he had had first hand experience. He nevertheless drank a large quantity of the 'scum' as his thirst had dictated, but it made him violently sick, which delayed him to such extent that he didn't catch up with his companions until he reached the shore off which the ship lay, he suffered no long term ill-effects from taking this foul liquor.

Johnann Forster had suffered from the excursion, he had not yet recovered from his Antarctic experience, and had to return to the ship by a different route from the main party, assisted by Sparrman and one of the natives as guide.[21]

Unlike most of the other islands encountered, Easter Island was devoid of trees, animals, and birds, except for the odd noddy[22] and the native's tame fowl, so that Wales had nothing to report on the natural history of this island. His usual measurements of latitude, longitude, the tides, and the weather were recorded, the latter had turned to heavy rain as *Resolution* sailed in search of more food and good drinking water on 17th March.

Cook's journal of the Easter Island visit contained a lot of the contents of the journal of Wales, he had not sufficiently recovered from what had been a serious illness, and spent the time merely pottering around the shore line and sending the others into the interior. He had nonetheless to complete his journal with a description of the island and the visit, and had first incorporated Pickersgill's account into his journal, but later when talking with Wales had decided this was a more articulate man who made better observations, and chose ultimately Wales' account to use.[23] The two had built up a high mutual respect while at Easter Island, Cook mentioned his indebtedness to Wales who carried out his duties ably and confidently. Cook later relied on a lot of the writings of Wales when completing his journal, both on board and back in London, a practice which Wales was more than happy to allow.[24]

Captain Cook was now desperate to find a place where he could stock the ship with food and drink for the rest of this stage of the voyage. He was still unwell, and during the next three weeks a lot of the company grew weak, surviving only on bread which was the only food they had any appetite for. Meanwhile Johann Forster miraculously recovered to such extent that he recorded in his Journal that 'everything agreed with him'.[25]

Cook knew the approximate latitude of the *Marquesas Islands* which had been first discovered in 1595 by the Spaniards Mendana and Quiros. *Resolution* followed the bearing for over two thousand miles, a calculated risk, but after three weeks sure enough the islands were sighted, much to Cook's relief.[26]

THE MARQUESAS APRIL 1774

Resolution sailed between the islands of Santa Christina[27] and La Dominica[28] of the Marquesas Group. Mendana had anchored in a bay at Santa Christina, and Cook was searching for the same place. In one of the bays they met with a wind which delivered such intense short gusts that the vessel was swept towards large steep cliffs which lay to the south west of the Bay, the crew had just managed to steer her clear, but being so light without many provisions, when another gust blew with such ferocity, she was flattened onto her beam-ends, and only saved from going down by the release of her top sails. After further manipulations the crew managed to anchor at the mouth of Vaitahu Bay at Tahuata.

The Native people were soon out in their canoes, but this time their approach was more cautious than had been experienced before. Wales patiently enticed one of them to the ship, and eventually he was able to deliver to him a sheet of writing paper. On receiving it the timid individual signalled to Wales to send the rope down again, and onto this he proceeded to tie a sort of stick, which could have been used as a weapon, or perhaps a sort of oar. After gaining the confidence of these people, other canoes approached, each containing a pile of stones with slings being worn around the waists of the occupants, but soon they were trading bread fruit to the crew for small nails, and towards evening a small pig was exchanged for a broken knife, when Wales wrote that he wished to see another knife in its throat. It had been some twenty or so weeks since the ship's company had last tasted fresh meat, and the sight of that pig was oh so tantalizing to the taste buds.

The violent wind continued all night, accompanied by heavy showers, but when the morning came the natives were around the ship early to trade bread fruit. On one occasion when obtaining a nail one of them refused to hand over a fruit, upon which the Captain immediately fired a musket ball towards the side of his head, he scurried off for a fruit and promptly sent it up to the ship.

Later that morning William Wales set off with Captain Cook in the pinnace to explore the shoreline, and to find a suitable place for erecting the Observatory. No sooner had they entered the boat, when one of the natives who was aboard jumped into his canoe with one of the ship's stanchions, whereupon the officers on board started to fire over him with muskets, and they killed him – despite Cook shouting at them not to. With all the mayhem, his shouts had not been heard. By the time Cook and Wales caught up with the canoe the stanchion had been thrown overboard by the dead man's companion, who sat in an uncontrollable frenzy while baling the blood out of the canoe.

There was no more to be done here for the moment, so the pinnace was rowed around the Bay with Cook and Wales taking soundings, and while they noted fresh water streams, they could see no fruit trees. The raging surf offered no safe landing place for the boat anywhere on the shoreline, so the Captain decided that after possibly taking on a little water and any fruit they could find, it would be better to find a more favourable port.

A further attempt to find a landing place was made the following day by a party of sailors with Wales who, because of the high swell here, was anxious to record tidal measurements. The party did manage to find a place to moor up among some rocks, which although this had proved difficult, was just tolerable. On landing Wales proceeded to take his measurements, to wind his watch, and to take some altitude readings.

The next time Wales went on shore he took a guard with him, and as was now his custom he walked quite a way inland but saw no sign of people, habitations, plantation or trees. Houses had been seen from the ship, but these were high up in the steep mountains of the Island and seemed to be fenced around. They returned to the boat, and before making their way back to the ship Wales again checked the tidal measurements and found that there had been a fall of as much as 4 feet from his earlier observations here.

The crew found that the food trading of this Island was much better than at Easter Island, and fruit, hogs, fowls, breadfruits, and plantains were all stored on board for the next stage of the voyage.

One morning a whole host of natives processed to the shore led by one of their Chiefs. Describing the scene, Wales remarked that where they had not been indulged with the sight of one female since they had arrived, this morning the party contained one woman who, although he described as being considerably on the wrong side of thirty, was nonetheless one of the most beautiful he had so far encountered anywhere in the Pacific seas. Being very fair, she was dressed much the same as the ladies of Otahitee, her facial features and her deportment were all so agreeable that if she be an example of the fair sex of the Island, then they must be exceedingly desirable. Her beauty had of course not escaped the attention of the other Gentlemen of Cook's crew, and there was much deliberation amongst them as to what position she held, for she had obviously joined the morning's party for a purpose, and although Wales doubted some of their suggestions, he preferred not to get himself into such dangerous arguments.

The tide measurements and other observations continued with unceasing regularity, and as they were a mere 10 degrees south of the equator, of especial importance here were the magnetic variation and dipping needle observations. For some decades seafarers had been aware of a variation in the magnetic compass needle from true north, and it was believed that the plotting of this variation around the world could be one of the contenders for solving the longitude problem at sea. The logging of this variation was an on-going exercise, and Cook's voyages were seen as a good opportunity to carry out this work.[29]

In tandem with the magnetic variation observations went dip needle measurements, whereby the needle was a compass, pivoted to move in the plane containing the magnetic field vector of the earth, it records the angle that the magnetic field makes with the vertical, which varies in different parts of the world, and the recording of this, like the magnetic variation, was an on-going study for the Admiralty.[30]

Wales was finding it a bother to keep adjusting the instrument as the dip changed, as it did on such a voyage when on the move. The continual adjustment was quite an irksome occupation, and highly inconvenient, but he did try before leaving this island to accurately adjust the instrument and effect an accurate reading, as this would be the best opportunity during the whole voyage to take the reading so near the equator, but there just wasn't time to do this before it was time to set sail again.

On leaving the island Wales recalled the voyage by Mendana and his description of the Marquesas Island group. Wales tried to interpret Mendana's account of his findings, and compared it to the actual islands and their features which he now witnessed. He resolved that the account, which was written by Quiros, did great honour to Mendana all those years ago.

Back on board Wales dutifully recorded his immediate experience of the previous island, while still fresh in his mind. He was sufficiently inspired by the natives to describe them as the finest race he had ever seen, and takes great pains to substantiate this conclusion, he then gives mention to their weapons, canoes, the trees, and the landscape.

Well-stocked with food, *Resolution* next headed south-west for the Society Islands. Sailing through the Tuamotu Archipelago caused Wales and the Officers on board much debate as to which islands had been seen and named before, not only by Roggeveen, but also Byron and Willem Schouten. This was certainly a part of the Pacific which caused much confusion, and the prolific accounts of previous voyages were serving only to confuse the present adventurers even more.

TAHITI & THE SOCIETY ISLANDS APRIL-JUNE 1774

Eventually on 21st April, 1774, *Resolution* moored again in Matavai Bay off Otaheite,[31] when Wales wrote that:

> ...it was soon crowded with our old friends, and if there
> be any truth in Physiognomy, they were extremely glad
> to see us; from what Motive, I will not pretend to say.[32]

The greetings over, Wales was eager to get the observatory erected and set up his instruments on *terra firma*, he had suggested to Captain Cook that it would be useful to calibrate the watches and determine their rate anew by using the longitude of Fort Venus, this would enable them to check the longitude of many places which they had visited recently, and which could then be used in the future to adjust the position of Easter Island, the Marquesas, and other small islands. A Guard was appointed, and Wales soon began to unload the tent and instruments with which he was well occupied for the next eighteen or so days, before carefully loading them back onto the ship. Wales also drew a chart of Matavai Bay while here.[33]

For the past five months since departing Queen Charlotte Sound in New Zealand, and suffering from both of the great extremes of temperature, Wales found Kendall's chronometer had lost just eight and a half minutes, an impressive achievement. The watch had performed better in the cold than the hot climate.

J R Forster was well again, and his confidence grew as he collected, studied, and recorded the abundance of plants that Tahiti had to offer, he was particularly anxious to explore areas which Joseph Banks hadn't had time to cover during the first voyage with Cook. Forster's obstinate, jealous behaviour did not improve however, and this was something which Cook, the other officers, and Wales had to endure. Forster's mood was not helped by the injuries he had sustained one night when, slipping in the trecherous terrain, he ruptured himself badly, enforcing him to wear a truss for years afterwards.[34]

With the urgency of observations over, Wales' could catch up with his Journal again, and he wrote at length of an incident which happened after he had returned to the ship one evening for supper, when a musket was heard to discharge near the observatory. Wales immediately returned to the tent, and found that one of the Guards had shot at a native, who had stolen a water butt and was swimming off with it down the nearby river. On hearing the shot the Native had returned to dry land, and was eventually found hiding in a bush, captured, and taken on board the ship.

The following day *Otoo*, the Chief of Tahiti, happened to visit the ship with some of his eminent retinue, amongst them was a relative called *Toowha*. Cook related to them the unfortunate events of the previous evening, and demanded that the man be punished, so that by example others would be deterred from repeating the despicable practice of stealing. *Otoo* at first was against Cook's request, but could find no convincing argument to stop the thieving, and so the prisoner was taken on shore and given two dozen lashes, which was witnessed by a thousand or so natives. The punishment had obviously angered the natives and their Chief, but then *Toowha* climbed up onto a small hill and spoke to them all for a full thirty minutes, he asked them how they could be so shameful, how they could steal from their visitors, their friends. He continued on how it was wrong to steal from those who offered them such articles as axes, knives, nails, feathers, and beads, they traded things they could spare for things their visitors could not, so why did their visitors have to suffer robbery? In conclusion *Toowha* suggested that they steal from their enemies, and not from their friends.

Otoo, his party, and a great number of the native population, were one day treated to a display by the ship's company, when the marines were exercised – going through their manouvres and firing many volleys. The audience was obviously amazed at the firing, and Wales gave the Marines great credit in showing the Tahitians just how inadequate their own weapons would be against the ones on the ship, the islanders were impressed enough to insist on a further display of the ship's great guns one evening.

The appointed time for the big guns display was delayed, due to a musket being stolen from one of the guards who just happen to nod off while on duty one evening, but this was soon retrieved by one of Otee's chief men once he heard of the incident, and eventually the big guns on board, and the twelve carriage guns were demonstrated to Otee. Wales described the Chief as being very tall and slender, but having a stoop, and although appearing to be stupid, nevertheless his actions and leadership prove him to be either wise, or having counsellors of great wisdom. He had a great interest in military matters, and there was evidence of a lot of war canoes being produced all over the Islands. Naval Reviews were carried out nearly every day, these being under the management of Toowha.

The gun exhibition over, the ship's company went ashore and were immediately treated to a mock display of the Native's spears.

Since 17th September, 1773 there had been a youth on board called *Odiddy* from the island of Raiatea, and here Otee did his utmost to persuade him to stay, offering him a wife and riches, all that was in his power to give him. Wales remarked that he would have been wise to accept these things, but Cook would have none of it, and insisted he returned to his native Island.

On 14th May, *Resolution* weighed anchor and left Matavai Bay, sailing ever westwards to arrive at Huahine the next day, an island which they had visited the previous year. When daylight broke it wasn't long before the Chief arrived on board, and the natives sailed up to the vessel bringing hogs, fowls, and fruit.

Wales busied himself with more tidal measurements and observations the next day, and that evening he and others enjoyed a dramatic production on shore, of which, from his description of the piece, he was well impressed:

> ...and soon recognized my old Friend the Uliatean Garrick amongst the Performers; who entertained us with two or three little Pieces which appeared to be Extempore: They were certainly *Pro-Tempore,* and his Part of them was most Excellently well performed; It was that of a Girl, and the Piece represented her as running away in the Ship from Otahitee with the English, and concluded with the Reception which she was supposed to Meet with from her friends at her return, which was not represented to be of a very indulgent Nature.[35]

Wales explains that the piece was an actual representation, and that the girl who was the subject of the play had reluctantly watched the performance, she was obviously sad to be reminded of the occasion.

The visit to Huahine was not without incident. The Forster's servant was attacked, petty officers on a shooting party were robbed, and later when a further shooting party was attacked and robbed, the Captain had to intervene and the culprits sought out.

Wales found that he dare not even go on shore here, just to observe the meridian altitude, without a guard, and after nine days the Captain thought it time to move on again, so the vessel headed for Raiatea Island once again and anchored at the harbour entrance.

A friendlier reception awaited the ship's company, and Wales records to his delight that they soon had the pleasure of seeing their old friends again, who appeared in good health, and were happy to see them all once more.

Wales felt he could relax more at this place, and so he did what he obviously enjoyed, and stretched his legs on one of his long walks into the interior of the island with a companion, when he came upon what he calls one of the most beautiful valleys he had ever seen. On one side of the valley, a little way up the hill they saw a small cottage, and in the valley floor a stream, of which he wrote that he could justify its appearance by describing as 'chrystaline', and almost broke into poetry as he went on to write of it falling from rock to rock with a tinkle sound, and continued 'murmuring along pebbles'. Curious, they climbed up to the cottage, where the inhabitant and his wives and family were obviously poor, and had only the stream water to offer their visitors. As far as their hunger was concerned their host could do nothing, but in an attempt to offer a crumb of comfort he had:

> ...placed himself on his back-side in an instant called forth more Music out of two pieces of dried sticks laid hollow, than I had before heard at these Islands...[36]

After the overture Wales and his companion distributed the meager lunch they carried amongst their host's family, the host, accompanying them part way back to their vessel, seized a opportune moment to relieve them of a couple of chisels before flying off through the woodland at speed – never to be seen again.

On returning to *Resolution* Wales learned that entertainment was laid on that evening, and he could scarce control his emotions when he heard further that the Princess *Poydoa*, whose dancing he had witnessed on the previous visit, was performing. His delight at the prospect of watching this, his favourite amusement, once again took him to the playhouse with a 'hop, skip and a jump', and needless to say he went into great detail in his Journal to record the event, especially the final drama, a farce, which portrayed the birth of a child – the mother sporting a large black bushy beard, the midwife, and the baby, all acted by men. This had Wales in stitches of laughter and he noted that it was all carried out with great decency for a male audience, while the ladies of the audience all sat sedate and reserved, like judges. Wales asked one of them why this was so, why did they not join in the laughter – he was told that the modest women didn't laugh at such things.

The next day Wales dined with the *Poydoa's* father, Chief *Oreo*, in the cabin. During the meal the chief managed to consume a full bottle of wine much to Wales' amazement, this eventually made the old gentleman noisy, and he insisted his companions accompany him ashore, when his daughter would again perform her dance, the *heavah*. As soon as the entertainment began Oreo disappeared, Wales concluding that his copious wine consumption had enforced a sleep, but this was not the case as he had been arranging for food, hogs, coconuts, and breadfruit to be gathered for loading onto *Resolution*.

The visit had been an enjoyable experience for the *Resolution's* Company, and all too soon on 3rd June the ship edged its way out of the harbour and headed westwards again, after a tearful farewell from the natives, who were told that this would probably be the last time that Cook and his companions would call this way. This remarkable demonstration of affection was duly recorded in Wales' Journal, and was in contrast to the silent sorrow shown by other natives when the vessel had departed.

Kendall's watch was proving to be a faithfully accurate timepiece. When Wales used it to compute the harbour observations, there proved to be just a 1⅔″ deviation from the reading at this place the previous year.

TONGA JUNE 1774

On 26th June the vessel anchored off the Island of Annamocka,[37] part of the Ha'apai Group of the Tonga Islands, Tasman had named this island *Rotterdam*. The natives were soon on board trading food for nails, and the next morning the Captain and a party of Officers were on shore looking for water, they found some ponds which were salty, stinking and insect ridden. When Tasman had landed here he had found clean water, and from his accounts the island had been well cultivated, but this was not found to be so when Wales had landed. When Wales took his walk over the Island, although the vegetation was lush and there was plenty of fruit, it lay rotting for want of harvesting, but he did find springs of water, The natives really impressed him, and he found their music and singing to be exceptional in sweetness and softness.

When the small boats returned to the Island the next day to collect water and food, the occupants suffered robbery of some articles by the natives. Several shots were fired from *Resolution*, which resulted in an unfortunate injury to one of the natives, this action terrified the islanders so much that the goods were immediately returned. The ship's surgeon went ashore and dressed the man's wounds, this action impressed the natives so much that thereafter no thieving occurred, and the parties continued to trade amicably.

The watch winding suffered a hitch while here, Cook and Cooper had both been on shore in the morning, and for this reason Wales recorded that the watch could not be wound at its usual time as there had to be three people present each day at each winding. The observations went ahead without hitch, before the watch started to slow down and then unfortunately stop before Wales had remembered to get the company gathered to wind it again, and although this didn't upset any calculations or testing, it did upset Wales somewhat, as he had hoped that he could carry it home in the knowledge that it had not stopped once during the voyage.

The watch incident was noted by Forster the elder, who made the most of this rare, minor blunder in Wales' professional competence by threatening to every officer on board that he would publish details of the event – tempers once again ran short.[38]

During the voyage J R Forster's relationship with the rest of the ship's company had gradually worsened, and it was obvious that he had taken a particular dislike to William Wales, possibly because he was a fellow scientist. The watch incident was not a major setback, and Wales soon had it set to the correct time again, but Forster had treated it as a chance to vent his jealous frustrations on Wales.[39]

On setting sail from Nomuka, Wales did not fill his Journal this time with a long description of the Island, it had been much the same as Tongatabu, and he was eager not to repeat too much of the information which was contained already in his writings. He did however think that he had perhaps neglected to describe the native boats, and so goes into a detailed account of the canoes, the size, the shape structure and rigging, the workmanship, the materials used, and he observes the way they were manned and manoeuvred – he was obviously impressed.

Sailing for the New Hebrides, the small island of Vatoa came into view, and Cook sent Gilbert to investigate. J R Forster asked if he could accompany Gilbert, but Cook refused to allow this, telling him to 'shut up, and await his pleasure'. When Forster protested at the Captain's decision, he went on to imply that public money was being wasted when such plant collecting opportunities were missed. Forster then went into a deep, resentful sulk, avoiding further disputes, and sitting silently with his equipment at the ready, waiting for signs from Cook which would indicate a change of heart – but this didn't happen. As Vatoa disappeared below the horizon, Forster reflected that those witnessing his penance were only there to further their fortune and rank, without any thought of scientific achievement.[40]

THE NEW HEBRIDES JULY-AUGUST 1774

Sailing south of the Fiji Islands, *Resolution* then reached the New Hebrides,[41] which had previously been visited by Quiros in 1605, and Bougainville in 1768 who had approached from the north of Fiji. Wales had read their various accounts of this Island group, and was anxious to see them for himself, he saw black smoke rising from what he assumed to be a volcano.

Cook was cautious, he steered around the top of Aurora,[42] and looked at Omba where the natives looked so threatening that he carried on to Pentecost, and eventually anchored off Malekula. Soon *Resolution* was surrounded by canoes, holding natives who were heavily armed with bow and arrow. They appeared eager to board the ship, which two or three of them proceeded to do and stayed on board a while, but Wales was busy below decks so didn't witness their visit. The next morning natives by the hundred swarmed on board, and this time their appearance was described by Wales:

> ...none had any Arms who came aboard that I saw except one, who had a small neat Club slung at his back. They are universally a small and ordinary race of People, not quite but very near as dark as the Negros, and do something resemble them in their Countenances,

although neither their Noses are remarkably flat or their Lips Thick. Their Hair also is quite short & curled like theirs, but not so soft and woolly. They go entirely Naked except the Penis for which they have a very fine Case, fringed; & a String to the end of it by which they tye it up to a sort of Belt or String that goes round their waist so very tight that the shape of their bodies is not much unlike that of an over-grown Pismire; but their limbs are well shaped & Clean made enough.

Most of them had a wild Boars Tooth, or some such like thing bent circular round their right wrist, and a round piece of wood with a hole through it on their left: the hole was so small that it would barely come over their hand. Some had very large Scabs or blotches on their Arms & Legs; but this was far from the general.

One of the natives was trying his utmost to gain access to one of the small boats which were moored alongside *Resolution,* and the crew's attempts to stop him caused an exchange of arrow and gun shots. When one of her great guns was fired onto the shore, this so frightened the natives that the ones who had been on board quickly jumped into the water, and swam to the shore.

The following morning Captain Cook and a party took a small boat to the shore, where several hundred of the natives waited with bows and arrows poised. The Captain leaped into the shallow water before the shore was reached, he was unarmed, and seeing this one of their chiefs handed his bow and arrow to another and entered the water to meet Cook open armed, on meeting the chief and Cook walked together hand in hand to the shore, with the Officers and Marines following. Cook indicated that he needed wood, and it was mutually agreed that the Company could cut down some trees, just so long as they stayed within the area of the beach.

Once the *Resolution* was again on its way, the natives, who had hitherto been keeping their distance, immediately appeared and were eager to trade, almost anything they could lay their hands on was brought to the ship, and the Chief offered Captain Cook a special gift of a pig.

In this island group were five small islands which were on the coral reefs, and named by Wales the *Maskelyne Islands* after the Astronomer Royal. At the end of his introduction to the 'Observations' Wales wrote:

> I cannot conclude, without observing that I have once, in the course of this work, stepped out of my province, and taken the liberty which I would wish not to be censured for. I had been at some pains to determine the situations of a group of small islands, to which I cannot find that any name has been assigned by Captain Cook: I have therefore ventured to call them by the name of a person to whom I owe very much indeed; one who took me by the hand when I was friendless, and never forsook me when I had occasion for his help; and who, I hope will not be offended at this public acknowledgement of his favours.[43]

It had been noticeable that the men of Malekula were the more adept at displaying their vanity than their female counterparts, who merely played a servile role, and did not exhibit any finery. This state of affairs meant that as the male natives observed the younger sailors labouring at their tasks, they assumed that they were female, and acted in a fawning flirting manner towards them. The sailors in turn assumed that the natives were homosexual, and this had apparently been endorsed by the elder Forster. This misinterpretation of Forster's provoked Wales into plotting a scheme which would prove him wrong, and the opportunity came whilst on Eromanga during a botanizing expedition with Forster. One of Forster's sailor helpers had gone into the bushes to relieve himself, and Wales mischievously seized the opportunity to secretly hint to the natives that they may take advantage of this opportunity, whereupon a couple of them disappeared into the bushes in hot pursuit. Witnessing this, some of the group called out that the sailor "Was a man!". Whence the mortified natives hastily returned embarrassed, and Mr Forster the elder was caused to amend his opinion of them.[44]

The exploration and charting of the New Hebrides Island group continued, they passed Whitsuntide Island, which Wales described as the most beautiful prospect he had ever seen, the view of rectangular fenced fields reminded him of England – he was feeling homesick.

The gentlemen on board, including William Wales, had been eating fish which had been giving them severe headaches and affecting their arms and legs, making them weak and numb, added to this they had experienced a severe heat on their skin, this had lasted several days before eventually they began to feel better.

The next landfall was Tanna[45] which was reached on 5th August. Here the Captain and crew were necessarily cautious when they went on shore, but they were shown and allowed to fill casks from a nearby pond, and so they got back on board without a skirmish and settled down for the night. The flames from the volcano on the Island, which Wales estimated to be about five miles from the harbour, could be seen throughout the night.

When morning came the natives arrived, and one in particular caused problems to the Captain. He repeatedly struck the ship with his club and acted in a hostile manner, eventually he offered his club to the Captain for a small medal which he grabbed, and then still clutching his club, sped away in his canoe as fast as he could. The Captain's shouts of protest were ignored, and Cook fired small shot at him, but to no avail as by this time he was too far away. Cook then called for one of the muskets to be fired, and this proved effective, in no time an old man appeared, he had been sent to them with presents and tokens of peace. Sugar cane was brought, and for this Cook exchanged much valued gifts in the hopes that eventually the natives would get the message, and peace would prevail.

The next attempt at landing was in order to collect fresh water, but this was witnessed by thousands of armed natives who were guarding the watering place. After some delicate actions from both sides an amicable state of affairs was reached, and the Company of the *Resolution* were able to return on board with an ample supply.

Wales' objective whilst here was to determine the rate of the watch, and while he would have been better doing this on shore, it was thought not safe to stay there overnight, even with a guard. Furthermore to carry the watch each day to and fro, and landing in a manner which was judged to be not at all smooth would have been far too risky. It was resolved that the watch would be taken on shore the first day, and on the following days readings which would be signalled from people offshore would suffice, and then the watch would be taken on shore again on the last day.

After a precarious landing onto a deserted beach the first day, the work began, and only after an hour did the natives appear. They were unarmed, and slowly Wales and his companions gained their confidence, enough for them to be able to help in loading the ship with water and fish, some of which was given to the natives, before the rest, which was mostly mullet, was taken back on board to feed the ship's Company.

The water from the pond was good and fresh, and the coconut trees were in fruitful abundance. The natives were only too pleased to collect the fruit for their visitors, and recompense was never an issue for these, and so a gradual trust was built. Wales took a wary excursion into the interior of the Island – not too far, but enough to find narrow tracks winding between the low shrubs, and although not a Native was in sight, nor any sign of habitation, he was not prepared to venture too far.

The instrument recording was now being carried out in a more relaxed manner, the watch and quadrant were taken on shore, dipping needle and tidal readings were made, and latitude readings recorded. The natives mingled around – not all of them were armed. The ship's Company continued to enjoy a diet of fresh fish, but the stay here so far as Wales was concerned seemed to be a monotonous round of killing time between data gathering,

Wales confessed his Journal to be swelled with all nonsense that came into his head at this point, likening it to 'Falstaff's belly', another reference to his obvious love of drama. The trouble was that his walks were rather curtailed, and this was a circumstance which didn't suit him at all, so frustrated was he, that after completing his observations that day, he asked two of the Officers to accompany him on a short walk into the Island's interior, they took their guns and set off. After the first quarter mile they found plantations of yam and tarro, and other vegetables which were foreign to the party, and then they reached houses, after another half a mile there was an abundance of fruit trees, fig, and nectarines. The plantations were orderly, and a village of about twenty dwellings sheltered beneath tall trees.

The houses were about 30 feet long by 10 feet broad, and made of sticks pushed into the ground and tied at the top to form a sort of tunnel, other buildings were open-sided and had square roofs, thatched with palm leaves. Hogs and fowls contentedly fed nearby, giving an impression of contented domesticity. The natives were cautious at first, but then on seeing that the party was so small, became more obliging and friendly, and on learning of their guest's needs to visit the far side of the Island, a number of them accompanied the party across the island, taking no weapons with them.

The ship's party was shown two islands at the far side of Tana which they called *Irroname*[46] and *Amatum*[47] before being guided back to the village, all the while the natives obligingly answered their questions, and gathered botanical specimens for them. On reaching the village again they were shown a short cut back to the beach, Wales summed up his afternoon's excursion as 'exceedingly delightful'.

The Island volcano showed its presence the next morning by violently throwing out a column of black smoke, with soil and large stones, this was accompanied by loud explosions. The force was in sharp contrast to the precision handling which Wales had to effect on the watch, which was not conforming to his computations at this point, and he wrote that he was becoming such a slave to it that he scarcely had time to eat.

The next day there was rain which poured down for the whole of the day, but not just of water, it appeared to be a strange compound of water, sand, earth, and asbestos, which Wales resolved must have been volcano sourced because the flora of the island was covered in the same material. On looking more closely at it, he discovered the same matter also made up the beach around the harbour.

Time was beginning to weigh heavy for Wales, when it was cloudy he was not able to take readings, and yet he couldn't leave the beach where his instruments were. Undaunted, he gathered some natives together and organized 'beach games' for them, these took the form of hitting stakes with their spears, and then a coconut set up on a stick, his Journal goes into the fine details of the results, and he records the distances from where the natives could best hit their target from, and the mechanics of their throwing technique.

In the evening the volcano was especially active, and the next morning again the weather was not suited to solar observing. William Wales took this opportunity to satisfy his curiousity and, together with several others from the ship's Company, climbed up the mountain towards the volcano's head. On and on they climbed over hills imagining they would arrive after four miles, but after completing that distance they appeared to be no further near to it.

The fact was that although the volcano appeared to be just active in the place they were heading for, other fires which they had assumed had been lit by the natives were of volcanic smoke exuding from cracks in the ground, and some seven miles from the main volcanic activity. The smaller appearances were rising from mole hill like structures of soft wet blue clay, measuring some eight feet in diameter. There was a strong sulphuric smell from these and they were encrusted with an alum-like substance.

The surrounding plant life was flourishing in the volcanic conditions, it was green and fresh, and the fig trees hung with fruit. Wales dug a hole in the earth, plunged a thermometer into it, and immediately filled in the hole again – after a minute the instrument rose to 210 degrees Farenheit, and showed the same temperature during the following ninety seconds, when the experiment had to stop, as it was not his own thermometer and the owner, who was perhaps J R Forster did not want him to carry on for some unknown reason. What Wales had hoped to do was to watch the temperature drop to the natural temperature of its surroundings after the initial high rise, which was always the way with a thermometer when first placing it into such a high degree of heat, but unfortunately he had not carried his own thermometer with him on this occasion, and so was not able to satisfactorily find the true temperature. One experiment which Wales promised himself he would do, was to locate a particular spring which he had heard of that was close to the shore, and not accessible by land, so he would have to take a boat there. He had heard that its water was so hot that it was possible to boil 'Perriwinkles'[48] in it.

The party was driven back by a group of natives who appeared hostile. They threatened with bows, slings and spears, and were persistently barring the way forward, so that the group of visitors decided to head back to the ship, their mission after all had been just curiosity. To Wales these natives were completely different to those he had encountered from the other side of the harbour, who were much more friendly, so they must have been of two different tribes – one friendly, and one more hostile.

Captain Cook was anxious to visit the friendlier natives at their dwellings, and Wales accompanied him to the village where he was now familiar to some of them. They were met as they entered the settlement, and the natives, welcoming them both as old friends, were only too happy to show them around this place, which Wales described as a 'perfect Paradise in the rural taste'. Having visited many of the houses where they had been invited to sit and eat and drink with the occupants, they were accompanied back to the beach by natives who carried fruit, yams, and sugar canes, which were gifts for their visitors.

One day the Chief, or *Areki,* of the Island paid them a visit, his name was *Geogy* – he was an old man, but was pleasant enough, although a little solemn.

The temperatures of the various springs were eventually taken by Cook and Wales, and recorded to Wales' satisfaction – the highest being 202° Fahrenheit. The next few days were spent observing and recording tides, altitudes, and calculations, and work here on board was continuing apace, Cook was anxious to set sail again, but the weather was not suitable.

One morning on board, while working on calculations, Wales heard a shot ring out. Apparently one of the guards had shot a native thinking that he had threatened him by drawing a bow. The native was shot through the elbow and ribs, and after staggering some way, he died. The ship's surgeon James Patten attended, but he told Wales that by the time he had reached him he was too late to be of service. Wales also spoke to John Whitehouse, the master's Mate, who witnessed the shooting.

That evening Wales met one of the natives he had come to know for a chat, he was a young man who had previously joined the ship's officers for a meal on board. The astronomer was interested to find out just how lethal their weapons could be, and this fellow really impressed Wales by his ability to shoot arrows, and to throw a spear with great accuracy and speed for some twenty yards, and at some sixty or seventy yards, albeit not with the same accuracy. In Wales' opinion this was the best spear throwing he had ever witnessed, comparing him to perhaps one of the heroes of Homer's works, or even Artistotle, or Pope's, the scene obviously brought his studies of the classics into the world of reality.

It is interesting to note that Cook was so impressed by the work done in writing up the observations by Wales, that he copied the account of the native's performance into his own Journal.[49]

Wales goes on to describe the natives, their hair, their stance, their dress, and their canoes, and also the fruits of the Islands, the flora and fauna are all listed in his Journal, before finally on 20th August, 1774, *Resolution* set sail once more, leaving Tanna to its inhabitants.

On heading east for a brief look at the islands of Aniwa and Futuna in the New Hebrides group, Cook turned the ship west again for a last look at Tana, before heading north west to the large island of the same group. Tana had impressed Wales, he recorded in his journal that he judged this to be one of the most beautiful and desirable islands they had yet seen in the South Sea. *Resolution* was then steered through the Bougainville Strait to the north of Malekula Island to reach Espiritu Santo, which it proceeded to encircle anti-clockwise.

Rounding Cape Quiros on the north east of the island on 26th August, 1774, the company sailed south into the large bay of St Phillip & St James. Wales noticed a large brook to the east of the bay, and a couple of smaller streams in the distance, he was looking for the rivers that Quiros described, and concluded that if these be they, he far exceeded poetic license. Neither had he seen the port of Vera Cruz containing many ships, which Quiros described – but then perhaps this was not the bay, perhaps there was another around the corner.

On anchoring some distance from the shore, the natives appeared, each dressed in a strip of cloth which was fastened by a string around the waist and passed between the legs, hanging low at the back and front almost to the knees, on the head each wore a feathered crown of cock feathers. They seemed friendly, and eventually they told of the bay being called *Tafonia,*, they were even coaxed near enough to the ship to receive some medals, nails, and cloth, which were lowered down to them on a string. But Cook did not linger here, he steered the ship north again to round Cape Cumberland and down the western side of Espiritu Santo, before heading off south-west to have a look at New Caledonia,[50] and before heading back to New Zealand.

NEW CALEDONIA SEPTEMBER 1774

The following week on 4th September, 1774, *Resolution* arrived at New Caledonia, one of the largest of the Pacific Islands lying to the north of New Zealand. Small boats were sent out to check the soundings, and were watched by the occupants of many native canoes, who seemed friendly enough. Then one canoe headed out from the shore, it seemed that one of the Island Chiefs was on board, and on arrival he offered fish to the visitors, responding to this gesture the Officer presented the Chief with trinkets and medals, which were received with much pleasure.

The Captain seemed well pleased that the natives were not causing him any problems, in fact they watched in some awe as he negotiated the vessel over the reefs, and when he sailed along the coast with a sounding boat at the head, they followed with their canoes in a large convoy – Wales likened the scene to a Man-of-War with a large fleet of Merchantmen in tow. When *Resolution* tacked, so did the canoes.

It was decided to anchor at a place on the main island, which lay about a mile from a small sandy island and which Cook had chosen as an ideal place from which to observe an eclipse of the sun, which was due in two days time. Wales learned later that this small island was called *Pudyoua*.[51]

Once at anchor, it was not long before the natives were on board the ship, they appeared honest and friendly, quite naked but for a penis covering of cloth or leaf, and some also with a cloth tied around their forehead. – Wales thought these people dressed the most like Adam than any others they had encountered, – that was before Adam started sewing fig leaves together. They had jet black frizzled hair and beards over a dark copper complexion, and carried exquisitely made weapons, which were thrown in the same manner as those of the people from Tanna.

The native canoes were all double hulled, with a platform spanning the two, and on which a fire generally burned. These were heavy vessels which were rigged with plenty of sails, and were not paddled, but rather operated with a large oar by a single person who sculled it along.

The next morning Wales was busying himself preparing for the forthcoming solar eclipse, he had landed on the small island of *Poudiou,* with Lieutenant Charles Clerke,[52] but they were followed there by natives in two canoes. Fearing he could not adequately guard his precious instruments, Wales made signs to them not to approach, and on seeing this they immediately turned around their canoes and retreated back to the beach, where they sat and observed the astronomer from a distance, much to his relief.

Wales had more visitors at noon, when the tide was low and the mainland accessible without a vessel, curious native women and children visited the island, but did not create any trouble for the observers. The women wore a short skirt, which Wales likened to a fringe of hemp, twisted into strings, and wrapped around the waist some twenty or thirty times.

When the time for the eclipse finally arrived it was cloudy, and Wales and Clerke were unable to observe it for the first half of the passage, but then it cleared, making the observing and recording the last half of it possible. They were joined by Cook for the observation, but Forster was not invited.[53] Wales measured the eclipse by Hadley's quadrant, believed to be the first time this method had been used, Cook wrote that he thought this a valuable discovery, and added to the use of the quadrant.[54] Wales wrote that the resulting quadrant calculations were as accurate as anything he could have done with the micrometer.

Wales, Clerke, and Cook, each recorded the end time of the eclipse, and these tallied to within a few seconds, and from this observation Wales was able to precisely determine the longitude of the place,[55] but subsequent tidal recording was hindered, this time by natives stealing his marking sticks. Wales soon managed to get around this when he chose well-placed half blown down trees to record the water levels, these couldn't be so easily stolen.

Meanwhile J R Forster had been trying to get ashore. Lt Cooper had set out in a small boat for the shore without giving Forster time to join him, and although another boat was available for him, Cooper had flatly refused to allow him to use it. Peace was not restored until Cook returned.[56]

That afternoon Captain Cook invited Wales to join him for a small boat trip along the coast, when they came by a small village. The houses were circular of about twenty feet in diameter, and walls of five feet high, they had a steep pointed roof, in which upper floors carried storage space. These houses were constructed of strong wooden posts with rails, thick with reeds, between, and a thatched roof. These dwellings must have been very disagreeable to live in, for they all had a fire hearth, yet there was no hole to allow smoke to escape. The door openings were hung with curtains, and the door posts were decorated with carving.

Around the houses were plantations of coconut trees, and yams. The vegetation was poor, and it appeared that the meager diet of the residents consisted of fish and a tree bark, which was chewed after roasting. But these people were good and honest, and they lived a clean life, which had impressed Wales.

The main island was named by its many districts, each with a Chief, or *Areki*. The name of the place where the ship lay was *Ballade*, and Wales managed to record a few of the local placenames, and their chiefs, in his Journal, before *Resolution* weighed anchor on the 11th September to explore further north along the coast, and beyond.

Having satisfied his curiousity about the land to the north, Cook then returned along the eastern shore of New Caledonia, south-east and to the west of the Loyalty Islands.

Wales noticed that on the Island further south the trees were of a much fresher green, these grew only on the higher ground, and the trees growing at a lower altitude appeared as ragged pillars of wood or stone. J R Forster was convinced these were basalt columns, such as the ones that formed the Giant's Causeway in Ireland, and claimed to clearly see the joints with his field glasses. The elder Forster's eyesight had long been a source of amazement to Wales, for he judged his own eyesight imperfect by comparison. Forster had told him he could see fruit growing on trees three miles distant with a spy glass – all to the credit of Jesse Ramsden, who made the common 2ft achromatic spy-glass used by Forster.

Jesse Ramsden was the same age as William Wales, and also hailed from Yorkshire. He was born at Halifax in 1735, and in the mid 1750s had arrived in London and became apprenticed to a mathematical instrument maker, a profession in which he excelled.

J R Forster was sensing that the ship's gentlemen were growing more hostile towards him, and dismissed this as being due to their envy of him, that their behaviour was of such low meaness, as a man of science, it was below his dignity to take heed of their enmity.[57]

From New Caledonia Island the ship sailed on to reach a large Island of low land, with a hill in the middle covered in the strange pillar trees – for Wales was by now almost convinced that Forster's basalt pillars were trees, and this was the case. Cook named the large Island *New Caledonia*, and the tree covered Island, *Isle of Pines*, and the trees he named *New Caledonia pines*.

Further on the ship encountered some hazardous reefs, Elliot described their dangerous situation on this dark night as anxious and perilous.[58] Wales wrote that this was a situation to be envied by very few, as the ship was steered back from whence it came, it had completed nearly a circuit of the Isle of Pines.

A brief visit was made to Amere Island where trees were felled, Wales reported an abundance of water snakes here, which he describes as a 'torpid' reptile ringed with black and white. These were prone to languishing in the sun, hence probably their description as 'torpid' by Wales.[59]

NORFOLK ISLAND

By 10th October the Ship had arrived at Norfolk Island, and Wales lost no time in joining some of the Company in a boat to the shore, where they managed to find a safe landing place among the high cliffs.

The vegetation of the island near the shore was thick with flax plants, the same as found on New Zealand, further inland the way became more accessible, with paths leading through woodland. Wales mentions the Pine trees, the now famous *Norfolk Island pines* which are so distinctive in foliage and shape from any other, their wood of red and course grain, which Wales suspects would make many a good main mast for a tall ship, even larger than *Resolution*.

Ever prepared, Wales had taken on shore a bag which he filled with wood sorrel, sow thistle, and what he called 'samphire', but Beaglehole thinks more likely the wild celery of New Zealand – much like samphire to Wales' English eyes. Also cabbages were gathered from the Cabbage Trees. A feast was in store, fresh food the like of which the ship's Company had not experienced for some time.

On the 11th October the ship sailed away from this Island, which Captain Cook had named after the Duchess of Norfolk. Wales recorded that this place had apparently not been trodden previously by humans, only birds, which appeared to be the same as those of New Zealand – which was to be their next port of call.

Endnotes

1   Personal communication. Duffin, K.E., *William Wales on Easter Island*. Unpublished poem.

2   Aughton, P, 2004. *Resolution – Cook's Second Voyage*. London, Weidenfeld & Nicholson. p.98.

3   Hoare, Michael E, 1976. *The Tactless Philosopher*. Melbourne, Hawthorne Press.

4   Beaglehole, J C (Ed), 1969. *The Journals of Captain James Cook on His Voyages of Discovery. II. The Voyage of Resolution and Adventure 1772-1775*. Cambridge University Press for the Hakluyt Society. p.310n

5   Modern name, *Rapa nui*.

6   Barrow, J (Ed), 1944. *Voyages of Discovery – Cook*. London, J.M. Dent & Sons Ltd.

7   Mazière, Francis, 1968. *Mysteries of Easter Island*. London, Collins.

8   Aughton, P, 2004. *Resolution – Cook's Second Voyage*. London, Weidenfeld & Nicholson.

9   Personal communication, Sonia Haoa Cardinali.

10 Quoted from: *The History of Tom Jones, a foundling* by Henry Fielding, first published 1749.

11 Original quote "we have the land all before us, to choose what spot we will" from *The Catholic Crusoe: Adventures of Owen Evans, Esq., surgeon's mate set ashore with five companions on a desolate island in the Caribbean seas, 1739"* by William Henry Anderdon. Published 1863,

12 Beaglehole, J C (Ed), 1969. *The Journals of Captain James Cook on His Voyages of Discovery. II. The Voyage of Resolution and Adventure 1772-1775.* Cambridge University Press for the Hakluyt Society. p.343n.

13 Due to Easter Islands volcanic formation, the ground was strewn with the resulting lava.

14 They were *Sophora toromiro.*

15 Hoare, Michael E, 1976. *The Tactless Philosopher.* Melbourne, Hawthorne Press.

16 Cameron, R, 1965. *The Golden Haze.* London, Weidenfeld & Nicholson.

17 Beaglehole, J C (Ed), 1969. *The Journals of Captain James Cook on His Voyages of Discovery. II. The Voyage of Resolution and Adventure 1772-1775.* Cambridge University Press for the Hakluyt Society. p.345.

18 Sharp, Andrew, (Ed), 1970. *The Journal of Jacob Roggeveen.* Oxford, Clarendon Press.

19 Aughton, P, 2004. *Resolution – Cook's Second Voyage.* London, Weidenfeld & Nicholson.

20 Beaglehole, J C (Ed), 1969. *The Journals of Captain James Cook on His Voyages of Discovery. II. The Voyage of Resolution and Adventure 1772-1775.* Cambridge University Press for the Hakluyt Society. p.347n.

21 Hoare, Michael E, 1976. *The Tactless Philosopher.* Melbourne, Hawthorne Press

22 Possibly the Sooty Tern.

23 Beaglehole, J C, Nov. 1957. *Some Problems of Editing Cook's Journals.* Melbourne, Historical Studies Vol 8, 29.

24 Beaglehole, J C (Ed), 1969. *The Journals of Captain James Cook on His Voyages of Discovery. II. The Voyage of Resolution and Adventure 1772-1775.* Cambridge University Press for the Hakluyt Society. p.cxxii.

25 Hoare, Michael E, 1976. *The Tactless Philosopher.* Melbourne, Hawthorne Press

26 Aughton, P, 2004. *Resolution.* London, Weidenfeld & Nicholson.

27 Modern name, *Tahuata.*

28 Modern name, *Hiva Oa.*

29 Gurney, Alan, 1998. *Below the Convergence.* London, Pimlico.

30 Gurney, Alan, 2004. *Compass.* London, Norton.

31 Modern name, *Tahiti.*

32 Wales, William. *Journal on the Resolution, June 21, 1772 to October 17th, 1774.* Manuscript now in the Mitchell Library, Sydney, Australia.

33 Beaglehole, J C (Ed), 1969. *The Journals of Captain James Cook on His Voyages of Discovery. II. The Voyage of Resolution and Adventure 1772-1775.* Cambridge University Press for the Hakluyt Society.. p.382.

34 Hoare, Michael E, 1976. *The Tactless Philosopher.* Melbourne, Hawthorne Press

35 William Wales 1734-1798, *Journal on the Resolution 21 June 1772-17 October 1774.* State Library of New South Wales. Manuscript Safe 1/84

36 ibid.

37 Modern name, *Nomuka.*

38 Thomas, N, & Berghof, O. (Ed)., 2000. A Voyage Round the World. by George Forster. Honolulu. University of Hawaii Press.

39 Aughton, P, 2004. *Resolution.* London, Weidenfeld & Nicholson.

40 Hoare, Michael E, 1976. *The Tactless Philosopher.* Melbourne, Hawthorne Press

41 Modern name, *Vanuatu.*

42 Modern name, *Maewo.*

43 Wales, W & Bayly, W, 1777. *The Original Astronomical Observations Made in the Course of a Voyage Towards the South Pole, and round the World in His Majesty's Ships the Resolution and Adventure, in the years MDCCLXXII, MDCCLXXIII, MDCCLXXIV and MDCCLXXV.* London, W & A Strahan.

44 Cameron, Roderick, 1965. *The Golden Haze.* London, Weidenfeld & Nicholson.p.210.

45 Modern name, *Tana.*

46 Modern name, *West Futuna.*

47 Modern name, *Aneityurn.*

48 Periwinkles, marine snails of the family *Littorinidæ.*

49 Beaglehole, J C (Ed), 1969. *The Journals of Captain James Cook on His Voyages of Discovery. II. The Voyage of Resolution and Adventure 1772-1775.* Cambridge University Press for the Hakluyt Society. p.507.

50 Modern name, *Kanaky.*

51 Cook later named this *Observatory Isle.*

52 Beaglehole, J C (Ed), 1969. *The Journals of Captain James Cook on His Voyages of Discovery. II. The Voyage of Resolution and Adventure 1772-1775.* Cambridge University Press for the Hakluyt Society. p.532.

53 Hoare, Michael E, 1976. *The Tactless Philosopher.* Melbourne. Hawthorne Press.

54 Beaglehole, J C (Ed), 1969. *The Journals of Captain James Cook on His Voyages of Discovery. II. The Voyage of Resolution and Adventure 1772-1775.* Cambridge University Press for the Hakluyt Society. p.532.

55 Aughton, P, 2004. *Resolution.* London, Weidenfeld & Nicholson.

56 Hoare, Michael E, 1976. *The Tactless Philosopher.* Melbourne, Hawthorne Press

57 ibid.

58 Holmes, Christine (Ed), 1984. *Captain Cook's Second Voyage, The Journal of Lieutenants Elliot and Pickersgill.* London, Caliban.

59 Beaglehole, J C (Ed), 1969. *The Journals of Captain James Cook on His Voyages of Discovery. II. The Voyage of Resolution and Adventure 1772-1775.* Cambridge University Press for the Hakluyt Society. p.560. fn2.

11

THE VOYAGE HOME

Oh! dream of joy! is this indeed
The light-house top I see?
Is this the hill? is this the kirk?
Is this mine own countree?[1]

It was just a week after leaving Norfolk Island that *Resolution* sailed into Queen Charlotte Sound for a third time. The ship's Company knew this would be their last visit, and soon they would be heading back across the Pacific, and then the Atlantic, heading homeward.

At Ship's Cove in Queen Charlotte Sound, New Zealand, the vessel was prepared for the journey home. A net was set to catch fresh fish, and Cook searched for signs of a visit by *Adventure,* he looked for the bottle in which he had left a note for Captain Furneaux in November 1773, telling what he intended to do – the bottle was gone. The Maoris came and told Cook of a shipwreck, and a massacre, but their varying tales could not be taken seriously.[2]

While setting up his observatory here, William Wales noticed that trees which were standing when he last set it up had been felled by saw and axes. He also noted that an Observatory had been erected in a different place from where he had last placed his, which was certain evidence that the *Adventure* and Bayly had been here since their last visit.[3]

In Queen Charlotte Sound Wales took numerous observations in an attempt to accurately record the Longitude of the place. Cook reports that he was impressed with the number of observations that Wales took in all the places they stopped, and he equals Wales' abilities to his assiduity.[4]

In complete contrast, J R Forster was apparently very frustrated with the work of Wales, and Forster's biographer wrote of him demeaning himself when he called into question Wales' scientific competence. Forster remarked that although Wales had visited the place three times, each for the duration of three weeks, he still wanted to stay to calculate the longitude of the place, thus proving negligence and the inaccuracy of the first observations, although the weather was fine for much of the time.[5]

Wales wrote in the Log that he was working on finding the greatest angle to which the ship listed when rolling in high seas, compared to calm weather. While in New Zealand he had fixed the graduated arc of a circle on one of the cross beams of the ship in his cabin, he pivoted a long slender rod on this, and weighted it at the bottom, the other end being a pointer to the degrees of movement. [6]

Soon after leaving New Zealand, Cook had written in his Log, that Wales had fixed up an instrument to measure the angle of the ship when it rolled, and that the greatest angle observed was 38°. The difference of angle when in calm weather, and going on a wind, was something which had often been mooted in the past.[7]

The *Resolution* crossed the Pacific to Tierra del Fuego in just over five weeks, the crossing was fast and relatively uneventful. On 19th December the ship reached Wateman Island and, no doubt looking forward to his eventual return home, Cook named the high point at its southernmost *York Minster*. On the next day the ship entered a creek which Cook named *Christmas Sound*, for it was here that they would celebrate Christmas.

On disembarking William Wales set up his observatory and instruments, he searched for a site which was firm and gave a clear view of the sky, which he eventually found on top of a rock. A guard tent was also needed, although it was not apparent that there were any indigenous people in the area.[8]

Two shooting parties went out on Christmas Eve and encountered an abundance of geese on an island, which they ultimately named *Goose Island*. A total of sixty two geese were bagged for the forthcoming Christmas celebrations.[9]

The feasting was a welcome experience after the hardships of the voyage, and due to the success of the shoot on the previous day, it was possible to allow one bird for every three men. The geese were roasted and boiled and made into pies, all washed down with the remaining Madeira wine which had improved with age, and according to Cook was:

...the only provision that was mended by keeping; so that our friends in England did not perhaps, celebrate Christmas more cheerfully than we did.[10]

Wales wrote in the log that they left Staten Land in a sort of 'Pet', but bearing no ill he stopped to give a short account of it. He had read Anson's account of this part of the voyage, and must have been fearful of the conditions around Staten Island, in 1740 when George Anson had sailed for South America in *Centurion* he had experienced extreme storms and gales, and lost many of his crew in these parts, and encountered the dreaded scurvy.[11] Wales on the contrary found it to be much better than the black bare rocks of *Terra del Fuego*. Here *Resolution* encountered a great storm, snow, sleet, and a great sea, which proved a good test not only for the vessel, but also for Wales' *clinometer* which he had rigged up in his cabin, this showed the maximum roll to be *42°*.[12]

Land was sighted again on 14th January, South Georgia stood covered with glaciers, ice, and snow. Cook surveyed the north coast, and at Possession Bay Forster and a party went ashore on a brief visit to collect penguins and other birds, and just a few plants that they managed to locate in this hostile place. *Resolution* finally pushed on to the South Sandwich Island group through thick fog, then onto Bouvet Island before Cook, resolved that his search for a southern continent was finally over, pointed his vessel north again and headed for Cape Town.[13]

In the afternoon Wales, Clerke, and Gilbert observed several distances of the sun and moon in intervals of clear weather, this proved their reckoning to have been accurate.[14]

CAPE OF GOOD HOPE

At Table Bay, the ship's Company reflected on their achievements, this was a busy place, and they were now back in the civilized world. Since they last anchored here two and a half years had passed, they had circled the globe and were now ready for home, but for now the work went on.

Cook found a letter waiting for him at the Cape from Captain Furneaux, who had made it back here twelve months before. At last Cook had news of the fate of *Adventure* and her company. The letter told of how, after parting from *Resolution*, *Adventure* had been battered by storm, and Furneaux decided to retreat to Tolago Bay in New Zealand to carry out repairs. On trying to follow Cook again it was obvious that the ships were now too far apart to find each other, and with not much hope of making Easter Island in the vast Pacific at the exact same time as *Resolution,* it was decided that it would be wiser for *Adventure* to turn back to Queen Charlotte Sound and prepare for the journey home, via Cape Horn and the Cape of Good Hope. Furneaux had again searched for Cape Circumcision on the way home, but to no avail. To Cook's horror the letter also told of ten of the *Adventure's* crew being murdered at Grass Cove, and eaten by the Moaris, prior to the vessel leaving Queen Charlotte Sound. Cook wondered if perhaps Furneaux had acted recklessly in some way to allow this to happen, he would reserve judgement until he learned more. For now he was just relieved to get news.[15]

Cook continued to make preparations for the rest of the voyage, and he went with William Wales to see the Governor for permission to erect the observatory and instruments, and they also agreed with the Widow Xieman for the use of the ground which they had used before, and where Mason and Dixon had carried out their observations of the Transit of Venus in 1761.

The Cape of Good Hope was a great meeting place for navigators, being a popular station for not only taking on supplies, but also exchanging both goods and tales of adventure. Unlike Cook, Wales found the company of the Spanish officers at the Cape quite amicable, and even gave them a sextant.[16]

J R Forster meanwhile was apprehensive at the approach of his homecoming, and wondered what news of his wife and family, but also worried that his friends and patrons would not be so amicable after three years absence. He was miserable at the thought of re-starting his whole life again, and at the now more advanced age of forty five, it would be even harder to regain the position in society that he had managed to achieve before he left. He would also bid 'farewell' to Sparrman here, who was keen to research in South Africa before returning to Sweden the following year, and once again corresponding with Forster.[17]

Capt Cook meanwhile had managed to locate an English East India Company ship bound for England, it was the East Indiaman *Dutton,* which was under the command of Capt Newte. Cook anticipated that *Dutton* would reach England quite a while before *Resolution,* which he planned would be anchored here for a while for essential refitting and re-caulking, before calling at other islands in the Atlantic. Cook wrote to Philip Stephens, the secretary to the Admiralty from Table Bay, reporting generally on the progress of the voyage after parting with *Adventure.* From William Wales he declared that he had received every assistance, and the watch of Mr Kendall had exceeded all expectations and been a faithful guide through all kinds of weather.[18]

Joseph Gilbert, master of *Resolution* was also impressed by the watch, declaring it to be the greatest piece of mechanism ever produced.[19]

Cook collected all logbooks, journals drawings and charts from the officers and petty officers, he had the men's chests searched, everything was given up and sealed by the Captain and all sent to the Admiralty in England with Captain Newte.[20] Supernumaries Wales, the Forsters and Sparrman were allowed to keep their own journals, on condition that they did not divulge anything about the voyage to England, before the Admiralty had given permission to do so.[21]

John Elliott particularly bemoaned the loss of his notes, he recorded that he had taken such pains to record his experiences on the voyage, and yet after giving in his Journal, he had nothing to prove he had ever been.[22]

Eventually Wales dismantled the observatory and instruments and carried them on board ship once more, where he would then compute his observations. *Resolution* was now bound for St Helena where she landed on 15th May, by a direct course, due to the 'goodness of Mr Kendall's watch' according to Cook.[23]

Cook wrote in his log that recent lunar observations made by Wales at sea, and comparing these with calculations by the watch before and leaving St Helena, resulted in only five miles difference at St Helena Island, than by Mr Maskelyne's observations here. Cook remarked that the longitude of places on land, could be found by the lunar method even at sea – with the assistance of a good watch.

ASCENSION ISLAND

Resolution had been accompanied from Cape Town by the English Indiaman *Dutton,* the two vessels parting company before Ascension Island, and the *Dutton* headed straight for London with the *Resolution* Officer's Journals for the Admiralty on board. Meanwhile Cook planned to spend a few days on Ascension, where, with Wales, the position of the island could be ascertained and duly recorded.[24]

Wales wrote that the Island of Ferdinando de Noronha was perhaps the most romantic of any in the world, being strewn with singularly shaped rocks, set on an irregular surface. With many plantations and the uncultivated parts covered with woodland, he found this place extremely beautiful.[25]

Numerous observations were made of Ferdinando de Noronha without landing there by Wales and Cook, to fix the longitude by the watch. It would be from these that the longitude of the adjacent east coast of Brazil could be determined.[26]

AZORES

Cook anchored off the Island of Fayal in the Azores, principally to allow William Wales to accurately calculate the longitude of the Islands. Wales and one of the officers went on shore to meet the acting English Consul Mr Dent, who not only allowed the observatory to be set up in his garden, but also opened his house for their accommodation, and served the ship's Company with some welcome fresh beef.[27]

The hospitality encountered on the Azores was impressive – the well cultivated island of Fayal had a good reputation for its wine. The provisioning of ships with water and wine and food was on a par with that experienced at Madeira.

The observations were carried out to the Captain's satisfaction, latitude, longitude, and the tides were calculated, and on 19th July Wales stowed the instruments and observatory back on board – for the last time – *Resolution* was now bound for England.

The ship anchored at Spithead near Portsmouth on 30th July, 1775, and Wales and Cook went on shore at noon with Kendall's watch. Wales compared it with the transit clock at the Royal Academy at Portsmouth, which is thought to have been the regulator made by Graham.[28]

The watches had been checked each day of the voyage, and whenever the ships anchored, and when it had been possible to set up the observatories on shore, they had been checked with the aid of the astronomical clock and quadrant. The results had been recorded, and these were ultimately published, K1 had performed beyond all expectations.

Wales was well impressed with John Harrison's work when he recorded at the end of his observations, that the Inventor had achieved accuracy of such an amazing degree, in the early 1760s, to the mechanics of time keeping. Wales further remarked that although there was still scope for improvement, no one should think himself more superior than Harrison until their time piece had stood the same challenging trials.[29]

Wales took a post-chaise back to London, carrying with him that precious and wonderful object the Watch, and in company with Captain James Cook, Johann and Georg Forster, William Hodges, and Richard Grindall, a clever young sailor of 25, who was to become a Vice-Admiral in later life, but who had married within an hour of his leaving for the voyage in 1772.[30]

At the latter part of 1772 after Cook had left Plymouth on his second voyage, John Harrison, then approaching the age of 80, had produced his timepiece H5, a watch in the same style as H4, and had approached the King who had put the watch 'on trial', after which it was given the royal approval. Eventually as a result of the King's intervention, Harrison was finally given the balance of his Longitude prize in June 1773.[31]

Cook returned with the all important longitude calculations, which accurately positioned a large part of the south Pacific, for which due credit was given to Wales.[32] It was now surely established that while Cook and Wales, prior to the voyage, had been proficient at calculating the longitude by the lunar distance method, and Wales had been instructed by Maskelyne to tutor the Officers in this method, both he and Cook were now firm supporters of the timekeeping method, having experienced their trials with Kendall's copy of John Harrison's invention.[33]

The company reached London on Monday 31st July, 1775, and after a jubilant reunion with Mary his wife, and children Sarah, William and Anne, William Wales took a coach the next day to Greenwich, and personally handed Kendall's

K1 timepiece over to Revd Mr Maskelyne, presumably John Arnold's watch was also handed over at this time.[34]

One of the items brought home by Wales, of which no doubt there would be many, was a piece of the *red tufa* from Easter Island, which we learn was given to John Ibbetson, the secretary to the Board of Longitude.[35]

The Journal kept by William Wales is often quoted by authors, who are writing of the second voyage of Cook, or of any related subject. The text was eventually part published by the Hakluyt Society as Appendix V to Cook's Journal. The editor J C Beaglehole was impressed with Wales and remarked:

> ...his interests were by no means confined to astronomy, a man of downright common-sense and some quiet humour.[36]

J C Beaglehole later expanded on the contribution that Wales had given to Cook in writing his Journals:

> ...Wales, an exceptionally intelligent and agreeable person, with a mind nourished on humane letters as well as on mathematics, would make his own contribution to the scientific records of the voyages in the published volumes of astronomical observations. He was not quite the sole source of supplementary information Cook had, and as we can follow what I shall call Cook's constructional method pretty clearly if we consider his account of Easter Island. Here, still weak from recent severe illness, he had had to confine himself to pottering about the beach, while he sent a party led by Lieutenant Pickersgill, and including Wales, to march over the island and observe all they could. Pickersgill wrote a brief report. Cook began with a simple copy of this, inside quotation marks. He copied

it into both Version One and an intermediary version I shall call X. But he also had discussion with Pickersgill and Wales and saw the latter's journal. So he wrote an additional account of the island in X, an amalgam of himself, Pickersgill and Wales. Then—I assume when he was doing his final rewriting in London, and had the use of Wales's journal to plunder as he liked—he abandoned the direct Pickersgill altogether, though still using his substance, and provided in Version Two something quite new, much longer, much fuller, with acknowledgements: 'This account of the excursion I had from Mr Pickersgill and Mr Wales, men on whose veracity I could depend'.....He was one of Cook's educators in literacy. Wales helps him with phrases, with paragraphs, with thoughts. He can build on them. He is generally discriminating. When he adverts to the heroes of Homer, he does not claim direct acquaintance. Mr Wales had told him. On the other hand knowing his usual mode of expression, we are a little startled when he brings in the all-devouring jaws of time. See, as one might annotate, Wales. The comparison could be continued for much longer. It would be an error to attribute too much. Cook's thought and style are alike stimulated by Wales: he even learns to balance his sentences, not without skill. But he remains Cook.[37]

For Wales' part his precept on the content of his Journals can be found in his entry for 13th May, 1774 when he wrote:

.....I have always thought the situation of a Traveller singularly hard. If he tells nothing that is uncommon he must be a stupid fellow to have gone so far, and brought home so little; and if he does, why – it is hum – aya – a tap on the Chin; – and – 'He's a Traveller.'[38]

It is recorded that William Wales assisted Captain Constantine John Phipps, later the second Baron Mulgrave, with the account of the voyage which he had undertaken towards the North Pole in June 1773.[39] Phipps had sailed on the vessel *Racehorse* accompanied by the *Carcass,* on which one of the midshipmen was the young Horatio Nelson. Also on board was Israel Lyons, who had taken one of Kendall's K2 chronometers with him on the voyage,[40] and like Wales, had worked on the Nautical Almanac computations. Joseph Banks' biographer describes Lyons as a 'remarkable specimen of the numerous class of self-educated persons who helped to make the eighteenth century'.[41] Phipps was a fellow Yorkshireman from near Whitby, and the navy sent him to carry out tests relating to the sea freezing, as part of their programme of searches for the elusive North-West Passage, he had sailed to the north of Spitzbergen, and found the ice barrier impossible to penetrate. His account was published in 1774, during Cook's second voyage.[42]

Cook had enjoyed the company of Wales on the voyage, a fellow Yorkshireman, and from a similar humble background. In Wales he had found a soul-mate, and had valued their discussions, particularly when discussing their dealings with indigenous peoples.[43]

The astronomer and broadcaster Patrick Moore summed up the quality of Wales' Journal, when he wrote of it being on a par with Cook's, and he remarked that Cook had always respected Wales, even after the astronomer had proved the Captain's observations to be wrong, Cook's admiration never wavered.[44]

Cook's later Biographer considers Wales to be one of the cleverest, and most amiable men on *Resolution*. Indeed when describing what Cook had achieved, with intense reading, and a desire for self-improvement in navigation, surveying, and observation skills with no formal education, and without close association with the scientists of the time, he could be describing the achievements of Wales.[45] The astronomer had not only recorded astronomical observations on the voyage, but his work had also encompassed tidal, barometer and thermometer readings, terrestrial magnetism, atmospheric electricity. He had recorded the angle of roll of the ship, and tested a wind gauge, he had recorded the saltiness of the water as well as its temperature, and throughout this work he kept exhaustive records, and taught the officers his skills, all of such vital importance in this Age of Enlightenment.

Undoubtedly Wales was a naturally skilled pedagog. By the end of the voyage the majority of the Officers had been instructed in observing the distance of the Moon from a star, or the Sun, and Cook remarked that Wales had tutored the officers to such a degree, that he couldn't tell any difference between Wales' observations and those of the officers.[46]

Endnotes

1   S T Coleridge (1772-1834).

2   Gurney, Alan, 1998. *Below the Convergence.* London, Pimlico

3   Beaglehole, J C (Ed), 1969. *The Journals of Captain James Cook on His Voyages of Discovery. II. The Voyage of Resolution and Adventure 1772-1775.* Cambridge University Press for the Hakluyt Society. p.570n.

4   ibid., p.580.

5   Hoare, Michael E, 1976. *The Tactless Philosopher.* Melbourne, Hawthorne Press

6   Beaglehole, J C (Ed), 1969. *The Journals of Captain James Cook on His Voyages of Discovery. II. The Voyage of Resolution and Adventure 1772-1775.* Cambridge University Press for the Hakluyt Society. p.587

7   ibid., p.587.

8   ibid., p.593.

9   ibid., p.596

10 ibid., p.598.

11 Heaps, Leo, 1973. *Log of the Centurion*. London, Hart-Davis MacGibbon Ltd.

12 Beaglehole, J C (Ed), 1969. *The Journals of Captain James Cook on His Voyages of Discovery. II. The Voyage of Resolution and Adventure 1772-1775*. Cambridge University Press for the Hakluyt Society. p.619.

13 Hoare, Michael E, 1976. *The Tactless Philosopher*. Melbourne, Hawthorne Press

14 Beaglehole, J C (Ed), 1969. *The Journals of Captain James Cook on His Voyages of Discovery. II. The Voyage of Resolution and Adventure 1772-1775*. Cambridge University Press for the Hakluyt Society. p.649

15 Aughton, P, 2004. *Resolution*. London, Weidenfeld & Nicholson.

16 Beaglehole, J C (Ed), 1969. *The Journals of Captain James Cook on His Voyages of Discovery. II. The Voyage of Resolution and Adventure 1772-1775*. Cambridge University Press for the Hakluyt Society. p.656n.

17 Hoare, Michael E, 1976. *The Tactless Philosopher*. Melbourne, Hawthorne Press

18 Beaglehole, J C (Ed), 1969. *The Journals of Captain James Cook on His Voyages of Discovery. II. The Voyage of Resolution and Adventure 1772-1775*. Cambridge University Press for the Hakluyt Society. p. 692

19 Beaglehole, J C *Eighteenth Century Science and the Voyages of Discovery*. University of Auckland.
    (Part of the New Zealand Electronic Text Centre Collection).

20 Beaglehole, J C (Ed), 1969. *The Journals of Captain James Cook on His Voyages of Discovery. II. The Voyage of Resolution and Adventure 1772-1775*. Cambridge University Press for the Hakluyt Society. p.654.

21 Gurney, Alan, 1998. *Below the Convergence*. London, Pimlico.

22 Holmes, Christine (Ed), 1984. *Captain Cook's Second Voyage. The Journals of Lieutenants Elliott and Pickersgill.* Caliban Books, London.

23 Gurney, Alan, 1998. *Below the Convergence.* London, Pimlico. p.32

24 Beaglehole, J C (Ed), 1969. *The Journals of Captain James Cook on His Voyages of Discovery. II. The Voyage of Resolution and Adventure 1772-1775.* Cambridge University Press for the Hakluyt Society. p.441.

25 ibid., p.670.

26 ibid., p.671.

27 ibid., p.674.

28 Howse & Hutchinson. 1969. *The Clocks and Watches of Captain James Cook 1769-1969.* London.

29 ibid.

30 Beaglehole, J C (ed), 1969. *The Journals of Captain James Cook on His Voyages of Discovery. II. The Voyage of Resolution and Adventure 1772-1775,* Cambridge. Cambridge University Press. p.682.

31 Whittle, Eric S, 1984. *The Inventor of the Marine Chronometer: John Harrison of Foulby.* Wakefield, Wakefield Historical Society.

32 Aughton, P, 2004. *Resolution.* London, Weidenfeld & Nicholson. p.177

33 Sobel, D & Andrews, W J H, 1998. *The Illustrated Longitude.* London, Fourth Estate.p.169

34 Beaglehole, J C (Ed), 1969. *The Journals of Captain James Cook on His Voyages of Discovery. II. The Voyage of Resolution and Adventure 1772-1775,* Cambridge. Cambridge University Press. p.cxi

35 Thomas, N, & Berghof, O (Ed)., 2000. A Voyage Round the World. by George Forster. Honolulu. University of Hawaii Press.

36 Beaglehole, J C Nov. 1957. *Some Problems of Editing Cook's Journals.* Melbourne, Historical Studies, Vol 8, 29.

37 Beaglehole, J C 1967. *Cook the Writer.* Sydney, Victoria University of Wellington. George Arnold Wood Memorial Lectures.

38 William Wales 1734-1798, *Journal on the Resolution 21 June 1772-17* October 1774. State Library of New South Wales. Manuscript Safe 1/84

39 E I Carlyle, 1900 *Dictionary of National Biography, William Wales,* Lond, Smith,Elder & Co.

40 Howse, Derek, 1989. *Nevil Maskelyne, the Seaman's Astronomer.* Cambridge, Cambridge University Press.

41 Smith, E, 1911. *The Life of Sir Joseph Banks.* London, Bodley Head.

42 Phipps, Constantine John, 1774. *A Voyage towards the North Pole undertaken by his Majesty's Command 1773.* London. J. Nourse.

43 Collingridge, V, 2002. *Captain Cook. The Life, Death and Legacy of History's Greatest Explorer.* London, Ebury Press.

44 Moore, Patrick. *William Wales.* in *The Journal of HMS Resolution 1772-1775 by Captain James Cook.* (Facsmile Edition),1981, Genesis Publications Ltd, Guildford p.91.

45 Hough, R, 1994. *Captain James Cook, a Biography.* London, Hodder & Stoughton.

46 Skelton, R A, F S A, 1954, *Captain James Cook as a Hydropgrapher.* The Mariner's Mirror. Vol 40, No.2. p 112.

12

THE SCHOOLMASTER

I was not trained in Academic bowers,
And to those learned streams I nothing owe
Which copious from those twin fair founts do flow;
Mine have been anything but studious hours.
Yet can I fancy, wandering 'mid thy towers,
Myself a nursling, Granta, of thy lap;
My brow seems tightening with the Doctor's cap.
And I walk *gowned* ; feel unusual powers.[1]

The second voyage of Captain James Cook, now completed, was eventually placed into the annals of our history as perhaps the most informative ever taken. *HMS Resolution* had been the first ship to cross the Antarctic Circle, and in all had crossed it three times during the voyage. Cook's voyages have been placed on a par with the exploration of space in the twentieth century,[2] and with just four deaths, three from accidents and one from disease, had a casualty list lower than any previous explorations of such length.[3] The whole experience was to affect the participants for the rest of their lives.

News of the success of the second voyage among British scientists and the naval fraternity was spreading fast, unlike the first voyage James Cook's achievements were not overshadowed by a botanist, and Cook, with his proud wife Elizabeth, now enjoyed a round of social engagements. He considered his future in retirement, and applied for a vacancy as one of the captains at the Royal Hospital at Greenwich, a sinecurial position which would allow him to write up his Second Voyage journals for publication.

In August 1775 *Resolution* sailed up the Thames to *Galleons Reach,* where she was inspected in beautiful sunshine by a party of admirers, headed by the First Lord, Sandwich, who was well pleased with the achievement of her crew. Solander wrote to Joseph Banks telling him of the euphoria of Sandwich, and how he had been "spreading promotions like confetti", and while Joseph Banks felt embarrassed at the voyage being successful when he had predicted otherwise, he soon forgot his resentments, and went on to commission Nathanial Dance to paint a portrait of Cook, which was to hang in Banks' London home.[4] Indeed from this point onwards, it was apparent that anyone who had sailed with Captain Cook was to be always highly regarded by Banks.[5]

The sea was now so strong in Cook's blood – and it was to call him once again. He was to go on to lead a third voyage, primarily to look for a North-West Passage, that elusive northern route, from the Atlantic Ocean and then through the Arctic and into the Pacific Ocean, which if found would open a trade route to the Orient, far shorter than the southern alternatives around the Capes of Horn and Good Hope.

Before the third voyage, James Cook was elected a Fellow of the Royal Society, by now well established as the authoritative body on all things scientific. Cook's election was indeed an honour, and among the proposers for his nomination was Nevil Maskelyne, the Admiralty Secretary Stephens, and John Reinhold Forster.[6] Cook was admitted to the Society on 7th March 1776.

After three years at sea, adjusting to the hustle and bustle of London life must have been quite daunting to the voyagers.

William Wales had left the city during the warm high summer of 1772, and the summer three years later was wet, and due to be followed by a very severe winter.[7] He was now back among his family and friends with his whole future to consider, how was he now to support wife Mary and their three children?

Mary Wales had suffered the loss of her eldest brother, Rev John Green of Denmark Street, London, while her husband was on the Cook voyage. John had performed their marriage ceremony at St Alfege Church in Greenwich, ten years previously, and his death in 1774 had been a tragic one, for while he was still teaching, the income from which provided him with his main form of subsistence, he also held the chapel in Fetter Lane, London. This chapel had been first built by the Moravians before the Great Fire of London, and after rebuilding it was used by John and Charles Wesley and George Whitfield. John Green introduced meetings here, similar to those practiced by the Quakers, and encouraged any person to speak. These eventually became public disputes, of which John Green was fond, until the *Arians* happened to visit, and by their preaching he questioned his own notions on the *Trinity,* which caused him to publicly admit that he had been wrong all his life, and indeed had published on the subject in error. This had thrown Green's mind into turmoil, and so great was his distress, that he never again lifted his head – and a week later he died.[8]

John Green had no surviving children, and in his will he left everything to his wife Sarah. He stipulated that on Sarah's death the residue was to go to his niece Rhoda Green, the 21 year old daughter of his brother William Green and wife Ann (née Rhodes).[9] Reverend John Green was laid to rest at Tottenham Court Chapel.[10] The memorial plaque placed inside the chapel was inscribed 'sometime Minister of this Chapel'.[11]

Wales took time to catch up with his old acquaintances, and there can be no doubt that when he returned the watches to Maskelyne, the two would discuss his future employment. He contacted William Bayly, and heard the story of the *Adventure* and her crew, and together the two astronomers called to see Reuben Burrow who had taken up the post of Maskelyne's Assistant at the Royal Observatory when William Bayly left in March 1771, a post he had held for two and a half years. In 1771 Burrow had married Anne Purvis, the daughter of a Leadenhall Street poulterer, and while working for the Astronomer Royal, had opened an academy at Greenwich.[12] Then in 1774, the year after leaving Maskelyne's employ, he had been chosen to assist Maskelyne with gravity experiments at *Schiehallion,* in Perthshire, Scotland, but the two had clashed when, on their return, Burrow refused to submit his observations due to Maskelyne receiving the Royal Society's Copley Medal, for the work of which Burrow felt he had done the greater part.

Wales and Bayly were bathing in the glory of their recent achievements on the Cook voyage, and dropped in on Burrow with the pretence that they needed his opinion on a certain subject. In truth they were out to chastise him, eventually they ended up at a tavern discussing the *Schiehallion* experiment, when Bayly, knowing that Burrow reviled Maskelyne, had inferred that Maskelyne had spoken favourably of Burrow at the Royal Society. Burrow questioned this, and then realized that the two were joking, resulting in a predictable Burrow protest. Reuben Burrow was a truculent stocky Yorkshireman, who was prone to temper tantrums at the least excuse and obviously had an inferiority complex.[13] He was described by Augustus de Morgan, the mathematician, as:

> ...an able mathematician, but a most vulgar and scurrilous dog, leaving notes in some of his books containing much cursing, obscenity and slander.[14]

Later that year at the local Bluecoat School – Christ's Hospital, Newgate Street in London – the post of Master of the Royal Mathematical School became vacant, owing to the death of Mr Daniel Harris on 4th November, 1775.[15]

The Christ's Hospital School, London, still survives as a highly regarded school, which is now set deep in the Sussex countryside near Horsham. Proud of its ancient foundation, its origins lie in the Dissolution of the Monasteries, when Henry VIII suppressed the religious houses and confiscated the property, bestowing the Grey Friars monastery in Newgate Street, London, to the City for the relief of the poor. After laying empty for six years it was Henry's son Edward VI who, on hearing Bishop Ridley's sermon on Charity, was stirred into working to establish three London Hospitals for the poor – Christ's Hospital in the old Grey Friar's monastery for their education, St Thomas's to care for their sick and Bridewell for correction of their criminals and vagabonds.[16]

Christ's Hospital School admitted its first children in 1552, some of them in these early days were babes in arms, but the infant intake was gradually decreased, until eventually children were only taken on from the age of seven. The uniform, which originates from that date, is still proudly worn by today's pupils, with only minor changes.

Leigh Hunt, who started at the school in 1791, described the uniform as:

> ...a blue drugget gown, or body, with ample coats to it; a yellow vest underneath, in winter time; small clothes of Russia duck; worsted yellow stockings; a leathern girdle; and a little black worsted cap, usually carried in the hand.. I believe it was the ordinary dress of children in humble life, during the reign of the Tudors. We used to flatter ourselves that it was taken from the monks;

and there went a monstrous tradition that at one period
it consisted of blue velvet with silver buttons...[17]

D'Arcy Thompson described the uniform when he was
admitted in 1837, when he was just seven. He first put on some
feminine garb, a 'frock', and then a shirt of material which
resembled horse hair, then yellow worsted stockings. Knee
breeches of a twilled cotton cloth, and a petticoat of yellow
were then covered in the long gown of blue. To complete the
outfit a girdle was tied around the waist of red leather, and
two tabs hung from the neck, like those of a cleric. D'Arcy
Thompson's hair was then cut so short that it resembled a
hair brush.[18]

The Foundation flourished, under a board of Governors,
Christ's Hospital became a Grammar School, with some
pupils going on to the Universities of Oxford and Cambridge,
and within it was a Writing School, which equipped boys for
apprenticeships. The school taught Latin, literature, religion,
and music, the school's chapel was the church of the Greyfriars
which stood within the confines of the Hospital.[19]

In 1665 when the Great Plague broke out with vengeance in
London, the School was considered lucky by losing just thirty
two pupils of the disease. This was followed by the Great
Fire the next year, and although most of its buildings were
lost, over 200 of the pupils had been transported some eight
miles north to the Nag's Head at Islington, and escaped the
inferno.[20]

To explain, the Nag's Head at Islington belonged to Christ's
Hospital, it had recently been given to them by a benefactor,
and was standing empty at the time of the Great Fire when the
pupils spent the night there before going on to Clerkenwell
for a few days, they were then housed at Hertford and Ware
whilst their old school was rebuilt[21]

Some of the buildings at Newgate Street were not entirely destroyed, four cloisters survived, and three wards, and several rooms, so that these were able to be repaired quite quickly and the pupils moved back late in 1667. With the help of benefactors, and under instruction from Sir Christopher Wren and his assistant Nicholas Hawksmoor, new buildings eventually rose from the ashes, to provide a stately complex of architectural splendour, incorporating the old cloisters, and including a new church, Christ Church, Newgate Street, was built on the site of the choir of the old Grey Friars church.[22]

During this period at the beginning of the Age of Enlightenment, mathematics, astronomy, and related sciences were becoming serious studies. In 1662 the Royal Society had been granted its charter by Charles II, Isaac Newton had been elected a Fellow in 1672/3 and had already prepared his *Principia* for publication. Among the governors of Christ's Hospital at this time were Sir Robert Clayton, politician and merchant banker, Sir Jonas Moore, originally a Lancashire mathematics teacher who had become the Surveyor General of the Ordnance, Sir Christopher Wren, originally a Professor of Astronomy at Oxford before becoming architect and surveyor of the King's Works, Sir Charles Scarburgh, physician to the King and a mathematician, Lord Treasurer Thomas Clifford, and Samuel Pepys who had been elected to the Royal Society in 1665.

Amid the rebuilding of Christ's Hospital, school plans were mooted by the Governors for the foundation of a Mathematical School within the Hospital, and a building erected to accommodate it. The plans were put to King Charles II through the Lord Treasurer Clifford and with help from the Duke of York who was then Lord High Admiral of England. Largely through the efforts of Samuel Pepys, the King was persuaded in 1673 to grant a Royal Charter for a Mathematical School for forty boys to be trained in mathematics, for the particular use and practice of navigation for the King's Service at sea. King Charles II was also persuaded to build an observatory at Greenwich, and this was opened in 1675, with John Flamsteed appointed as the first Astronomer Royal.[23]

A course of study at the Royal Mathematical School was planned through the efforts of Jonas Moore, Isaac Newton, Edmond Halley who was then at Oxford, and John Flamsteed who also provided tutoring for the School's Boys at Greenwich.[24] But it was Samuel Pepys, secretary to the Admiralty, who had been the main driving force from the creation of the idea of a Mathematical School, through the funding of it from Government sources, to the eventual granting of the Charter.[25]

In 1775 there had been three candidates for the vacancy of Mathematical Master when William Wales secured the position, an admirable appointment, which was to give him a job and a home for himself and his family for the rest of his life. The Court Minutes show he had gained the post by a large margin:

'William Wales Elected Master of the Royal Math'l & Mr Stones Schools'

This Court being summoned for the election by Ballot of a Master to the Royal Mathematical and Mr Stones Schools, in the room of Mr Daniel Harris deceased the Petitioners were, Reuben Burrow 20, Benjamin Donn 3, and Willm Wales 92. Whereupon the President declared William Wales duly elected, who being called in and acquainted therewith, he returned the Court his most humble thanks, and promised to discharge his Duty with the utmost Care and Fidelity: And the Court referred it to the Committee of Almoners to give him his Instructions and settle him in his Houses.[26]

Petitioner Benjamin Donn (1729-1798) was a teacher of mathematics and navigation from Bideford in Devon. The other unsuccessful candidate was Reuben Burrow, who according to Danson 'the establishment' rose to prevent him from securing the position, whether this was the Royal Society, or the Astronomer Royal, or the Christ's Hospital Committee of Almoners who policed the running of the school, is not clear.[27]

So what of George Gilpin, that faithful servant of William Wales who had accompanied him on the second Cook voyage? Described as a *quiet y(ou)ng man* by John Elliot, a Midshipman on *Resolution*,[28] Gilpin's first record in the annals of this scientific world appear when he was aged 18, and the ship's company were first mustered. He was born in 1754 at Leeds in Yorkshire and was most probably known to William Wales before the voyage. His father Joshua Gilpin was working in Leeds as agent at the coal staith of Mr Charles Brandling:

> We are informed that one of the four learned gentlemen which the Emperor has sent out as Astronomer upon a voyage round the world (as mentioned in our last) was a native of this town, being the younger son of the late Joshua Gilpin, agent at Charles Brandling Esq's coal laith (sic)—He went out under Mr. Wales, also born near Wakefield, under whom he gained his Knowledge in Mathematics and astronomy, in a voyage round the world with Capt Cook in the years 1772,1773,1774 and 1775.[29]

It is relevant that Charles Brandling was also an employer of Joshua Green,[30] a brother of Charles Green and his sister Mrs William Wales, George Gilpin eventually married one of their nieces, Lydia. That George Gilpin had attended the Academy of John Green, another brother, and that William Wales had tutored him in that place, is also a possibility. Gilpin did offer the information later in his life that he had left school around 1768 at the age of 14, when he had learned some Latin and a little Greek.[31]

A later record confirms the families' ties:

> ....to be Lett for the Remainder of a Lease 19 years to come. A Farm in Spen lane, Cookridge, Liberty in Addle, in occupation of Wm Potts and widow of Joshua Gilpin. Enquire of Wm Potts, of Leeds Coal staith, or of Joshua Green of Middleton.[32]

Considering the events of Gilpin's life it is surely no surprise when we learn that in March 1776 he became assistant to the Astronomer Royal Nevil Maskelyne, the post had been left vacant by John Hellins who had taken over from Reuben Burrow in 1773. Maskelyne had great problems keeping his assistants, and Hellins' work had proved far from satisfactory, so Maskelyne had in effect sacked him, in his place Gilpin was to stay for the next five years.[33]

The site of Christ's Hospital, in London formed roughly an oblong area bordered by Newgate Street to the south, Giltspur Street to the west, Butchers-hall Lane to the east and to the north was the Town Ditch and the grounds of St Bartholomew's Hospital.

In 1775 Christ Church occupied the south-eastern corner of the school grounds, originally established in the choir of the church of the Greyfriar's, it was destroyed by the Great Fire and rebuilt by masons John Shorthose and Richard Crooke, in Portland stone to Wren's design, and completed in 1687, the steeple being added after 1700. Christ Church was one of the larger City churches, with broad aisles and huge galleries, its interior was impressive, and served the Hospital well as it's school chapel.

The complex of school buildings stood to the north west of the Church around a central courtyard, the Greyfriar's Cloisters known as the *Garden* were flanked on the west by the Great Hall, while to the north was the Whittington Library which had been founded in 1429 by Richard Whittington. The Mathematical School was to the west of the south range, and the Writing School to the north of the west range.[34] The Mathematical School's gateway at one time formed the school's western entrance, over which a statue of Charles II stood, he had signed the charter of the School, and this particular building was erected in 1710, the architect was Sir Christopher Wren.[35]

One visitor to the new Mathematical School building in 1710 was Zacharias Conrad von Uffenbach, who described it:

> ...in it there stood several cupboards with glass doors, in which were various globi and a certain number of mathematical instruments, though for the most part geometrical. There stood also here a couple of fairly large wooden models of ships of most elegant and curious workmanship; they can be taken to pieces, so that the children, who make a special study of ship-building, may be shown all the parts of a ship. In a great cupboard near the door were some four hundred mathematical books...[36]

A particularly good description of the cloisters was written by a 19th century pupil:[37]

> ....Another game we had which was played in the "Giffs" (the G soft, the name? derived from the initial letters of "Grey ffriars," of whose monastery the "Giffs" cloister was the only remaining relic). A description of the "Giffs" may not be out of place here. A person entering the school from Christ Church Passage would

pass through the gate guarded by "Biggy Rabs," and would find himself at the meeting of two cloisters, one straight in front of him, known as the "Library Cloy," the other at right angles to this, immediately on his left hand; this was the cloister known as the "Giffs." Turning to the left he would have to descend some stone steps, about six of them, to find himself in a rather gloomy corridor, lighted on his right by mediaeval arched windows barred perpendicularly with iron bars. The cloister was fairly wide. On his left hand were doors belonging to the shoe room, etc. Passing along the cloister he would rise by the same number of steps to the original level. The cloister formed the southern side of a quadrangle known as the "Garden. Having reached the top of the steps, over which was Twelves staircase, another cloister would be found on his right leading to the "Greks' Cloy," which in turn led to the "Library Cloy" on the east side of the Garden."....

"Biggy Rabs" referred to above was Mr Robinson, one of the beadles who guarded the main entrance to the school, and the "Greks" refer to the Grecians, head boys of the Grammar School.[38]

In 1940 Christ Church was gutted by fire when hit by an incendiary during the Second World War, but Wren's tower, with its beautiful steeple, survives.[39] (see Illustration No 9)

To the north of the Mathematical School originally stood a large old house which had suffered great damage in the 1666 fire, and not being entirely destroyed was repaired and used as the residence of the Mathematical Master, but was a dark and gloomy place and not entirely suitable for its purpose, and so was used by various servants, and for a long time was the home of the Porter.[40]

The entrance to the complex was via Newgate Street, into Christ Church passage, and under the eastern end of the south range which extended over the southern cloister, this was the Girl's Ward or dormitory above the southern and western ranges of the cloister were the chambers for the drying of laundry, and rooms known as the *dungeons,* for the temporary solitary internment of boys who had committed offences. The ground floor housed the Porter's Lodge, the Porter was the superintendent of the Beadles of the school, who under the Steward watched over the boys while they were at play. The Surveyor had his office here also, he not only drew plans for new buildings, but was also responsible for any repairs to the existing buildings.[41]

To the west of the central complex and parallel with the western wall of the Hall was the Grammar School, and standing apart from the main western range was the Infirmary used for the care of the sick, and run by the matron who superintended fourteen nurses, responsible for the cleanliness, health, and comfort of the children and their general behavour. At the head of the medical department was the Physician/Surgeon, and an Apothecary was resident within the walls immediately adjoining the Infirmary, it was his responsibility to examine the children on admission. Also a dentist visited the Infirmary one day a week, and the school had on its staff a watchman, street-keepers, a cook, cobbler, barber, shaver and a shoe-maker as well as a wardrobe keeper, who was in charge of the custody and distribution of the children's wearing apparel.[42]

The children of Christ's Hospital ate in the large hall, which stood on the western side of the Garden. The room measured 130 feet by 34 feet, and here the pupils ate their scanty diet, dry bread and a little beer for breakfast. Dinner was more varied, on Sundays and Thursdays it was boiled beef and broth, Monday was bread and butter and milk and water, and on Tuesday roast mutton was served. On Wednesday it was bread and butter again with rice milk, boiled mutton and broth on Friday, and on Saturday the boys ate bread and butter and pease porridge. Supper was always a large piece of bread with a choice of either cheese or butter to accompany it.[43]

An old school rhyme reflects the boys' thoughts on this fare:

"Sunday, all saints;
Monday, all souls;
Tuesday, all trenchers;
Wednesday, all bowls;
Thursday, tough Jack;
Friday, no better;
Saturday, pea-soup with bread and butter."[44]

There is no doubt that on hearing the above rhyme, William Wales would have been reminded of his many austere meals on board *Resolution*.

Reading through the recollections of the pupils, it is evident that, as in most schools, as well as developing their own rhymes they also used their own particular *words*, the definitions of which were peculiar to Christ's Hospital, as well as nicknames for the staff. Such confusion prompted Edmund Blunden to Appendix a 'mini-dictionary' of Christ's Hospital words in his history of the school.[45]

Across the area north of the central square of buildings originally ran the old city wall of London which had been surrounded by a great water course. On the founding of the School here, this ditch had been used as a drain, but had proved such a risk to the children's health that it was soon covered over, but throughout the history of the school's occupation it had always been called the *Ditch*. On the extreme eastern side of the Ditch stood the *Treasurer's* house, a large fine looking residence with a portico, built about 1690, it had a large garden which ran south down the eastern boundary of school, and the entrance into Counting Yard which ran parallel to the garden, in 1776 this was occupied by Thomas Burfoot Esq., his job was to control all the monies paid in and out of Christ's Hospital, and to chair the various committees, he was assisted by the *Receiver*.[46]

Next to the Treasurer's House to the westward were a row of houses assigned to the Head Master, the Matron, and the Mathematical Master,[47] and it was into the latter that William Wales, his wife, and young family Sarah, William and Ann Hagley would have moved in the latter part of 1775.

William Wales' appointment of Master of the Royal Mathematical School in Christ's Hospital was a prestigious one. Among past masters had been John Robertson, who with Daniel Harris had assisted Thomas Penn in setting practical examinations for Charles Mason and Jeremiah Dixon, who were the candidates for surveying the Maryland-Pennsylvania Boundary Survey and has come to be known as the *Mason Dixon Line*. It was Jeremiah Dixon who had accompanied William Bayly to Norway to observe the Transit of Venus in 1769, an event also observed by Daniel Harris who had observed the Transit from the Round Tower in Windsor Castle. In 1754 Robertson had published *The Elements of Navigation,* and a year later became mathematical master at the Royal Naval Academy at Portsmouth.

John Robertson's scheme of education for the Mathematical School was revised by William Wales, when the boys first entered the school their syllabus was part classical, but chiefly mathematical – covering arithmetic, algebra, the Elements of Euclid, trigonometry, and conic sections. The complete nautical course would have been completed by the ten pupils who took the examination at Trinity House each year.[48]

This was to become a significant time in the history of Christ's Hospital, of which William Wales' installation was a part. New boys were being admitted all the time, boys like Lancelot Pepys Stephens for example whose mother's death in 1768 had left his father Lancelot Stephens with three children to raise, a task he found he was unable to maintain without assistance.[49] The family lived in Deveraux Court just off Temple Bar in London, between Fleet Street and the Strand where Mr Stephens was proprietor of Tom's Coffee House. For his son to enter Christ's Hospital, Lancelot Stephens needed to be a freeman of the City of London, and he bought his membership into the Company of Combmakers, by redemption, for the sum of forty six shillings and eight pence, in 1774.[50] In 1775 the boy's father died.

When children were considered for admittance into Christ's Hospital the regulations were strictly adhered to, and quite often revised. The regulations in 1777 as laid down were as under:[51]

One third of presentations to be *non-free,* and sons of clergymen to be considered free.

Age of admission from *seven to twelve.*

Two children of the same family admissible, in which there are four unprovided for.

Foundlings and paupers ineligible.

Children of livery servants, unless free of the city, as well as all deformed, ruptured, and diseased children, to be rejected.

No child to be received, for whom there is any *probable* means of support.

Certificates to the above qualifications to be produced from the minister, churchwardens, and three principal householders of the parish, from which a child may come; with an engagement to discharge the child at the proper age.

The certificates to be strictly examined by committee or court.

Another boy who was admitted just after William Wales' appointment was Arthur William Trollope, aged 7, whose mother had died in 1769 leaving his father Thomas, a merchant of London in poor circumstances with several children to provide for.[52]

Both Lancelot Pepys Stephens and Arthur William Trollope were to play important roles in both the history of the school and the personal life of the Wales family.

Christ's Hospital school had experienced spells of lapses in discipline since its foundation, largely due to the inexperience of its staff. In 1775 the 'Head Master', or Upper Grammar Master was Rev Peter Whalley who had held the post for fifteen years which, according to Blunden, were years of unambition. Whalley edited and wrote various works, but left Christ's Hospital in 1776, and eventually, due to his extravagant wife, he got into difficulties and retired to Flanders. The Under Grammar Master was Rev James Boyer. Edmund Blunden calculated that the buildings had housed an average of 800 boys, each one remaining there for six years.[53]

The boys of Christ's Hospital, whatever their behaviour, were afforded at times certain privileges in London, not least of these was the right to enter the Tower of London free of charge, a privilege which was often enjoyed, for in 1771 there was a charge of six pence for a single person to see the lions. The Tower was a great place for Londoner's to spend their leisure time, and besides the Crown Jewels, the Tower housed

1. Kirkthorpe Church & Graveyard, Yorkshire c1900.

2. Prospectus for Rev John Green's Academy in
Denmark Street, London.

3. Portrait of Rev. John Green.

4. The Tent Observatory.

5. Portrait of Mrs Mary Wales by John Russell RA.

6. Point Venus with Transit of Venus Memorial, Tahiti.

7. Easter Island Statues.

8. Mount Wales, Fjordland, New Zealand.

9. Christ Church,
Newgate Street,
London.

10. William Wales'
Teaching Chair, in the
Museum, Christ's Hospital
School, Horsham.

11. Portrait of
William Arthur
Trollope.

12. Graveslab of John and Mary Wales, Kirkthorpe
Churchyard, Yorkshire.

13. Sundial found at Fort Prince Wales, Hundson's Bay.

14. Memorial Plaque, Clavering Church, Essex

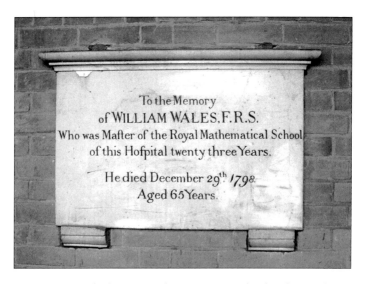

15. Memorial Plaque at Christ's Hospital School, Horsham

an armory museum, the Mint, and the Royal Menagerie, which dated back to the first half of the thirteenth century and the reign of Henry III, when there was a tradition of royalty receiving exotic animals from around the world. Henry had decided that the Tower was the best place to house these wild, and sometimes ferocious beasts, and there the collection stayed for six hundred years. In the 'Age of Enlightenment' people were eager to educate themselves and any exhibit, whether in cage or glass case was to be seen, especially after Cook's voyages.[54]

A recent publication of the School indicates that the late eighteenth and early nineteenth centuries were known as the *Golden Age* in the School's history, academically. While the Royal Mathematical School pupils were under William Wales' eagle eye, those of the Grammar School suffered the raging temper of Rev James Boyer, he was a disciplinarian of the highest order.[55]

The Mathematical School building, abutting the extreme south-western edge of the complex, overlooked the burial ground to the south and an area of ground to the west known as *Grey Friars,* at the very top of the building Wales had an observatory. During his first days he realized that he must first be a strict disciplinarian, in order to enforce restrain on pupils under his charge who were getting out of control, as explained in 1834 by William Trollope:

> ...When Mr William Wales was elected to the mastership, in 1775, he found the school in the most desperate state of anarchy and confusion; the boys were the terror to the whole community; and it required the most determined perseverance of that able mathematician, and strict disciplinarian, to establish his authority over his new pupils. Under his judicious and effective care, however, the school attained to that

high reputation, in which it has since been effectually upheld the vices and immoralities, which had taken deep root in this branch of the establishment were speedily eradicated; the duties of the school were rigidly enforced; and sixteen was the age, beyond which he seldom allowed a boy's continuance in the school.

Mr Wales was, indeed, precisely the man for the station, which he was thus called upon to fill. A practical sailor himself, and the co-navigator of Captain Cook, he knew the requisite qualifications of a seaman; and his whole aim was to fit his boys for the profession in labours he had to battle it hard for the mastery; and severity for a time was the order of the day. He was not long, however, in subjuing the spirit of insubordination; and his whole soul was thenceforward engaged in the improvement of those committed to his charge. Strict and punctual in his discipline, he was frank and open in his temperament; and he was more loved for the goodness of his heart, than feared for the heaviness of his hand. There was a fund of genuine humour about him, and a joyous expression of countenance, which took at once a pleasing provincial dialect, frequently elicited the hearty mirth of his juvenile auditors. Many are the living witnesses to the success of his instructions; while it will be readily acknowledged, that by his energies the Royal Mathematical School of Christ's Hospital was first seen to realize the objects of its foundation, and gave the promise of becoming one of the first naval seminaries in the world.[56]

The forty boys of the Mathematical School foundation were called the *King's Boys*, and wore a badge to distinguish them from the rest of the pupils, which was sewn through ten outer holes onto the left shoulder of their uniform coat. The badges were originally of solid silver, but these were replaced by silver plated badges when, during the latter half of the 18th century, some impoverished boys were found to be selling them.[57] The dye for the RMS badge was kept in the Tower of London for safe-keeping.[58] The badge was kept by the boys when they left the school, and served as a security against them being pressed into the Navy.[59] Also at the school were twelve boys of the *Stone's* foundation,[60] this was a preparatory class from which the King's boys were eventually chosen, and was established from an annual sum given by Governor Sir Henry Stone of Skellingthorpe in Lincolnshire, for the 'better maintenance and education of the children of King Charles's foundation'.

In 1780 John Stock left in his will £3000 to Christ's Hospital the interest and dividends from this to be used for the maintenance of four fatherless boys between the ages of 8 and 10 years old, two of whom would be trained as tradesmen, and eventually put out to apprenticeship at the age of 15, one of these to be put to the Draper's Company. The other two boys would be sons of deceased lieutenants of the Royal Navy, and be educated for the sea service in the Mathematical School. These boys wore a small badge, depicting a figure of Britannia with an anchor.[61]

The task before William Wales, apart from having to discipline the boys, can be gleaned from a revision of Charges and Orders of the Officers published in 1785, when those of the Master of the Mathematical School were strictly laid out, and briefly established. That he should constantly and diligently attend upon the children from 7 o'clock to 11 o'clock in the morning, for the eight months from 1st March, and from 8 o'clock to 11 o'clock in the morning for the remaining four months of the year. In the afternoons, on Tuesday from 1 o'clock until 5 o'clock for the 8 months from 1st March, and from 1 o'clock until 4 o'clock for the remaining 4 months, also on Thursday afternoons throughout the year from 1 o'clock until 3 o'clock.[62] Assuming this to be for six days of the week, this equates to 31 hours a week for the 8 months from 1st March and 23 hours a week for the remaining 4 months.

Under the teaching syllabus of the Sciences of Arithmetic, Navigation, or Mathematics, the Children were to be instructed in:

I. Decimal, sexagesimal, and logarithmetical Arithmetic, the Extraction of Roots, and first Principles of Vulgar Fractions.

II. The usual Methods of finding the Golden Number, Epact, the Moon's Age, the Time of her Southing, and also the Time of High-Water in any Port.

III. The Principles of Geometry in the Construction of such Problems as are useful and necessary in the following Articles.

IV. Plane and spherical Trigonometry in the Resolution of all the various Cases of rectangular and oblique angular Triangles.

V. The Use of the terrestrial Globe in finding the Latitudes and Longitudes of Places, their Angle of Position, and the distance between them. Also the Use of the celestial Globe in finding the Latitudes and Longitudes, right Ascensions, Declinations, Amplitudes, Azimuths, and Altitudes of the Sun, Moon or fixed Stars; together with the Times of their rising, setting, and culminating.

VI. Plane sailing; namely, the working of Traverses, the Resolution of all plane sailing Questions; with their Application to sailing in Currents and turning to windward.

VII. Mercator's and middle Latitude sailings, exemplified in the Resolution of all the usual Questions.

VIII. Projection of the Sphere; and the Application of spherical Trigonometry in the Resolution of such Questions in Astronomy as are necessary in finding the Amplitudes, Azimuths, Altitudes, right Ascensions, Declinations and angular Distances of the Sun, Moon, and fixed Stars.

IX. The Doctrine of Parallaxes; and the Methods of computing their Effects on the Altitudes and angular Distances of celestial Objects.

X. The Use of Instruments proper for observing the Altitudes, Azimuths, and angular Distances of the Sun, Moon, and Stars; such as the Quadrant, and Amplitude, or Azimuth Compass; with the Use of the Observations in finding the Variation of the Compass, the latitude a Ship is in, as well from the meridional Altitudes of the Sun, Moon, and Stars, as by means of two Altitudes of the Sun and the Time which elapses between the Observations; also in finding the Longitude of the Ship by a Time-keeper, and by the observed Distance of the Moon from a Sun or a fixed Star.

XI. The Use of the plane and mercator's Charts.

XII. The Use and Application of the preceding Articles in the actual Working of Day's Works, and correcting the dead reckoning by Observations.[63]

Further stipulations followed regarding the non admittance of any children without an order from the General Court, or the Committee of Almoners. Ten of the King's boys annually must be educated, to such a degree that they were fit for sea service in the opinions of the Master and Wardens of the Trinity House, by whom they were examined, the candidates being first approved for sea service by the age of 16 by the Master of the Mathematical School, who would then present them to a Committee of Almoners, before their Examination at the Trinity House. A boy gaining entry into the Mathematical

School must be competent in English, Writing, and Arithmetic up to the third Rule above. Any ten of the most backward King's Boys, the Master was at liberty to send to the Writing School if he thought them to be backward in this skill. Boys from the Grammar School were taught in Mathematics here each Tuesday afternoon, to enable them to encompass the subject better at University.[64]

The Master must not only keep a Register of names of boys under his care in the morning and afternoon, but also inspect their clothing, general appearance, and cleanliness, reprimanding them or their Nurse for any apparent neglect. It was the Master's duty to correct any boy under his care who did not behave or show good manners. If, during the day, the Master should think it possible that any of his Scholars would be idle, during that evening he must appoint them a task which would employ them to their best advantage, which he would inspect the next morning, as a warning to the other boys not to waste their time. It was the Master's duty to take care of all equipment, books, globes, maps, and mathematical instruments at the School. The school holidays were set as Easter – 11 days including Sundays; Whitsuntide, a week; Bartholomew-tide, 3 weeks; and Christmas 15 days including Sundays; all these as well as Saints' Days and other holidays, as had been the custom of the establishment. The Orders closed with a note that they laid down just some of the principal Duties of the Office, and further recommended that the Master promote the welfare of his pupils by every means in his power.[65]

Wales had inherited a group of boys who were described by contemporary pupils as hardy, brutal, and often wicked, they were athletic, bigger and older than the majority of the other pupils, and of the military class among the boys.[66]

Leigh Hunt described the 'King's Boys' as absolutely reluctant to move when lesser beings got in their way when he wrote:

> ...I remember well my astonishment when I first beheld some of my little comrades overthrown by the progress of one of those very straightforward marine personages, who walked on with as tranquil and unconscious a face as if nothing had happened. It was not a fierce-looking push; there seemed to be no intention in it. The insolence lay in the boy not appearing to know that such inferior creatures existed. It was always thus wherever he came. If aware, the boys got out of his way; if not, down they went, one or more; away the top or the marbles, and on walked the future captain —
>
> In maiden navigation, frank and free.[67]

Each of the King's Boys, who left the Mathematical School and had passed the Trinity House Examination, then received a testimonial of his good conduct, a watch, an outfit of clothes, and books as well as mathematical instruments, a Gunter's scale, a quadrant, and a sea-chest, he also kept his RMS badge.

The reputation of the Mathematical School was evidently known to Captain Cook, and prior to him leaving on the third voyage, in April 1776 he wrote to the Admiralty asking them for authority to apply to the School for one of the Mathematical boys who was ready for naval service. This was agreed, and Matthew Paull was discharged from the school by James Cook and joined the crew of the *Resolution*. In this case it is felt that William Wales had been heavily involved in negotiating the provision of one of his prize pupils for his friend Cook.[68]

Prior to Wales' appointment to the RMS, an average of just one pupil a year was being assigned to HMS vessels, and such was his impact, the year after his appointment in 1776, he was able to discharge a total of seven boys to His Majesty's Naval Service from the Mathematical School, after that the average steadied to about five boys annually to HMS vessels, while others joined East Indiamen.[69]

The School had a long established association with the Honourable East India Company. In 1694 the Christ's Hospital Court Minutes show that the Company would be pleased to accept into their service 10 boys from the Hospital as apprentices, for which the Hospital Governors allowed £4 per head to the Company towards their transportation, this was an annual arrangement. Many Old Blues gained fame and fortune while with the East India Company, and many from the Royal Mathematical School became captains of their ships.[70]

On 24 March, 1776 the scientific world of London learned of the death of John Harrison at Red Lion Square, London. Harrison died on his 83rd birthday, and he was duly buried in the vault on the south side of St John's church, Hampstead, his wife died the following year.[71] The reason that John Harrison was buried at Hampstead is not known.[72]

It is undoubted that Captain Cook's approval of K1, during the second and third voyages, was instrumental in encouraging clockmakers to produce more and cheaper models of the marine chronometer for navigation. Harrison's legacy was to save countless lives, his life's work opened up the world to safer and faster navigation of the world's oceans for exploration, trade, defence, and leisure.[73]

In 1767 George Witchell had become the Headmaster of the Royal Naval Academy at Portsmouth, moving from London where he had been one of the *Nautical Almanac* calculators, and it was to this institution that some of William Wales' pupils went to complete their training as naval officers, this continued Witchell's association with Wales until Witchell's death in 1785, when the headmaster became William Bayly, another of Wales' associates, this time from Cook's second voyage.

The installation back into London Society, by his appointment to the Royal Mathematical School in 1775, was no doubt a relief to William Wales, and the following year in 1776 his acceptance into London's scientific circles was confirmed by his election to the Royal Society. The application described him as:

> *A Gentleman deeply skilled in Astronomy, and other branches of Mathematical learning, and Author of a restitution of the two books of Apollonius Pergeus, concerning determinate sections. Advantageously known to the Society by his observations, made by their order, in the years 1768 and 1769 in Hudsons Bay, on the transit of Venus &c. And since that time, by his Appointment to accompany Captn Cook in his 2nd Voyage round the World.*
>
> *Being desirous to be admitted as fellow of this Society, in whose names are hereunto subscribed, do, from our honest knowledge of him, and our acquaintance with his works, testify, that we believe him deserving of the honour, & that he will become a worthy & useful Member. Balloted & Elected Nov. 7th 1776.*

The signatories were an eminent group of thirteen members of the Royal Society, Beaglehole remarks that it was more usual for three to six only to nominate members[74]:

Charles Morton (1716-99) – physician, librarian, and secretary to the Royal Society

Charles Hutton (1737-1823) – mathematician, teacher

George Witchell (1728-85) – headmaster of Royal Academy, Portsmouth

Mat Duane (1707-85) – lawyer and antiquarian

John Landen (1719-90) – mathematician, land surveyor, and land-agent to Lord Fitzwilliam

John Lloyd (1749-1815) – lawyer

James Cook (1728-79) – explorer, navigator

Samuel Horsley (1733-1806) – prelate, scientist

Matthew Raper (1705-1778) – scientist.

Nevil Maskelyne (1732-1811) – Astronomer Royal

James Stuart (1713-88) – architect and artist

Dan Solander (1733-82) – naturalist (on Captain Cook's first voyage)

William Mountaine (c1700 -1779) – teacher of navigation and Trinity House examiner

William Wales and his wife Mary had another cause to celebrate at this time, their second son Joshua was born, and they named him after Mary's late father. Baby Joshua was duly christened at Christ Church, Newgate Street, London on 5th December, 1776[75] – and joined his siblings Sarah aged 9, William aged 8, and Anne Hagley aged 6, in their house at Christ's Hospital.

Despite celebrations, the family's thoughts would also be turned to Yorkshire and to Warmfield about this time, and the family of William's brother John. Since his wife Mary's death in 1769, John had been left with a family of four to bring up, three girls, and their brother John now aged 10, it was time to think seriously about a career for the young lad. The family was also to mourn the death of William and John's sister Sarah in May 1779, aged 39. Sarah had never married, and no doubt had been a great help to her brother John in helping to raise her nephew and three nieces.

It is perhaps evident from his future career that young John Wales made his way down to London, sometime during the late 1770s, when he would probably have stayed in his Uncle's household, and on assuming responsibility for his education, William Wales would tutor him privately in mathematics, navigation, and particularly surveying. A family grave indicates John went abroad in 1779,[76] he had volunteered in 1783, at the age of 17, to enter the service of the East India Company's navy, the *Bombay Marine,* as a midshipman. The *Marine* not only protected the Company's mercantile vessels, but also surveyed the coasts around Arabia, Persia, and Media.[77] According to John's niece he distinguished himself in the wars of Tippo Saib, so much so that by the age of 19 he was made Captain.[78] John quickly rose through the ranks of the navy, to become the first Marine Surveyor General of India.[79] He was later described "as an officer of rare professional and scientific attainments, who had imbibed" (from his Uncle) "that taste for astronomy which gained him a considerable reputation in India".[80]

John Wales' entry into service with the East India Company would no doubt have been helped by his uncle's links with that Company, via not only his position at Christ's Hospital, but also his association with Nevil Maskelyne, brother-in-law of Robert Clive of India, Clive had died in 1774. John was a contemporary of Lt Archibald Blair, an officer of the Bombay Marine who carried out many surveys for the Company, including the Andaman Islands where *Port Blair* was named after him – some of Blair's surveys were published by the Admiralty.[81] Archibald Blair was eventually to become John Wales' brother-in-law.[82]

Archibald Blair's brother was the astronomer Robert Blair, and as such was probably known to William Wales. Robert was Professor of Astronomy at Edinburgh University, and had written and experimented at length on Hadley's Quadrant which had been added to the Nautical Almanac.[83]

The fact that William Wales tutored Richard Blechynden in maths and astronomy is a significant fact in the story of Wales' nephew John's future in India. Blechynden arrived in India in 1782 at the age of 22, and worked as a surveyor, architect and builder. His diaries chronicle a life in Calcutta in the colonial households, and how they interacted with the Indian population. The diaries reveal that Blechynden was a close friend of not only John Wales, but also other members of the Wales family.[84]

William Wales' reputation as a teacher was undoubted, even before his appointment to Christ's Hospital, his instructions to Samuel Hearne at Hudson's Bay, and the resulting work done by Hearne did not go unnoticed within the Company. In 1778 Wales received a letter from his friend William Redknap, the Secretary of the Hudson's Bay Company, telling him that the Committee were planning to send out persons who were proficient in mathematics and astronomy from their factories, to travel inland as Surveyors, and would attain high rank within the Company according to their performance, he asked William Wales to recommend persons for this service.[85] Wales wrote back proposing Philip Turnor among others.

Turnor was from Laleham in Middlesex and had a farming background, but it is also documented that Philip Turnor was one of the compilers of the Nautical Almanac, a practical astronomer and a mathematician, according to his pupil David Thompson.[86] Turnor had in fact carried out other work for Nevil Maskelyne, and it was just before his death in 1800 that he was employed as a computer of the Nautical Almanac.[87] It is possible therefore that Turnor was known to Wales through his work for Maskelyne, and Wales subsequently received five guineas from the Hudson's Bay Company in gratitude for recommending Turnor to them.[88]

Turnor was posted to York Fort on Hudson's Bay. He tutored Peter Fidler and David Thompson in practical navigation, just as Wales had tutored Samuel Hearne on the same subject. It is this course of events which demonstrates the huge part that William Wales played in the very founding of the nation of Canada, and establishing its place on the world map.

It is a fact that the Masters at Christ's Hospital took on private pupils, and there is a report that Clowdesley Shovell had once been tutored privately here.[89] Writing in 1923 Edmund Blunden was undecided on the authenticity of this legend,[90] but then in 1984 when J. E Morpurgo revised Allan's work, he states that although the Royal Mathematical School was in no way to be blamed for Shovell's 'inglorious end', but he was 'almost certainly a private pupil'.[91]

William Wales now had a static observatory, for years he had been used to observing the heavens from that portable structure, which he had of necessity lugged around the world with him, but now he had one at Christ's Hospital. It was erected at his own expense when he became a master[92] and it must have been something quite special to him. It was from here that he observed the solar eclipse on 24th June, 1778, and he read his report to the Royal Society a couple of weeks later.[93]

In the *Solar Eclipse Observation* report, Wales positions the Royal Mathematical School's latitude at 51° 30' 55" North, and longitude at not quite half a second in time West of the cupola of St Paul's cathedral.[94] This report gives a hint of the spectacular view he must have had from his observatory, to

Wren's masterpiece of St Paul's virtually at the end of the road. Of the equipment he had, he mentions his use of a most excellent watch by Larcum Kendall, and explains that it goes while it is winding up, and counteracts the effects of temperature change, he mentions a Hadley's quadrant made by Ramsden, and a micrometer and telescope both made by Short, with which he used a magnifying power of 75 times for the start and finish of the eclipse. There is also mention of him using the ball at the top of the spire of St Bride's Church in Fleet Street as a landmark during his observations.[95]

When William A Trollope wrote his history of the school in 1835, published some thirty six years after his grandfather William Wales' death, he described the valuable apparatus which once furnished the observatory above the Mathematical School, some of which had been used in the observation of a transit of Venus. There had been a clock of some quality, telescopes, and a transit instrument among others, all helped to instruct the pupils under the care of William Wales, but all had long since gone, including the observatory, so that only sextants, quadrants, and a few uncared for model ships remained for the King's Boys' instruction.[96]

Around mid 1778 the president of the Royal Society, Sir John Pringle, resigned from the office, and in November of that year William Wales wrote to Lord Mulgrave, assuring him that he would not only vote for Mr Banks, but urge all the members he was acquainted with to do the same.[97] Sir Joseph Banks was duly elected president of the Society later in 1778,[98] and this automatically gave him a position on the Board of Longitude.

The Wales family at Christ's Hospital was growing fast, on 6th March, 1778 a third daughter was christened at Christ Church, Newgate Street. Mary Judith Wales was named Mary after her mother.[99]

Mary's brother Joshua Green was in town during 1778, as agent of Charles Brandling of the Middleton coal mine in Yorkshire, Joshua was again representing Brandling at a House of Commons Committee, this time petitioning for Brandling to supply more coals to the neighbourhood of Leeds.[100] Joshua had eight years previously founded the Leeds Pottery with his fellow agent Richard Humble, and other partners.[101]

There is evidence that Wales was not in the best of health around this time, and with his growing family he needed to plan as much as possible for their future. His son William, who had until 1774 probably been tutored by his uncle John Green, was in need of a more formal education, one which would take him on to University. In the Christ's Hospital records dated 19th March 1778 appears:[102]

To the Right Honourable, Right Worshipful, and Worshipful the Governors of Christ's-Hospital, London.

The humble Petition of William Wales in the Parish of Christ Church, London.

Humbly Sheweth that the Petitioner has a Wife and four Children, one of whom a Son named William, of the Age of Eleven years, having made a considerable Progress in Classical Learning, your Petitioner is very desirous of sending to the University, but having been sometime in an ill state of Health, and his Life being therefore the more precarious and his Income not being more than equal to the Exigencies of his Family, he cannot afford the Charge of compleating his Son's Education for the Church, And Therefore he humbly beseeches your Worships, in your usual Pity and Charity to distressed Men, poor Widows, and Fatherless Children, to grant the Admission of his said Child into Christ's-Hospital, named WILLIAM WALES of the Age of Eleven years and eleven months, there to be Educated and brought up among other poor Children.

There is in the above an obstacle, in that William Wales junior was only ten years of age in 1778, not nearly twelve as the document shows, but when one goes onto read the document further it is apparent that William was not admitted into the school until 31st May 1780, when his father had become a Freeman of the City of London, and Company of Stationers, and had thereby satisfied the condition for his son's entry.

Entrance into one of the London guilds, was gained by having served an apprenticeship to one of the Guild members, or by patrimony, i.e. having a father who was a Freeman, or entrance by Redemption, by payment, or by being deemed worthy or distinguished enough to receive an Honorary freeman, entries by this means were comparatively few.[103] William Wales became a Freeman by redemption on 2nd May 1780,[104] and was admitted to the Livery on 6th June 1780. For this he would pay an Annual Quarterage, and the Stationer's Guild records show him paying these up to his death.[105].

Admission by Redemption was not viewed as a quick means of entrance into the guilds, rather it was a way of introducing new skills into the city's economy, and candidates considered to have been vetted by their respective company were then admitted at the discretion of the Court of Aldermen. Having obtained the Court's permission, the entrant was then admitted to one of the city companies, before taking his company freedom ticket to the chamberlain's court at the Guildhall, and only then was he or she admitted to the city freedom.

The Stationers and Newspaper Makers Guild had connections with books and allied trades, printing, publishing, book selling, book binding, paper making, graphic design, communications industries, as well as stationery, packaging, and newspaper making.[106] The scientific world in the eighteenth century was so reliant on the printed word and, those columns, after columns, after columns, of computed figures, calculated by Wales for such a large proportion of his working life meant that this was an appropriate Guild for him to chose to enter – thus William Wales junior was *Clothed*, and officially admitted into the care of Christ's Hospital school, on Thursday 1ˢᵗ June, 1780.

The next day saw the start of a week in which London was gripped by a tumult of violent uproar. Responding to a statute, which had been granted on the relaxation of some of the conditions imposed on Catholics, a meeting of Protestants was called by Lord George Gordon in St George's Fields, and the event sparked an outrage, resulting in thousands of people marching on Westminster. When this did not quell their anger the protesting mob ran amok, and started a week of violence against the houses of Members of Parliament, Lords and Commons, the Court houses, prisons, and other buildings throughout the city, setting them on fire.[107]

By Tuesday the Gordon rioters had reached Newgate prison, where they demanded release of their companions, who had been interred for demolishing the chapel there, but when the Keeper went to seek out the Mayor to get his permission for their release, he returned to find the gaol on fire, and all the prisoners released.[108]

Witnessing the violence in Newgate Street that night was William Wales. At the entrance to Christ's Hospital some of the freed prisoners from Newgate gaol had stopped to knock off their fetters, and then had proceeded to demand entrance into the Hospital complex. Wales intervened, fearing for the life of the pupils, staff and their families, he managed to reason with the prisoners, firmly assuring that they had little to gain by destroying the security of defenceless children. Such was his power as a disciplinarian, he averted what could have been the total destruction of Christ's Hospital, and no further threat was offered by the riotous mobs throughout the rest of the disturbances.[109]

Mary Wales' nephew William Taylor[110] had also witnessed the riots in London, aged about twelve he was on his way to Leeds, where he was to work at his Uncle Joshua's pottery, and had seen the mob set fire to many houses before he left in a stage wagon. The journey to Leeds took 8 days.[111]

Two months later at the beginning of August another baby joined the Wales household at Christ's Hospital – John Wales, son of William and Mary, was baptized at the Christ Church, Newgate Street on 4th August, 1780.[112]

Endnotes

1   John Milton (1608-1674). *Paradise Regained*.

2   Kaye, Margaret, 2003. *The Greenwich Effect*. Moray, Librario.

3   Muir, J R, 1939. *The Life and Achievements of Captain James Cook*. London, Blackie & Son.

4   Gurney, A, 1998. *Below the Convergence*. London, Pimlico. p.144

5   Smith, Edward, 1911. *The Life of Sir Joseph Banks*. London, Bodley Head. p.167.

6   Beaglehole, J C, 1974. *The Life of Captain James Cook*. London, A & C Black. p.450.

7   Website: http://booty.org.uk/booty.weather/climate/1750_1799.htm.

8   Wilson, Walter, 1808. *The History and Antiquities of Dissenting Churches and Meeting Houses in London, Westminster and Southwark including the Lives of their Ministers.* London, W. Button.

A fuller account of the last days of John Green can be found in *The Monthly Repository of Theology and General Literature.* Published in 1810 by Sherwood, Gilbert and Piper, on p 10 is 'Mr Marsom's Account of the Rev Mr. Green'.

9   Will of John Green, PRO Probate Records. Ref. PROB 11/999.

10 Will of Sarah Green, PRO Probate Records. Ref. PROB 11.1220.

11 Website: British History Online: www.british-history.ac.uk

12 Matthew, H C G & Harrison, B (Eds), 2004. *Oxford Dictionary of National Biography.* Oxford, Oxford University Press.

13 Danson, Edwin, 2006. *Weighing the World.* Oxford University Press.

14 de Morgan, Augustus, 1864. *Notes and Queries,* 3rd series, 5, p.361.

15 Kimber, Isaac & Edward. The London Magazine, Vol 44, p.603.

16 Allan, G A T, 1984 Revision by J E Morpurgo. *Christ's Hospital.* London, Town & Country.

17 Johnson, R Brimley, 1896. *Christ's Hospital Recollections of Lamb, Coleridge, and Leigh Hunt.* London, George Allen.

18 Blunden, Edmund, 1923. *Christ's Hospital, a retrospective.* London, Christophers.

19 ibid.

20 Old Blues Committee, 1953. *The Christ's Hospital Book.* London, Hamish Hamilton Ltd.

21 Allan, G A T, 1984 Revision by J E Morpurgo. *Christ's Hospital.* London, Town & Country.

22   Blunden, Edmund, 1923. *Christ's Hospital, a retrospective.* London, Christophers

23   Trollope, W A, 1834. *A History of the Royal Foundation of Christ's Hospital.* London, William Pickering.

24   *Christ's Hospital, a Short History.* Published Christ's Hospital School, Horsham, W Sussex.

25   Ollard, Richard, 1974. *Pepys, a Biography.* London, Hodder & Stoughton.

26   Guildhall Library, London. Christ's Hospital Manuscript. Court Minute Books. 12806/12 p.202. Minute dated 1775.

27   Danson, Edwin, 2006. *Weighing the World.* Oxford University Press.

28   Elliot, J & Pickersgill, R, 1984. *Captain Cook's Second Voyage.* London, Caliban.

29   *Leeds Intelligencer.* Tuesday, October 15, 1782.

30   Griffin, John D, 2005. *The Leeds Pottery 1770-1881,* The Leeds Art Collection Fund.

31   Hall, Marie Boas, 1992. *The Library and Archives of the Royal Society 1660-1990.* London, The Royal Society.

32   *Miscellany.* Thorsby Society Publications, 1935, v 33, p.216.

33   Howse, D, 1989. *Nevil Maskelyne, the Seaman's Astronomer.* Cambridge, Cambridge University Press.

34   Baker, T M M, 2000. *London Rebuilding after the Great Fire.* Chichester, Phillimore & Co. Ltd.

35   Johnson, R Brimley, 1896. *Christ's Hospital: Recollections of Lamb, Coleridge and Leigh Hunt.* London, George Allen.

36   Von Uffenbach, Zacharias Conrad, Translated and edited by W.H. Quarrell and Margaret Mare, 1934. *London in 1710.* London, Faber & Faber.

37   LaTouche, W M D, 1928. *Christ's Hospital, from a Boy's Point of View.* Cambridge, W Heffer & Sons Ltd.

38   ibid.

39   Betjeman, John, 1974. *The City of London Churches.* Andover, Pitkin Pictorials Ltd.

40 Trollope, W A, 1834. *A History of the Royal Foundation of Christ's Hospital*. London, William Pickering.

41 ibid.

42 ibid.

43 Johnson, R Brimley, 1896. *Christ's Hospital: Recollections of Lamb, Coleridge and Leigh Hunt*. London, George Allen.

44 Thornbury, Walter, 1878. *Old and New London*. London, Cassell, Petter & Galpin & Co.

45 Blunden, Edmund, 1923. *Christ's Hospital, a retrospective*. London, Christophers.

46 Trollope, W A, 1834. *A History of the Royal Foundation of Christ's Hospital*. London, William Pickering.

47 ibid.

48 Trollope, W A, 1834. *A History of the Royal Foundation of Christ's Hospital*. London, William Pickering. p.121

49 Guildhall Library, London. Christ's Hospital Manuscript No.12818. Children's Registers Vol II. 1774. p.119.

50 London Metropolitan Archives, Freedom of he City Admission Papers.

51 Trollope, W A, 1834. *A History of the Royal Foundation of Christ's Hospital*. London, William Pickering. p.121.

52 Guildhall Library, London. Christ's Hospital Manuscript 12818. Children's Registers Vol II. 1775. p.81.

53 Blunden, Edmund, 1923. *Christ's Hospital*. London, Christophers.

54 Hahn, Daniel, 2003. *The Tower Menagerie*. London, Simon & Schuster UK Ltd.

55 *Christ's Hospital, a Short History*. 2004. Published Christ's Hospital School, Horsham, W Sussex.

56 Trollope, W A, 1834. *A History of the Royal Foundation of Christ's Hospital*. London, William Pickering.

57 The badge depicted three figures representing Arithmetic holding a tablet of figures, Geometry with a triangle and compasses and Astronomy, wearing the hat of Mercury and

with a quadrant and sphere. A pupil stands in front of them as a ship sails by and angels hover above in a bright cloud. The motto around the edge is *Auspicio Caroli Secondi Regis, 1673.*

The dye used for the badges was kept in the Tower of London, such was it valued.

58 Thornbury, Walter, 1878. *Old and New London.* London, Cassell, Petter & Galpin & Co.

59 Johnson, R Brimley, 1896. *Christ's Hospital: Recollections of Lamb, Coleridge and Leigh Hunt.* London, George Allen.

60 The badge of the *Twelves,* as the Stones boys were known, was worn on the right shoulder.

61 Trollope, W A, 1834. *A History of the Royal Foundation of Christ's Hospital.* London, William Pickering.

62 Charges and Orders for the Several Officers of Christ's Hospital: Revised by the Committee of Almoners. Published 1785. London.

63 ibid.

64 ibid.

65 ibid.

66 Johnson, R Brimley, 1896. *Christ's Hospital: Recollections of Lamb, Coleridge and Leigh Hunt.* London, George Allen.

67 Leigh Hunt, 1906. *Essays and Sketches.* London, Oxford University Press. The World's Classics edition.

68 Thornton, Cliff, *The Boy from Christ's Hospital School.* Cook's Log, the Journal of the Captain Cook Society, 2008. vol 31, No 1, p.41.

69 Personal communication, Cliff Thornton, President of the Captain Cook Society.

70 Allen,G A T, 1984. *Christ's Hospital.* London, Town & County. (Revised edition by J E Morpurgo)

71 Sobel, Dava, 1996. *Longitude.* London, Fourth Estate Ltd.

72 According to Col H Quill's book *John Harrison* published by the Antiquarian Horological Society in 1976, the entry in the Burial Register is recorded as "Thomas Harrison".

73   Whittle, Eric S, 1984. *The Inventor of the Marine Chronometer: John Harrison of Foulby.* Wakefield, Wakefield Historical Society.

74   Beaglehole, J., 1974. *The Life of Captain James Cook.* London, A & C Black. p.450.

75   Parish Registers of Christ Church, Newgate Street, London. The page from the actual Registers shows the scars of an incendiary bomb which hit the Church during the Second World War.

76   See Chapter 17.

77   Keble Chatterton, E, 1971. *The Old East Indiamen.* London, Conway Maritime Press.

78   Mrs Mary Wales Fenton. *Memoir of Mrs Abigail Manners.* (by her daughter). Methodist New Connexion Magazine, October 1848. p.438.

79   Phillimore, R H, 1945-58. *Historical Records of the Survey of India.* Dehra Dun.

80   Lowe, Charles Rathbone, 1877. *History of the Indian Navy (1613-1863).* London, Richard Bentley.

81   Dawson, Commander L.R., (Compiler), 1830. *Memoirs of Hydrography.* Eastbourne, Henry W Keay.

82   Archibald Blair married Elizabeth Morris Dixon in September, 1799.

83   Taylor, E G R, 1966. *The Mathematical Practitioners of Hanoverian England 1714-1840.* Cambridge, Cambridge University Press. p.305.

84   Peter Robb, 2011. *Sex and Sensibility* Oxford University Press, India.

85   Hearne, Samuel & Tyrell, Joseph Burr, 1934. *Journals of Samuel Hearne and Philip Turnor.* Toronto, Champlain Society.

86   Moreau, William E (Ed), 2009. *The Writings of David Thompson,* Volume I. Montreal & Kingston McGill-Queen's University Press.

87   Croarken, Dr M *Providing Longitude for all: the eighteenth century computers of the Nautical Almanac.* Journal of Maritime Research, September 2002.

88   Hearne, Samuel & Tyrell, Joseph Burr, 1934. *Journals of Samuel Hearne and Philip Turnor.* Toronto, Champlain Society.

89   Allan, G A T, 1949. *Christ's Hospital.* London, Ian Allan Ltd.

90   Blunden, Edmund, 1923. *Christ's Hospital.* London, Christophers.

91   Morpurgo, J E, 1984. Revised Edition of G.A.T. Allan's *Christ's Hospital.* Shepperton, Ian Allan Ltd.

92   Hutton, Charles, 1815. *A Philosophical and Mathematical Dictionary.* Vol II, p.l129

93   Wales, W, 1778. *Observations on the Solar Eclipse which happened June 24, 1778.* Phil.Trans.R.Soc., Vol LXVIII., pp1013-1018.

94   On the 1777 one inch map of Surrey by Andrews and Dury, they used the meridian through St Paul's Cathedral, London. Also General Roy used St. Paul's to define the meridian in 1790, just prior to the Ordnance Survey being founded a year later. This also was the one used by Wales in this instance, although the one at Greenwich, established by James Bradley, was used for the Nautical Almanac Calculations from1767.

95   Wales, W, 1778. *Observations on the Solar Eclipse which happened June 24, 1778.* Phil.Trans.R.Soc., Vol LXVIII., pp1013-1018.

96   Trollope, W A, 1834. *A History of the Royal Foundation of Christ's Hospital.* London, William Pickering.

97   Letter from William Wales to Lord Mulgrave, Sir Edward Sabine Collection No 14., University of Cambridge

98   Smith, E, 1911. *The Life of Sir Joseph Banks.* London, Bodley Head.

99   Parish Registers of Christ Church, Newgate Street, London.

100   Journals of the House of Commons (1803 reprint). Ed. Brotherton Library, University of Leeds. Vol. 37, pp.14,15.

101 Griffin, John D, 2005. *The Leeds Pottery 1770-1881*. Leeds, The Leeds Art Collections Fund.

102 Guildhall Library, London. Christ's Hospital Manuscripts, Children's Registers, 12818A/50. p.129

103 Aldus, Vivienne E, 1999. *My Ancestors were Freemen of the City of London*. London, Society of Genealogists..

104 McKenzie, D F, 1978. *Stationers' Company apprentices, 1701-1800*. Oxford, Oxford Bibliographical Society.

105 Personal communication, The Worshipful Company of Stationers and Newspaper Makers, London.

106 Public Relations Office,1997. *The Livery Companies of the City of London*. London, Corporation of London.

107 Boswell, James, 1930. *Life of Samuel Johnson*. London, G Bell & Sons Ltd.

108 ibid.

109 Trollope, W A, 1834. *A History of the Royal Foundation of Christ's Hospital*. London, William Pickering.

110 William Taylor was the son of Elizabeth Taylor (nee Green), sister of Mary Wales.

111 Obituary of William Taylor in *Annual Monitor* for 1854, New Series, or *Obituary of the Members of the Society of Friends in Great Britain and Ireland for the year 1853*, pp.138-149.

112 Parish Registers of Christ Church, Newgate Street, London.

13

THE FORSTER AFFAIR

"To clear this Doubt, to know the World by Sight,
To find if Books, or Swains, report it right;..."[1]

With the recent voyage behind them, it was time for William Wales and William Bayly to prepare their *Astronomical Observations* for publication. Since returning to London, Bayly had been employed computing Nautical Tables for Nevil Maskelyne,[2] but then he was chosen to go as astronomer on the third voyage, and so it was left to William Wales to complete the editing of the work.[3]

The *Observations* volume was published in 1777 at the expense of the Board of Longitude, it included charts and plates, and sold for one guinea a copy. The work included an *Introduction* written by William Wales, in which he wrote a history of astronomy up to it's publication, and explained how 'proper' persons had been employed to carry out the calculations for the first *Nautical Almanac*. In his biography of Cook, Andrew Kippis described this work as 'displaying in the strongest light, the scientific use and value of Captain Cook's voyage'.[4]

Now settled into his new position at Christ's Hospital's Royal Mathematical School, Wales was to prove a useful 'editor' to the relevant authorities.

Following Cook's first voyage in 1771, it was imperative that an official account of that circumnavigation be published without delay, before the market became flooded with unofficial accounts. Dr John Hawkesworth, recommended by Charles Burney, was chosen by the First Lord, Sandwich, to edit the accounts of the voyage for publication. It was further decided that the Journals of Cook and Banks should be published together with the accounts of Byron, Wallis, and Carteret, the three circumnavigators who had preceded Cook.[5] The work was eventually published in June 1773.[6]

The Journal Accounts were published in three volumes, the second two of which covered the *Endeavour* voyage. When Cook read a copy, which had been sent to Cape Town for him to read before he returned from the second voyage, he was upset, especially by Hawkesworth's apparent unfounded claims that Cook had been aware of the manuscript before publication, and also Hawkesworth's obsession of acknowledging the account of Joseph Banks more than his own, in fact the engravings had also been credited to Banks, rather than the official artists Parkinson and Buchan, who never even received mention.[7]

Cook returned to London, to learn that John Hawkesworth was dead. Hawkesworth had been upset by the critical reviews that his work on the various Journals had received, and this had probably contributed to his ill health and eventual death, which occurred in November 1773, just five months after the Account of the Voyages had been published.[8]

By the time Johann Reinhold Forster, and his son Georg had returned to London from the second voyage, news of the elder's reputation on board had already reached the capital, and although Forster senior must have had knowledge of this, he no doubt still expected to receive the acclaim and rewards which Joseph Banks had experienced after the first voyage. To his chagrin, his return to London was met with silence from the press, and although he was not so worried by this lack of celebrity status, he was concerned of a lack of scientific recognition, and financial reward. He had a large family to support, and while he was confident that he would be allowed to write up the official account of the *Endeavour Journals,* and receive £6000 for this work, he also remained confident that his communications with Daines Barrington, Sandwich's agent, had secured for him the post of editor of the *Resolution* Journals, although this was only a verbal agreement.[9]

The elder Forster decided on keeping a low profile for a while, he was evidently being ignored, and so turned his attention to the livestock he had brought back from South Africa for Queen Charlotte. Intending to impress the King and Queen with these exotic animals and birds, they somehow came to the attention of Sandwich's mistress Miss Martha Ray, who would have liked some for herself, but Forster refused her request, guarding them for the Queen to whom he presented them at a levée held at Kew in August.[10]

Eventually Lord Sandwich cautiously agreed that Forster should submit some of his account of time spent at Dusky Bay in New Zealand for consideration, and if approved, he could be given the job of writing up the official account of the voyage, and receive a fifty-fifty share of the profits with Captain Cook. At this turn of events J R Forster set to work immediately, preparing the account in English, French, and German, confident that expensive plates, which had been paid for by the Admiralty, would be included in his work. There was no stopping his enthusiasm, and he related his position as official author of the second voyage account to scientists far and wide, they crowded to his home to witness the work, and the collections he had brought back from his travels. He also had his portrait painted.[11]

By October 1775, Sandwich was aware that Forster was dealing with what he described as certain inaccuracies, and vulgar expressions in Cook's journals, these were totally alien to Sandwich who had come across no such entries. Furthermore, undercover forces from the world of literature, were intent on persuading Sandwich to call a halt to Forster's commission, and this culminated in Sandwich ordering Forster to cease the Work, and not to expect the Admiralty to give him the engraved plates which they had kept for the eventual publication of the Work.[12]

The person eventually chosen by Lord Sandwich to edit Cook's second voyage account[13] was a Scottish clergyman, Dr John Douglas, a canon of Windsor, who had moved to London and as well as being a clergyman, was an inveterate writer of political pamphlets. Wales' work was subsequently included in a third edition of this work which appeared in 1784, when a chapter of his account on the location of *Cape Circumcision* was included, this work was also published in pamphlet form in 1784.[14] A French translation of this pamphlet appeared in 1788. Forster, apparently undeterred by Sandwich's decision however continued his work on Cook's second voyage, confident that his friends would back him in its eventual publication. In January 1776 Forster called on Daines Barrington, still indicating to him that he expected to receive those engravings.

The whole affair came to a head in April 1776, when both Forster and Cook were called to the Admiralty, and in the presence of the Earl Sandwich, the First Lord, and Philip Stephens, the Secretary to the Admiralty, signed an agreement. This detailed that Cook's Journal, as edited by Dr Douglas, would contain the nautical and ethnographical observations of the voyage, and Forster's work on his own Journal, would only describe his own work in the fields of natural history, ethnography, and his own philosophical remarks – it was further agreed that the Admiralty would have sole right to decide on how the costly plates were published, and in which volumes.[15]

On examining the first pages of Forster's work, Sandwich was not impressed, and insisted that Forster had broken their agreement by not sticking to his own narrative. After attempting many negotiations, all of which ended in stalemate, Forster ultimately was left to write his piece independent of the Admiralty, and in his own way. This would eventually be published under the authorship of his son Georg,[16] in March 1777.[17]

The engraved plates were a concern to the elder Forster at this time, to make his work a success he really needed them to be included, and after Cook left on the third voyage, Forster approached Cook's agents in the hope of securing them, but without success. Six weeks after Georg Forster's account appeared Cook's was published, and within it were the coveted engravings. J R Forster's work[18] was published the year after. These publications proved a luxury which Forster could not afford, and many volumes remained unsold, throwing him deep into debt.[19]

Georg Forster's *Voyage* was eagerly scrutinized by William Wales, almost as soon as it was published. Wales was greatly upset by Forster's writings,[20] who had for example virtually blamed Wales and Cook for the malfunction of Arnold's timepiece while on board, and Wales was anxious to reply to this criticism, and other slurs which were apparent in the work.[21]

On 24th June, 1777 Wales put pen to paper and wrote to Georg Forster, this the first correspondence between the two which was to culminate in two works published the following year, laying out the Wales' Remarks and Georg Forster's Reply as under:

Remarks on Mr Forster's Account of Captain Cook's Last Voyage Round the World, in the Years 1772, 1773, 1774, and 1775. by William Wales, F.R.S. Published in London, and printed for J Nourse, opposite Catherine-Street, Strand. 1778.

Reply to Mr Wales's Remarks by Georg Forster, F.R.S. Published in Londonand printed for B White, Fleet Street; J Robson, Bond-street; and P Elmsley, in the Strand. 1778.

In the former work, Wales opens by explaining his reasons for publishing these Remarks:

...There are few situations wherein a peaceable man finds himself less at ease than when involved in a dispute; and nothing less than personal provocations could have induced me to take up my pen on this occasion. Mistakes in philosophy might, for me, have remained long uncontradicted; and I am not certain that even nautical and geographical ones, which, in my opinion, are of infinitely more consequence than the former, would have drawn me into a dispute, at least with Dr. Forster and his son. I have been farther stimulated by the ill-natured remarks, which have been frequently made in consequence of these misrepresentations, both in writing and conversation, on the conduct of those who were concerned in the voyage; which, as they are founded on misrepresentations, are the more provoking to persons who find themselves injured by them. It is true, I am, perhaps, as little concerned in them as any person who was on board; but many others, whom I have every reason to love and esteem, are particularly

315

pointed at; and, what is more, are not now present to defend themselves; on which account, I esteem it more my duty to take up.[22]

On the title page of his publication Wales repeats lines which Forster saw fit to print on his title page on the Account of the Voyage, quoted from *César de Missy*, "*La Vérité, le Suisse, et le Roi*," and translated into English as under:

The truth cannot in silence be dismissed;
And however it be halted along the way,
This will be seen as an outrage one day,
Whose fatal fruit was shame at least.[23]

When Wales' work was reviewed, the writer suggested that:

...frontispieces could not be trusted, as was evident from the book now 'in front of us', which Mr Wales had included not only in judgement against Mr Forster, but also as a truly fitting introduction to his own work.[24]

Wales then continues to debate whether the Account of the Voyage in question should be attributed to Georg, or to his father, and quickly comes to the conclusion that although Georg's name is on the title page, and at the end of the preface, his father being referred to in the second or third person, the content is in the father's language and sentiments, and written with such arrogance, self-consequence, and asperity as to leave him in no doubt that it is Johann's work.[25]

A further preamble follows in which Wales explains that it is his intention, by publishing his *Remarks*, to defend the character of himself and his friends, by merely recording the arguments and matters as facts, and that any passionate and hasty reflections of his emotions must be suppressed. He then goes on to try and work out why Dr Forster should falsify facts to such extent, when writing of events during the voyage, suggesting that he may have been provoked into doing so by some of the ship's company – or maybe he was dismayed when the attention he had obviously expected to be commensurate to that afforded to Joseph Banks on the first voyage, did not materialize. The Doctor had certainly been most dissatisfied with his accommodation when first inspecting his quarters at Plymouth, and he had not been afforded the attention from the Ship's Company that he had expected his position would command, which had aroused him into venting his anger in a most ungenteel manner, so that he continually grumbled about his lot, and a week never passed without him being in dispute with one person or another, this soon alienated him from the other 120 persons on board.[26]

Wales begins his criticism of Dr Forster's *Account* by examining the *Preface* of the work, which he describes as "a master-piece of misrepresentation, and chicanery". He notes that Georg Forster refers to the agreement drawn up between Cook and his father and signed by the Earl of Sandwich, in which it was specified which of the elements of the Voyage Account would be covered by each of them working independently, and that the plates contained therein would be a joint gift to them by the Board of Admiralty. Despite this the Forster's had pleaded ignorance of the content of that agreement by going ahead with the publication, and would not adhere to the terms of the agreement, blindly going on to publish, despite the disapproval of the Earl of Sandwich.[27]

Georg Forster continues in his *Preface* to offer facts, which Wales can only describe as intended to prejudice the reader against Captain Cook. The first of these was that whenever *Resolution* was anchored, Cook was employed in victualling and refitting the ship, with no time to attend to anything else, unlike the Forster's who had more importantly surveyed the land for manifold objects which would be of use to science, and were described without the intrusion of nautical digressions, which would no doubt be the content of Cook's writings. A further remark by Forster, which Wales assures was included to defame Cook, was that the Captain's account of many observations of consequence would be no doubt suppressed, if Cook supposed the content to be obnoxious to certain authorities, whereas Forster's account had no need of such censorship.[28]

Wales' picks out further items from the *Preface*, which in his opinion were included merely for ungenerous and unjust reasons, and were very little to do with the account of the second voyage. He then proceeds to criticize some eighty six points from the main body of the *Voyage Account,* which he describes as 'Forster's revenge', in each case commenting on them, sometimes at length. (see Appendix VII). The reader is referred to a recent edition of the *Remarks* which includes Georg Forster's *Voyage* and *Reply* to Wales by Georg Forster, published in the year 2000.[29]

William Wales finishes his *Remarks* by concluding that although he had laboured through a long, tedious, and incorrect work, he had nonetheless found it entertaining in places, and had ultimately achieved the truth. He had at all times given the facts, which had been witnessed by himself and others, whom he had been at pains to contact in order to corroborated the facts. The task had been laboured, as few of these people remained near London, and even in England, but were now scattered abroad, and the task of contacting these witnesses had delayed the publication of his work, but he was now confident that his *Remarks* were supported by the most respectable authority, and that he had achieved justice for himself and fellow ship-mates.[30]

Wales' *Remarks* were published in pamphlet form in December 1777, in April 1778 he paid his printer £13.15s.8d for 500 copies.[31]

Georg Forster's *Reply* was published the same year as Wales' *Remarks*, in this work Georg Forster retaliates by throwing personal insult at Wales, not only commenting sarcastically on his Yorkshire accent, but by criticizing his social position, and class, even his lack of formal education in Latin and the classics. This childish taunting continues when Forster suggests that Mr Wales' work could overshadow that of Newton and Halley.[32]

In his resulting *Remarks* the younger Forster includes in his 'Advertisement' of the work, what can only be described as a sentiment which conveys that to have to reply to Wales is a bother:

> ...The paths of controversy lead through a desart: they are dry, uninteresting and uninstructive. I shall therefore try to be as brief as the subject will permit, and as dispassionate as my opponent is enraged.[33]

In this era of transition in philosophy and science, the discipline of Wales' was exact and reliant on accurate conclusions, which were justified by reason. These skills had been honed in his contributions to the *Ladies' Diary,* and in his calculations for *Nautical Almanac* which had been scrutinized by comparers, his involvement with the Transit of Venus calculations had also demanded accurate skills, such was the importance of their results – whereas the natural history of the Forster's, was based more on the quality of description. This difference of discipline did nothing to relieve the tension between them during the voyage. Forster in fact suggests that where his involvement in the voyage had been a waste of time, and a nuisance, Wales' voyage had been the absolute making of his career. Such was the difference between their roles, nevertheless it is a fact that to have been without natural historians on the voyage, would have not been a great tragedy, whereas to have been without astronomers and navigators, could well have ended in disaster.[34]

The Forster's seem to have been given carte blanche to carry out their observations, whereas in contrast, the detailed instructions given to Wales before the voyage, further indicated the scientific importance of his role.[35]

Georg Forster reminds Wales that it was parliament who had appointed he and his father to go on the voyage, and despite being German, they had proved their ability, by understanding languages of the South Sea natives and by their command of the English language in which they had such ability in both the spoken and written word. But Wales had no particular professional interest in interaction with the natives, he merely observed and recorded, and proves to be an articulate reporter, he was a natural inquisitor of broad interest, and unlike Forster relied on first-hand accounts of events, when he failed to witness them himself.[36]

The *Monthly Review* of the time explains in a nutshell:

> ....The Reader is not to suppose that Mr Wales's Remarks are solely confined to matters of a personal nature, or to the defence of himself and shipmates. His performance may be considered as an useful, and, indeed, necessary companion and corrective to Dr. Forster's work. At the same time it contains several pertinent observations relating to subjects of more general importance.

Richard Wells in his scholarly dissertation on the Forster affair, as well as analyzing Wales' *Remarks* and Forster's

Reply, quite rightly states that the dispute offered a great opportunity for Wales to get some of his own observations on the culture of the people of the South Seas published, and it is thanks to the publication of his *Remarks* that we learn so much more of his vast knowledge on a variety of subjects. On Forster's hinting that Wales was perhaps an atheist due to his rational views, Wells indicates that this was a prime example that science was evolving into industrial advancement, which was to became apparent in the following century. In both scientific advancement, and the history of voyages of discovery, Wales was to leave a lasting impression.[37]

The wrangle between Forster and Wales took place during the time of Cook's Third Voyage around the world. After spending time in New Zealand and the islands around Tahiti in the South Pacific, Cook had sailed into the North Pacific, and to Nootka on what is now Vancouver Island. From Nootka he had sailed up the coast to Alaska in a bid to find an entrance into a North-West Passage, but when the weather and the seasons caught up with him he headed south to Hawaii and warmer climes. It was in Hawaii at Kealakekua Bay, to the horror of his crew, that he was killed during a skirmish by natives on 14th February, 1779.[38]

Captain Charles Clerke switched from commanding the vessel *Discovery,* for *Resolution,* with 1st Lieutenant John Gore commanding the former. A month after Cook's death the two ships, with crews deep in shock, had sailed to Kamchatka from Hawaii, where Clerke had entrusted the Governor Major Behm, who was about to relinquish his governorship and return to London, with the return of Cook's Journal, some charts, and other journals, together with a long letter to the Admiralty. The ships had then resumed searching for an entrance into a North-West Passage, in line with what they believed had been Cook's intentions, but having sailed north from Kamchatka they again were faced with bad weather, and the way choked with ice, and to add to their troubles Clerke became very ill, and so they headed back to Kamchatka. It was just before reaching Petropavlosk on the Kamchatka Peninsula, that Captain Charles Clerke died, at the age of 38, and there he was buried. When the two ships left for home Lt Gore then took overall command of the ships.[39]

The whole of the Forster affair, however important it seemed to William Wales at the time to put the record straight, must have seemed pretty trivial to him when, on 10th January, 1780, the Admiralty broke the news from Clerke's letter that Captain James Cook was dead. The news appeared in the *London Gazette* the next day, and grief swept the country – even the King had been reduced to tears.[40]

Endnotes

1   Rev Thomas Parnell, (1689-1718). *The Hermit.*

2   Croarken, Dr M *Providing Longitude for all: the eighteenth century computers of the Nautical Almanac.* Journal of Maritime Research, September 2002.

3   Wales, W and Bayly, W. 1777. *The Original Astronomical Observations Made in the Course of a Voyage Towards the South Pole, and round the World in His Majesty's Ships the Resolution and Adventure, in the years MDCCLXXII, MDCCLXXIII, MDCCLXIV, and MDCCLXXV,*London. Ed. W. Wales. J. Nourse, J Mount & T Page: W & A Strahan.

4   Kippis, A, 1878. *Narrative of the Voyages Round the World, performed by Captain James Cook.* London, Bickers & Son. p.232.

5   Beaglehole, J C,1974. *The Life of Captain James Cook.* London, A. & C. Black.

6   Hawkesworth, Dr John, 1773. *An Account of the Voyages undertaken by the order of His Present Majesty for making discoveries in the southern hemisphere, and successively performed by Commodore Byron, Captain Wallis, Captain*

Carteret, and Captain Cook in the Dolphin, the Swallow, and the Endeavour. Drawn up from the journals which were kept by the several Commanders, and from the papers of J Banks. London, W Strahan & T Cadell.

7   Hough, R, 1994. *Captain James Cook, a Biography.* London. Hodder & Stoughton.

8   Robson, John, 2000. *Captain Cook's World.* Rochester, Chatham Publishing.

9   Hoare, Michael E, 1976. *The Tactless Philosopher.* Melbourne, Hawthorne Press.

10 ibid.

11 ibid.

12 ibid.

13 Cook, James, 1777. *A Voyage towards the South pole and Round the World, in His Majesty's Ships, the Resolution and Adventure*, 2 volumes, London. Edited by J Douglas.

14 Wales, W., 1784. *A Defence (against P.C. Le Monnier) of the Arguments advanced in the Introduction to Captain Cook's Last Voyage against the existence of Cape Circumcision.* A pamphlet.

15 Hoare, Michael E, 1976. *The Tactless Philosopher.* Melbourne, Hawthorne Press.

16 Forster, J George A 1777. *Voyage round the World, in His Britannic Majesty's Sloop, Resolution, Commanded by Capt James Cook, during the Years 1772,3,4 and 5, 2 vols,* London: B. White, J. Robson, P. Elmsly and G. Robinson.

17 Hoare, Michael E, 1976. *The Tactless Philosopher.* Melbourne, Hawthorne Press

18 Forster, J R, 1778. *Observations made during a voyage Round the World (with Captain Cook) on physical geography, natural history, and ethic philosophy.* G. Robinson.

19 Hoare, Michael E, 1976. *The Tactless Philosopher.* Melbourne, Hawthorne Press.

20 See *Appendix VII* for a list of points raised by Wales with George Forster.

21 Hoare, Michael E, 1976. *The Tactless Philosopher.* Melbourne, Hawthorne Press. p.173.

22 Wales, W 1778. *Remarks on Mr Forster's Account of Captain Cook's Last Voyage Round the World, in the Years 1772, 1773, 1774, and 1775.* London, Printed for J Nourse.

23 ibid.

24 Griffiths, R & G E, *The Monthly Review or Literary Journal.* Vol 58, Jan-June 1778. p.127.

25 Wales, W 1778. *Remarks on Mr Forster's Account of Captain Cook's Last Voyage Round the World, in the Years 1772, 1773, 1774, and 1775.* London, Printed for J Nourse.

26 Wales, W, 1778. *Remarks on Mr Forster's Account of Captain Cook's Last Voyage Round the World, in the Years 1772, 1773, 1774, and 1775.* London, Printed for J Nourse.

27 ibid.

28 ibid.

29 Thomas, N, & Berghof, O (Ed)., 2000. A Voyage Round the World. by George Forster. Honolulu. University of Hawaii Press.

30 Wales, W, 1778. *Remarks on Mr Forster's Account of Captain Cook's Last Voyage Round the World, in the Years 1772, 1773, 1774, and 1775.* London, Printed for J Nourse.

31 Ledgers of Wm Strahan, British Library.

32 Wells, Richard H, 2008. *William Wales and the Conflict of Sciences during Cook's Second Voyage.* Unpublished Dissertation, Centre for Eighteenth Century Studies, University of York

33 Thomas, N, & Berghof, O (Ed)., 2000. A Voyage Round the World. by Georg Forster. Honolulu. University of Hawaii Press.

34 Wells, Richard H, 2008. *William Wales and the Conflict of Sciences during Cook's Second Voyage.* Unpublished Dissertation, Centre for Eighteenth Century Studies, University of York.

35 ibid.

36 Wells, Richard H, 2008. *William Wales and the Conflict of Sciences during Cook's Second Voyage.* Unpublished Dissertation, Centre for Eighteenth Century Studies, University of York.

37 ibid.

38 Beaglehole, J C, 1974. *The Life of Captain James Cook..* London, Adam & Charles Black.

39 ibid.

40 ibid.

14

THE EDITOR[1]

"A room without books is as a body without a soul."[2]

At the same time as having to contend with the Forster affair, William Wales was overseeing his publication of the voyage *Observations*,[3] this appeared in May 1777, when 500 copies were printed for the Board of Longitude.[4] William Bayly had left on Cook's third voyage in 1776, and it was left to William Wales to edit their observations from the second voyage for the Board of Longitude. In the work Wales entered some remarks from his journal, and a useful piece on the scientific equipment taken on the second voyage, as well as two scientific diagrams, and illustrated with one of William Hodges *seascapes*, and a chart of Point Venus.[5]

In 1780 Wales and Bayly's *Situations of the most Essential Islands discovered during the Second Voyage* appeared in an Appendix in Andrew Wakely's classic Navigation Manual, first published in 1665, and printed through many editions up to 1796.[6]

Then in 1781 a second edition of the *Requisite Tables* was published. This had been edited by Nevil Maskelyne, with the 'Explanation' written by William Wales. These tables now included the sines and logarithm tables, and together with the *Nautical Almanac*, provided the vital information needed to compute longitude, 10,000 copies were printed.[7]

In June of 1781 William Wales read to the Royal Society his paper of hints on using Logarithm Tables, this was duly published in the Transactions.[8]

In 1781 there appeared as if 'out of the blue' a publication by William Wales entitled *An Inquiry into the Present State of Population in England and Wales; and the proportion which the present Number of Inhabitants bears to the Number at former Periods,* priced at two shillings.. In it Wales explains that as demography is such an important subject to everyone who is concerned about the prosperity of their country, he makes no apology for writing this work, he goes on to explain that his interest in this subject was aroused reading an Essay, which had been published at the end of a book on Assurances, by Mr Morgan in the Spring of 1779.[9]

William Morgan was an actuary on lives and survivorships to the Society of Equitable Assurances, and at the end of his book[10] appears a piece by his uncle, Rev Dr Richard Price, entitled *An Essay on the Present State of Population in England and Wales.* In the book's introduction, also written by Dr Price, he explained that Mr Morgan's work indicated that the population of the England appeared to have been decreasing fast for many years, in contrast to its neighbours. Price also explained that in order to achieve a more dependable future for the Society, he had at its request, assisted with adjusting the Society's Tables of Life-Annuities, Assurances, and Reversions, by using the *Register of Mortality* of Chester.

Price's *Essay* showed that when calculating the population figures, he had drawn on the accounts of surveys for House and Window Taxes, for Hearth Taxes, and from the books for the collecting of Hereditary and Temporary excise. The latter tax, being the only excise to exist before the *Revolution,* was paid on strong beer, wines, and spirits, and showed a marked decrease of income. The causes for the decrease he listed as war, and the necessary increase in supplying men for our army and navy, another cause was migration to overseas settlements, to the increase of luxury, public taxes, and debts, to the over-population of London, and the unhealthy problems caused by it, he sums up the situation:

> ...how unhappily we are distinguished by some of the worst causes of depopulation; and with what particular force they have been operating for the last *twenty* years. At present we are sinking under new incumbrances and difficulties. The most valuable of our dependencies are lost. Another foreign war is begun. Trade is declining; our strength is wasting; and at the same time, that load of debts which has pressed so heavily on our population, is increasing faster than ever. —Never, certainly, were the resources of a state so anticipated and mortgaged.. —Never before did imprudence and extravagance bring a great kingdom into such peril.[11]

Price's words deeply affected William Wales. Was the nation in such a deplorable state? Was the evidence from the surveyors of windows etc. sufficient to conclude that the kingdom was in such peril? Was the evidence from the excise reliable when smuggling had been practiced at such length? Surely not![12]

Wales' disbelief in the figures urged him to write to acquaintances around the country. Enclosing a questionnaire, he asked them to find out about a number of houses in their respective townships or villages in 1750 and 1780, about the recent building and decay of houses, how many had been enlarged, and how many had been included in the window tax surveys, Wales suspected that not all had. Finally he asked if the opinion could be sought from a few 'sensible' people, long resident in the respective places, as to whether they thought the population had increased or decreased. The replies which came back were in some cases informative, yet others related that the writers had met with some opposition, even violence!

Wales thought the reports of resistance to his enquiries hardly credible, but he was to experience this first hand when he personally took his questions to the people in one of the large towns in Yorkshire, and was immediately attacked by a crowd of women. His quick-thinking however saved him from what he describes as 'the fate of Orpheus', when he managed to whisper into the ears of some of the crowd, that his enquiries may well benefit them, by persuading the King to settle annuities on them if they raised their offspring as useful members of society. This move had the desired effect, the news spread fast, and to his relief he met with no more opposition from the townspeople.[13]

Wales knew that he would never be able to continue interrogating people to any extent in the manner he had first adopted. He remembered something he had read in the *Philosophical Transactions of the Royal Society* on the subject of demography.[14] This was a paper by Dr Thomas Percival on the State of the Population in Manchester and its surrounds, after a survey of the places was carried out 'with great accuracy' in 1773, Dr Price had first read the paper to the Royal Society in November 1773. The figures had then been compared with those shown by the parish registers.[15]

From this it is evident that Wales resolved to extend this survey, by asking the various clergy of his acquaintance to furnish him with numbers from the birth and death records of their respective parishes, a strategy which was to prove much more effective, as laid out in his publication.[16]

When Wales' population study was published it received a scrutiny in *The Critical Review*, The author of the review remarked that it was not easy to calculate the decrease of population, and it was refreshing to be able to read the views of an author, whose desire to investigate the truth was free from any influence of political prejudices. The Reviewer concluded that Wales' deductions on the method of calculating the state of the nation were far more agreeable than other writers on the subject – that was until an accurate survey could be organized.[17]

Wales' population enquiries carried on after the publication of his book, in 1782 he wrote to Dr John Heysham, physician of Carlisle, enclosing some sixty blank forms to be completed for the parishes of Cumberland. He explained to Heysham that by comparing the proportion of births, with the number of people living in the same places, for half the places in England, they would then be able to calculate a number for the population of the whole kingdom, more accurate than had yet been proposed.[18]

The various letters between Dr John Heysham and William Wales reveal some of the domestic details of Wales' life at Christ's Hospital, like the time Mr Archdeacon Law had called, and left some *Bills of Mortality* on an occasion when the family were not at home, all the maidservant could say was that it was a Mr Law, leaving Wales at a loss as to whom he was to thank for this personal delivery.[19] Wales goes on to say that it is deplorable that there is no law of the land to regulate the careful registering of births and deaths, it would be another 56 years before such a law would be enforced in England and Wales.

A letter by William Wales to Dr Heysham in December 1781, tells of parcels of forms being despatched from London to Carlisle, in London the coach left from the *Bull & Mouth* Inn, this stood in Bull and Mouth Street which ran east from Christ's Hospital. In this letter Wales apologies for the delay in answering Heysham's letter of 27th November, he had apparently been too ill to answer it immediately.[20]

In a letter which Wales sent to Heysham in about 1783, we learn of an incident which occurred in his home village of Warmfield, when he wrote:

> ...I remember, many years ago, as they were digging a Coal-Pit in the neighbourhood of the place where I then lived, that in the midst of a perfectly solid rock, of the nature which I think they call Toadstone in Derbyshire, a small spherical cavity of about an inch diameter, was broke into, and in this cavity were found 20 small, red insects, so nearly resembling those which run in the grass and are called by the farmer *Tings*, that they could not be distinguished from them by any person that saw them; they all died almost as soon as they were exposed to the air. I have heard also of Toads being found in large blocks of Marble. – How are we to account for the presence of these animals, etc on the principles generally received?[21]

Knowing that William Wales' father worked in the coal industry, he would have had an excellent opportunity to learn of such things. The subject of demography certainly encompassed diverse subjects in the eighteenth century.

It was the work done by these 'population' pioneers which culminated in the ten year census. The need for counting the people had been first mooted by Parliament in 1753, and eventually a *Population Act* was passed in 1800. The first count of the population under the Act was taken on 10th March the following year, and apart from 1941, during the Second World War, a census has been taken every ten years since.

When Wales' *Inquiry into the Present State of Population in England and Wales* was published in 1781, his friend Reuben Burrow had armed himself with a copy, this came to light in 1857, when it was noted that Burrow had written inside his copy 'his vile and most execrable book'.[22]

William Wales was very much a family man, and he and his wife Mary were no doubt delighted when William's faithful assistant, and of late the assistant of Maskelyne, George Gilpin, married into the family in 1781. On 20th May, 1781 George married Lydia Green, daughter of Mary's elder brother William, by licence at the church of St Bartholomew-the-Less in London where she is described as a 'spinster of this parish', while George, as assistant to the Astronomer Royal, was of the parish of Greenwich.[23]

The appearance of Lydia Green in this parish is interesting, it is not clear where her parents lived at this time, two of her siblings married and settled in Yorkshire, while the third, William, according to family legend settled in Greenwich, and became a farrier.[24]

The church of St Bartholomew-the-Less lies to the north of the site of Christ's Hospital, an octagonal church within the confines of Bartholomew Hospital, of which it is the parish church,[25] indicating that Lydia Green was probably working at the hospital when she married.

George Gilpin left Maskelyne's service in July 1781, having been assistant at the Royal Observatory, Greenwich for five years, he was replaced by Joseph Lindley from Heath, near Warmfield in Yorkshire, William Wales' birthplace. To be the assistant of the Astronomer Royal and married, was not very practical, it seems that the assistant's duties involved not only living at the Observatory, but also being available for observing from 7 am to 10 pm seven days each week, and he was expected to get up in the night when specific events occurred, so not very practical arrangements for a married man.[26]

The following year, on 6th May 1782, George and Lydia Gilpin's first child George was baptized at Clerkenwell.[27] George senior meanwhile, was engaged by William Bolts to prepare for a voyage with Johann Heinrich Zimmerman, the German who had been coxswain on the *Discovery* during Cook's third voyage. On the vessel *Covenzell,* they planned to sail around Cape Horn to Nootka Sound on Vancouver Island, Canada, where they would take on furs and sell them in China and Japan, returning via the Cape of Good Hope under a new enterprise – *the Triestine Society,* which had been set up by William Bolts.[28]

To George Gilpin's disappointment, plans for the above voyage were abandoned, and he returned to London from Trieste in Italy. In August 1784 George and Lydia Gilpin's daughter, also called Lydia was baptized at the church of St George the Martyr, Queens Square, when their address was Fisher Street.[29] He wrote to Zimmerman in 1784 that he still hoped to sail if ever the voyage did take place. Also engaged to go had been George Dixon, master armourer, and William Walker, carpenter's mate – both had been on *Discovery.*[30] Gilpin had no doubt been originally chosen because he had been tutored in navigation by William Wales, and while Zimmerman was in Trieste with Gilpin, he was apparently taught navigation, presumably by Gilpin, whom he asked to obtain a chronometer for him from London when he returned.[31]

In March 1785 George Gilpin applied for the post of clerk to the Royal Society, there was one other applicant, Thomas Coppard who had assisted Mr Robertson, librarian to the Society.[32] Mr Robertson had resigned from the post following evidence of his neglect on several occasions,[33] Mr John Robertson had taken over the post from his father who had been a former Master of the Royal Mathematical School at Christ's Hospital.[34] Gilpin, now aged 30, who left school at the age of 14, and had learned Latin, Greek, and recently Italian, was now a 'practical astronomer' but admitted he knew nothing of libraries. After interview it was Gilpin who obtained the position of Clerk and Housekeeper,[35] and he and his wife Lydia, and their growing family moved into Somerset House in the Strand, part of which had become the home of the Royal Society in 1780, the Society's previous headquarters had been at Crane Court off Fleet Street.[36] At Somerset House the Society had a small observatory, which was usually superintended by the Secretary.[37]

Prior to Gilpin taking up his post, William Wales had ordered from the Royal Society no less than 18 of the silver medals, and 4 of the bronze, which the Society had commissioned in honour of Captain Cook, no doubt Wales ordered them on behalf of friends and acquaintances.[38] Purchased in several batches,[39] there is evidence that his budget was rather stretched at this time.

Among the many friends and acquaintances of William Wales, who had been furthering their careers in the world of navigation and science, was Samuel Hearne. Hearne had achieved promotion with the Hudson's Bay Company, which culminated in him being appointed commander of the Prince of Wales Fort on the shores of Hudson's Bay in 1775, but in 1782 Hearne was forced into surrendering the Fort to La Pérouse,[40] the French Admiral, who would go on to be commissioned by the King of France to explore the Pacific three years later.

Hearne, along with other prisoners, were allowed to return to London, but the following year he returned to Churchill and built a simple house of wood, which was named Fort Churchill. He found the indigenous population decimated due to smallpox and starvation, trade had declined, and eventually Hearne, whose health had also deteriorated, returned to London in 1787 to retire.[41]

Among William Wales' private pupils in the 1780s was John Pond[42] who was to go on to Trinity College, Cambridge, and eventually replace Maskelyne as Astronomer Royal, at Maskelyne's recommendation.[43] This would be about the time another pupil, Wales' nephew John left for service in the East India Company's naval service.

The Wales family gained yet another member when Mary gave birth to their seventh child, another son who was baptized at Christ Church, Newgate Street in May 1783. They named him James – maybe after James Cook.[44]

The family's home at the school now rang to the shouts of seven children, and news came of the possibility of a new house, when it was learned that John Smith Esq had left money for a new Grammar school to be built, which would entail several master's houses being demolished.[45]

A review of the buildings in 1783 acknowledged William Wales' position there, when it included:

> ...This is a school of great reputation, and has always hitherto been under the conduct of one of the first mathematical men in England. The present master is Mr William Wales, who is sufficiently known to the world for his scientific knowledge and abilities...[46]

Among the new boys admitted to the school in 1782 were Charles Lamb and Samuel Taylor Coleridge, whose recollections of the school in later life described William

Wales with great affection. One pupil who was showing great promise was Arthur William Trollope, who unfortunately had news of his father's death in 1784. He was now an orphan at the age of 14, and the youngest of four children, and together with his three siblings, a beneficiary under his father's will.[47]

Lancelot Pepys Stephens, another orphaned pupil, had also shown promise. Stephens was the senior Scholar in his School, and qualified as a Christ's Hospital Exhibitioner to be sent to Pembroke College, Cambridge, where he was admitted on 5th July, 1784. An allowance was granted by the Christ's Hospital court for L P Stephen's support while there, and a sum of money for his apparel, caution money, and settling fees.[48]

Wales was obviously gaining a reputation in the publishing world at this time, he was correcting errors before publication of work by John Goodricke (1764-1786).[49] Goodricke was born in the Netherlands, and was profoundly deaf. He had been educated at Warrington Academy, and pursued a career in astronomy, investigating variable stars, which gained him fellowship of the Royal Society in 1786, having been awarded their Copley medal in 1783. Goodricke died prematurely in 1786 at York, he was the first to provide an explanation of the eclipsing variable star in the constellation Perseus, called *Algol,* which he found to be a binary star.[50]

Perhaps the most pressing of Wales' editorial commitments at this time, was assisting Dr John Douglas in the editing of the account of Cook's third voyage.[51] From the letters Wales sent to Douglas between 21st May 1781 and 5th August 1784, it is evident that Wales often called on Douglas, borrowing and returning voyage accounts and other books, and commenting on them. Once in March 1784, Wales apologized to Douglas, for not venturing out during the cold weather to call on him as promised. Another letter dated 1784 asks Dr Douglas if he has 'Matty's' book[52] concerning the squabbles in the Society, and if he has read it, then he would thank him if he could borrow it, as he could not prevail on himself to lay out half a crown on it.[53]

A letter written to Dr Douglas, dated 30th March, 1784, shows Wales to have been a strict critic of deficiencies in reporting standards, when he read other people's Logs, he explains to Douglas that in Captain King's Log he had seen many bad reckonings, but has made the best he could from it, and likewise that of Bayly's book, which was as bad.[54]

The eventual publication of Cook's third voyage Journal was produced in three volumes, at the end of volume three were appended Wales' tables of the route of the ships which he had prepared for Dr Douglas, who in conclusion, wrote:

> ...the editor and the public were indebted to the abilities and perserverance of Mr Wales, of Christ's Hospital, who undertook this laborious task merely with a view of serving the widow of his deceased friend, Captain Cook.. From his information, likewise, several passages in the introduction have been derived...[55]

It had been part of Wales' brief to report on Cook's quest to find the location of *Cape Circumcision* during the second voyage, which had originally been sighted and named by Lozier Bouvet. Wales had assisted Cook in the search for this 'fabled' land, and their conclusions were included in the form of a chapter in the above *Account of the Third Voyage*, as previously explained, this account was also published separately in pamphlet form.[56]

The Royal Society was increasingly playing a huge part in William Wales' general routine. On 30th November, 1784 at its anniversary meeting at Somerset House, Wales was sworn in to the Council for the following year, and thus became part of the President Joseph Bank's executive committee, the body responsible for running the Society. Also elected to the Council were Henry Cavendish, Constantine Lord Mulgrave, Rev Richard Price, John Smeaton, and Samuel Wegg among others. Following the meeting the Society dined as usual at the Crown and Anchor Tavern in the Strand.[57]

In 1785 George Witchell died, a long-term colleague of Wales and a signatory to Wales' election to the Royal Society, his will was discovered to have been amended. When the will was originally written in 1777, George Witchell had named his executors as his eldest son Thomas, and also Charles Barton, who had worked as a comparer on the Nautical Almanac, and a schoolmaster at Greenwich Academy. On being shown the will by his father however, Thomas Witchell had said he did not wish Charles Barton to be a joint executor with him, as they were not on friendly terms, and he had requested that his father change his mind and choose another executor, his father however did not appear to agree at the time. On George Witchell's death his will had been found in a book case, and to the surprise of his son had found that George had obliterated Charles Barton's name and substituted that of William Wales. The will was duly proved at the Prerogative Court of Canterbury, and Witchell's estate was to be divided equally between his six children.[58]

It was while on the Council of the Royal Society, that Wales was called as a witness in the case of Sayer & Bennet v Moore, at the Guildhall, when Action was brought for copying Charts by the plaintiffs Sayer & Bennet, The Governor of Newfoundland, Admiral Campbell, F.R.S. confirmed that on comparing the charts, Mr Moore's were correct and an improvement on charts, while Mr Sayer's had errors. Wales had been called on to inspect the charts in question, charts of Newfoundland, and the West Indies, and confirmed Campbell's findings. Mr Moore was awarded damages of £10,000.[59]

A further publication in which Wales was involved was entitled *Astronomy in Five Books*. The original author was Roger Long (1680-1770), a Professor of Astronomy, Fellow of the Royal Society, and Master of Pembroke College, Cambridge. In the later extended version of this work Wales is listed as a subscriber, but it is also noted that after the author's death in 1770, he edited and completed books 4 and 5 together, with Richard Dunthorne who had been the first comparer of the *Nautical Almanac* calculations.. Richard Dunthorne died in 1775, so the work was left to William Wales, who completed the work, and it was published at Cambridge in 1784.[60]

In 1785 William Wales had been ensconced in Christ's Hospital for ten years. He had not only proved himself worthy of the position, but was also taking on pupils for private tutoring and earning other income editing and writing,[61] he surely deserved a rise in salary, and duly penned his application to the Committee that:

> ...ever since he was chosen Master of the Mathematical School in this Hospital has, with the utmost assiduity, employed every hour which is not allotted to the Duties of the School toward improving his Income for the support of his large Family. that the maintenance of his Family has been constantly governed by the strictest frugality that Decency would permit, but that, nevertheless he unhappily finds that he has frequently been under the necessity of taking from that little Stock, which former Industry and a smaller family had enabled him to lay up; and which he can not hope, under the present circumstances of his situation, ever to replace. That his Salary until the last half year remained

at the Sum it was originally established at, and that, through an unfortunate mis-apprehension of his own, he omitted to apply for a Gratuity similar to those, which had been granted, and are now annexed to the Salaries of other Masters. That partly in consequence of the establishment of a new Foundation, but more especially in consequence of the introductions of a great number of new articles, which the late great improvements in the art of Navigation have rendered necessary to be taught in the School, the labour of his Office will be much greater in future than fell on any of his Predecessors: and he trusts that the labour arising from this latter cause will not be thought the less of because the necessity of introducing it was pointed out by himself.[62]

The Committee deliberated, and agreed to recommend to the General Court an increase in Wales' salary to one hundred and sixty five pounds per annum, backdated to Christmas last, but on being read to the Court it was further moved, and seconded, that it be increased to one hundred and seventy pounds per annum, which was voted upon, agreed, and ordered accordingly.

William Wales redeemed the inefficiencies of the early Mathematic teachers according to Pearce, probably because as well as being a mathematician, he also had the advantage of being a sailor of scientific direction. In 1786, being dissatisfied with equipment issued to his pupils when they left the Mathematical School, he informed the Governors that some of the books and charts allocated to his boys were useless due to recent great improvements in navigation, and that the quadrants and other instruments were equally antiquated. The Governors listened, and agreed that the books and charts be discontinued, the price saved being put to more up to date quadrants and instruments for the RMS boys.[63]

The working relationship between George Gilpin and William Wales was still in evidence ten years after the Cook Voyage when, in 1785, the Royal Society Council minutes reported that an account of the astronomical instruments, which had been purchased by the Society, and details of the manner in which they had been disposed of was read to the Society, and inserted in the Guard Book, this had been signed by both Wales and Gilpin.[64]

In August 1785 Wales and Gilpin took a journey to Norfolk to visit friends, they returned with observations they had made, and in a letter to Ez. Walker it is clear they surveyed the north of the county, concluding that no part of it lay more northward of latitude 53 degrees, they took two chronometers, comparing them at Somerset House on their return, the conclusions showed a difference, which was explained by Wales – that one of the watches had been influenced by a very strong magnet.[65]

The Cook voyages proved to have a huge impact on many aspects of British life, even capturing the imagination of the theatre. John O'Keefe, an Irish actor and dramatist wrote a pantomime for Christmas 1785 entitled *Omai, or a Trip around the World,* this was performed at the Theatre Royal, Covent Garden in London at great expense. It was a great hit with the London audiences and ran for fifty performances that year, and then continued for a further two seasons. The voyages to the South Seas, and the indigenous peoples portrayed in costumes copied from the drawings of Hodges and Webber, had really captured the public's imagination.[66]

The first biography of Captain James Cook was written by Andrew Kippis, a dissenting minister, who in 1786 had become one of the tutors at the Hackney dissenting college in London, and was a Fellow of the Royal Society.[67] When writing the biography he was curious about the life history of

Charles Green, and knowing that William Wales was Green's brother-in-law, asked him to supply details for the book. Wales' prepared a piece about Charles Green which appeared in Kippis's first edition of the Cook biography, without Wales' information the early history of Green's life could still be largely unknown.[68]

The boys at Christ's Hospital were ever curious about William Wales' experiences during his voyage with Cook, and no doubt William junior who was still a pupil there, was very proud of his father. In turn his father must also have been proud of his son who had entered the Upper School, and here automatically elevated to the status of *Grecian*, just one Grecian per year, one who had shown exceptional talent and promise of an excellent future, was sent on to University. Eventually on 14th March 1786, the now Upper Grammar Master Rev Mr James Boyer declared to the Committee of Almoners that William Wales jnr, being the Senior Scholar in his school, qualified as Exhibitioner to go to University later that year, the Court duly approved that he be sent to St John's College, Cambridge from Michaelmas 1786.[69]

The family was saddened during the summer of that year when news came of the death on 8th July 1786 of William Wales' widowed mother Sarah at Warmfield, she was 88. According to her grand-daughter Abigail, Sarah had been a strict Churchwoman all her life, until in her 85th year she had decided to convert to Methodism as her son John had done.[70]

Sarah Wales was interred in Kirkthorpe churchyard on 10th July.[71] Her spinster daughter Sarah had died a Warmfield in May 1779 aged 39.[72] This left just her son John at Warmfield with his three daughters Mary aged 21; Sarah, 18; and Abigail, 17. The three girls had succeeded to their grandmother's school, and together with their needlework managed to maintain themselves in a respectable manner.

Certainly Abigail had received almost all her education from her grandmother,[73] as it is assumed did her sisters, and probably their brother had instruction from her in is younger years.

In April the following year William Wales' brother John died aged 51, he was described as 'Calculator for the Board of Longitude',[74] evidence that William had secured his brother employment. John Wales completed calculations for 80 of the months for the Nautical Almanac editions covering 1779 to 1796, his salary sometimes being accepted on his behalf by his brother William.[75]

John Wales' body was interred at Kirkthorpe churchyard in the same grave as that of his wife Mary. Their three daughters were still spinsters when their father died. (see Illustration No 12)

Endnotes

1   For a list of William Wales' Works Published see *Appendix V*.

2   Sir John Lubbock, Lord Avebury, (1834-1915).

3   Wales, W & Bayly, W, 1777. *The Original Astronomical Observations Made in the Course of a Voyage Towards the South Pole, and round the World in His Majesty's Ships the Resolution and Adventure, in the years MDCCLXXII, MDCCLXXIII, MDCCLXXIV and MDCCLXXV.* London, W & A Strahan.

4   Ledgers of Wm Strahan, British Library.

5   Beaglehole, J C, (Ed), 1969. *The Journals of Captain James Cook on His Voyages of Discovery. II. The Voyage of Resolution and Adventure 1772-1775.* Cambridge, Cambridge University Press.

6   Wakeley, A., 1780. *The Mariner's Compass Rectified; containing Tables, shewing the true Hour of the Day, the sun being upon any Point of the Compass: With the true Time of the Rising and Setting of the Sun and Stars, and the Points of*

the Compass, upon which they Rise and Set: With Tables of Amplitudes. Which Tables of Sun-Dials, Semidiurnal-Arches, and Amplitudes are calculated from the Equator to 60 Degrees of Latitude, either North or South. With the Description and Use of those Instruments most in Use in the Art of Navigation. also a Table of the Latitudes and Longitudes of Places. London, W. & J. Mount, T. Page & Son.

7   Howse, Derek, 1989. Nevil Maskelyne, the Seaman's Astronomer. Cambridge, Cambridge University Press.

8   Wales, William, Hints relating to the Use which may be made of the Tables of Natural and Logarithmic Sines, Tangents, etc. in the numerical resolution of affected Equations. Philosophical Transactions of the Royal Society, Vol lxxi, No 3, pp.454-478.

9   Wales, William, 1781. An Inquiry into the Present State of Population in England and Wales. London, C. Nourse.

10   Morgan, William, 1779. The Doctrine of Annuities and Assurances on Lives and Survivorships, Stated and Explained. London, T. Cadell.

11   ibid.

12   Wales, William, 1781. An Inquiry into the Present State of Population in England and Wales. London, C. Nourse.

13   ibid.

14   ibid.

15   Percival, T, Observations on the State of Population in Manchester, and other adjacent Places. Philosophical Transactions of the Royal Society, Vol LXIV, p.54-66.

16   Wales, William, 1781. An Inquiry into the Present State of Population in England and Wales. London, C. Nourse.

17   Smollett, T G (Ed), 1781. The Critical Review, Or, Annals of Literature. London, A. Hamilton.

18   Letter from William Wales to John Heysham dated 10th June 1782. Heysham Collection, Carlisle City Library.

19   Letter to Dr John Heysham from William Wales dated 28th August 1781. Carlisle Library, Bibliotheca Jacksoniana, Shelf mark M839.

20 Letter to Dr John Heysham from William Wales dated 10th December 1781. Carlisle Library, Bibliotheca Jacksoniana.. Shelf mark M839.

21 Letter to Dr John Heysham from William Wales, undated. Carlisle Library, Bibliotheca Jacksoniana, Shelf mark M839.

22 *Notes and Queries,* Vol. 4, 2nd S. (91) Sept 26 1857. p.242.

23 Parish Registers of St Bartholomew-the-Less, London. Marriages.

24 Personal communication, Heather Lill, New Zealand.

25 Betjeman, John, 1974. *The City of London Churches.* Andover, Pitkin Pictorials.

26 Croarken, Mary *Astronomical Labourers: Maskelyne's Assistants at the Royal Observatory, Greenwich 1765-1811.* Notes & Records of the R S, (2003), Lond. 57 (3) pp. 285-298.

27 Parish Registers of St. John the Baptist church, Clerkenwell, London. Baptisms.

28 King, Robert J, 2010. *Henrich Zimmermann and a Proposed Voyage.* Journal of the Captain Cook Society, Cook's Log, Vol 33, No 2. p.14.

29 Parish Registers of St George the Martyr, London, Baptisms.

30 King, Robert J, 2010. *Henrich Zimmermann and a Proposed Voyage.* Journal of the Captain Cook Society, Cook's Log, Vol 33, No 2. p.14.

31 ibid.

32 Hall, Marie Boas, 1992. *The Library and Archives of the Royal Society 1660-1990.* London. The Royal Society.

33 Thornton, Cliff, 2008. *Cook's Log.* The Journal of the Captain Cook Society. Vol 31, No 4, p.13.

34 Website of the Royal Society, London. http://www. royalsociety.org/about-us/governance/executive-director/

35 Hall, Marie Boas, 1992. *The Library and Archives of the Royal Society 1660-1990.* London. The Royal Society.

36 The Royal Society archives in London record that the two people who stood surety for Gilpin after his election were

William Wales and Joseph Slack, the latter of Castle Street, Aldgate, London, and no doubt the brother of Sarah Slack who married Rev John Green, Wales' brother-in-law. Joseph Slack had also been one of the witnesses at the wedding of William Wales and Mary Green some twenty years previously.

37 Hutton, Charles, 1815. *A Philosophical and Mathematical Dictionary.*

38 Thornton, Cliff, 2009. *Cook's Log.* The Journal of the Captain Cook Society. Vol 32, No 2. p.21.

39 Personal communication, Cliff Thornton.

40 Willson, Beckles, 1900. *The Great Company (1667-1871).* London, Smith, Elder & Co.

41 Mackinnon, C S, 1979. *Dictionary of Canadian Biography.* University of Toronto Press.

42 Papers of John Pond, Royal Greenwich Observatory Archives.

43 Ronan, Colin A, 1967. *Their Majesties' Astronomers.* London, The Bodley Head.

44 Parish Registers of Christ Church, Newgate Street, London.

45 Thornbury, Walter & Walford, Edward, 1878. *Old & New London.* London, Cassell, Petter & Galpin.

46 Ralph, James, 1783. *A Critical Review of the Public Buildings.* London, J.Wallis.

47 Will of Thomas Trollope, PRO Probate Records. Ref. PROB 11/1122.

48 Guildhall Library, London. Christ's Hospital Manuscript. Court Minute Books, 12806/12. pp 410.

49 Personal communicaltion, Letter from W Wales dated 18th August 1784 in the collection of Mr René Vlug, of Culemborg, Holland.

50 Website of The National Maritime Museum, Greenwich. http://www.nmm.ac.uk

51 Cook, James & King, James, 1784. *Introduction to a Voyage to the Pacific Ocean. Undertaken, by the Command of his Majesty, for making Discoveries in the Northern Hemisphere. To determine the position and estend of the West Side of*

North America; its distance from Asia; and the Practicability
of a Northern Passage to Europe. Performed under the
direction of Captains Cook, Clerke and Gore, in His Majesty's
Ships the Resolution and Discovery. In the years 1776, 1777,
1778, 1779 and 1780. London.

52 In 1785 the Royal Society published Paul Henry Maty's book
An History of the Instances of Exclusion from the Royal
Society, which were not Suffered to be Argued in The Course
of the Late Debates, with Structures on the Formation of the
Council, and other Instances of the Despotism of Sir Joseph
Banks, the Present President, and of his Incapacity for his
High Office. (website http://books.google.com)

53 British Library, Egerton Ms 2180,

54 Beaglehole, J C (Ed), 1969. The Journals of Captain James
Cook on His Voyages of Discovery. II. The Voyage of
Resolution and Adventure 1772-1775. Cambridge, Cambridge
University Press.

55 Cook, James & King, James, 1784. Introduction to a Voyage
to the Pacific Ocean. Undertaken, by the Command of his
Majesty, for making Discoveries in the Northern Hemisphere.
To determine the position and estend of the West Side of
North America; its distance from Asia; and the Practicability
of a Northern Passage to Europe. Performed under the
direction of Captains Cook, Clerke and Gore, in His Majesty's
Ships the Resolution and Discovery. In the years 1776, 1777,
1778, 1779 and 1780. London.

56 Wales, W, 1784. A Defence (against P. C. Le Monnier) of the
Arguments advanced in the Introduction to Captain Cook's
Last Voyage against the existence of Cape Circumcision.
London.

57 Kimber, Isaac & Edward, 1784. The London Magazine or
Gentleman's Monthly Intelligencer. p.459.

58 Will of George Witchell, PRO Probate Records. Ref PROB
11/1127.

59 Moore, John Hamilton, 1794. The New Practical Navigator:
being an epitome of navigation, containing the different

methods of working the lunar Observations and all the requisite tables used with the nautical almanack in determining the latitude and longitude.

60   Website of WorldCat: http://worldcat.org/title/astronomy-in-five-books/oclc/019569500

61   See *Appendix VI* for Notes on Remunerations received by Wales during his career.

62   Guildhall Library, London. Christ's Hospital Manuscript. Court Minute Books, 12806/12. pp. 423/4.

63   Pearce, E H, 1901. *Annals of Christ's Hospital.* London, Methuen & Co.

64   Howse, F & Hutchinson, B, 1969. *The Clocks & Watches of Captain James Cook 1769-1969.* London, The Antiquarian Horology Society.

65   1813. *The Philosophical Magazine, a Journal of Theoretical Experiment and Applied Physics. Vol.41.* Taylor & Francis. p.333

66   Moorhead, Alan,1966. *The Fatal Impact.* London, Hamish Hamilton.

67   Robson, John, 2004. *The Captain Cook Encyclopædia.* London, Chatham Publishing.

68   Kippis, A, 1788. *The life of Captain James Cook.* London. pp.176-8.

69   Guildhall Library, London. Christ's Hospital Manuscripts, Court Minute Books, 12806/12 p.464. Minute dated 1786.

70   Mrs Mary Wales Fenton. *Memoir of Mrs Abigail Manners.* (by her daughter). Methodist New Connexion Magazine, October 1848.

71   *St Peter's Parish Church Warmfield (Kirkthorpe) Burials 1758-1812.* Published by the Wakefield Family History Society, 2004.

72   ibid.

73   Mrs Mary Wales Fenton. *Memoir of Mrs Abigail Manners.* (by her daughter). Methodist New Connexion Magazine, October 1848.

74 *St Peter's Parish Church Warmfield (Kirkthorpe) Burials 1758-1812*. Published by the Wakefield Family History Society, 2004.

75 Personal communication, Dr Mary Croarken.

15

THE ANCIENT MARINER

I pass, like night, from land to land;
I have strange power of speech;
That moment that his face I see,
I know the man that must hear me:
To him my tale I teach.[1]

We can only imagine the variety of duties which William Wales faced in his position as head of the Royal Mathematical School, and it is evident that his prolific output of published material was interspersed with other responsibilities. He was not only playing a major part in the education of Britain's future naval officers, but also endeavouring to ensure an adequate supply of navigational literature for them, when in 1786, there appeared a fifth edition of Robertson's *Elements of Navigation*, which he had revised and corrected before it went to Mr Nourse the publisher.[2]

Wales often wrote items for the *Monthly Review*, a magazine founded in 1749 by Ralph Griffiths, a non-conformist bookseller, Wales' contributions to this periodical spanned almost 20 years from 1778 to 1796. One particular piece was the review of *An Introduction to Astronomy. In a Series of Letters from a Preceptor to his Pupil:* by John Bonnycastle, Mathematical Master of the Woolwich Royal Military Academy, which had been published in 1786. Wales went to great lengths to explain why Bonnycastle had thought it necessary to publish the book as an aid to introduce individuals to the subject of astronomy, without having to stumble through complicated mathematical principles and calculations. Wales ends his review with:

> ...The Author of the work under consideration appears to us to possess the art of explaining the subjects he treats in a more plain and familiar manner than we have met with before; and of dressing them up in a language neat, clear, and comprehensive; for which reason we recommend him to those who wish to know the first principles of astronomy, without enquiring how far he conducts them in it, or where he picks up the materials on which he works.

> At the same time that we do justice to the merits of his book we shall take the liberty of hinting to him that he has slipped into some considerable mistakes in it; particularly in his 8th, 9th, and 22nd letters, which he will readily discover without our being more particular respecting them. Perhaps, also his book would not be worse thought of a few years hence if he had taken less notice of some fanciful hypotheses of a popular astronomer, as they are not only improbable in themselves, but are, in some instances, flatly contradicted by strict mathematical reasoning. Let us add that we read his 13th letter, on the reformation of the calendar, with pleasure and profit.[3]

It was reported that several of Bonnycastle's friends – in particular one Reuben Burrow – considered that Wales had been unfair in his review of Bonnycastle's work and, determined to seek reprisal for his friend, he anxiously sought Wales' next publication, which after obtaining a copy, promptly defaced it with notes, describing it as paltry, and handed it to Bonnycastle advising him to use the notes to write a sharp review for publication.[4]

The work cited in the above by Wales was his *Method of Finding the Longitude at Sea by Chronometers*, which was published in 1794. As Reuben Burrow died in June 1792, this could hardly have been the work handed to Bonnycastle for review, but rather an earlier work by Wales.

The consequence of Cook's voyages was still having a great effect on the world. One of the food sources discovered was that of bread-fruits, which were harvested from native trees in the South Sea islands. The existence of this had been known to Europeans since the late 16th century, but the value of this fruit was not discovered until William Dampier had tried it in the late 17th century, and the accounts of Cook voyages endorsed his findings.

Sir Joseph Bank's friend Valentine Morris was appointed Captain General of the British West Indies in 1771, and had experienced the frequent lack of food in that part of the world, but it was Hinton East from Jamaica who eventually wrote to Banks in 1784, suggesting that if Banks could only find a way of getting bread-fruit plants to him he would transplant them in the West Indies, where they could prove of great benefit. East visited London two years later, and Banks proposed the idea to the King, and in 1787 Sir Joseph Banks was planning the whole operation.[5]

An expedition to Tahiti was planned on a vessel to be called the *Bounty*, with William Bligh as commander and purser. Bligh had been *Resolution's* sailing master on Cook's third voyage.[6]

William Wales' reputation as a leading mathematician, teacher and scientist was undoubted at this time – this had been hard won. Wales was no academic, but the 'Age of Enlightenment' had sucked potential scientists and mathematicians to the capital city like a giant sponge, and the best of them, through sheer hard work and determination, succeeded in their various fields. As Master of the Royal Mathematical School in Christ's Hospital, Wales was double-qualified to recommend boys for service in the South Seas, and in 1787 it was Thomas Hayward whom Wales recommended in a letter to Joseph Banks for the forthcoming voyage on *Bounty*:

> "...I beg leave to trouble you with the name of the Young Gentleman who is desirous of going with Capt Bligh and whom I mentioned to you sometime since. It is Mr Thomas Hayward, son of Mr Hayward, a surgeon at Hackney."[7]

It is suggested by a book on the voyage that Thomas Hayward's father was the brother-in-law of Charles Green, the astronomer who sailed on *Endeavour*,[8] the obituary of Francis Hayward, M.D. who died in 1831, says that he was married to a sister of the late Nathaniel Green, who had been the British Consul at Nice, and of their nine children Thomas was trained under Mr Wales, an eminent nautical mathematician.[9] So far as the author is aware there is no family link between Thomas Hayward and Charles Green of the *Endeavour*.

Thomas Hayward was accepted onto the *Bounty* as midshipman, another of Wales' 'acquaintances' was also on board, the Kendall chronometer which had accompanied him around the world and which he had guarded with his life. Hayward was to experienced the famous 'mutiny' and, loyal to his Captain, he was forced into the small boat with Bligh and others to endure the long journey home.

In 1785 William Wales recommended one of his pupils, Joseph Woodcock to Nathaniel Portlock – who was Master's Mate on *Discovery* on Cook's third voyage.[10]

Past colleagues and friends meandered through the decades of William Wales' life, many associated with his editing skills. Not least of these was Samuel Hearne whom Wales had first encountered at Churchill in 1768, on the shores of Hudson's Bay. Hearne left service with the Hudson's Bay Company and returned to London in 1787, he was not in good health. During his retirement he was to discover that both the Admiralty, and the world of science, were interested in the work he had carried out while exploring the interior of Canada, and he was advised by them to work on the Journal which he had kept of his experiences.[11]

After Charles Green's death, it was left to William Wales to sort out his papers and edit the *Endeavour* observations, together with the astronomical observations of the previous voyages of Wallis, Byron, and Carteret. The results of Wales' work, illustrated with maps of New Zealand, and the eastern Coast of New Holland, as Australia was then known, and with original drawings by Captain Cook, was eventually published in 1788, it had been a mammoth task with a title of astronomical proportions. Wales had indicated that, although the papers had been given to him in April 1778, owing to the imperfect state of Mr Green's papers he had laid them to one side in the hope that Captain Cook could assist with some of their interpretation when he returned from the third voyage. Meanwhile, there were other tasks which Wales was working on for the Board of Longitude, there was his teaching career, and coupled with some bad health he had experienced, the preparation of the work had of necessity been delayed for some time – but once published it was a work of great value to seamen.[12]

Wales' work on the Observations of the four voyages of Byron, Wallis, Carteret and Cook took its place alongside the published journals of those expeditions edited by Dr John Hawkesworth and published in 1773.[13] Of Samuel Wallis' voyage on *Dolphin,* we know by the survival of a letter, that Wales was in correspondence with John Harrison, the Purser on the voyage who was a person with mathematical skills, and a friend of Robertson's.[14] Hawkesworth's work had been received with huge expectation – but much criticism, and had caused him so much worry and ill-health, that he had been driven to a premature death six months after it's publication.[15]

In 1789 William Wales read a paper by his fellow Yorkshireman John Smeaton to the Royal Society.[16] Smeaton, now aged 65, enjoyed pursuing his interest of astronomy in later life, and was contributing several papers to the Royal Society at this time.[17]

The Wales household had a huge shock in October 1789 when they learned of the death of their dear eldest son William, he had died at his lodgings while at St John's College, Cambridge, after spending three years in his studies there, he was buried on 29th October at All Saints Parish Church, Cambridge.[18] Many years later in India, his younger brother John revealed that William had died of venereal disease.[19]

Back in Yorkshire the following year, two daughters of William Wales' brother John were married. Sarah Wales married George Womack and Mary Wales married Richard Womack at Kirkthorpe church, in December 1790. Richard Womack was a collier, and George a tailor, they were both local lads, and cousins. Sarah and Mary's youngest sister Abigail then went to live with her sister Mary for a while, until her marriage in 1792 to Rev Joseph Manners.[20]

George Vancouver had apparently kept in touch with William Wales over the years. In 1781 Wales had examined a sextant for Jesse Ramsden, which Vancouver had not been happy with, and assured Ramsden that it was accurate to one quarter of a minute. Wales also asked Ramsden to provide Vancouver's sister, as requested, with his telescope and a dark glass for his sextant, promising to pay 'immediately'.[21] Vancouver had just qualified as a lieutenant, and had been appointed First Lieutenant on HMS *Martin* which was bound for the West Indies in 1782.[22]

It was in 1790 that George Vancouver once again came to the notice of William Wales. Vancouver had been appointed by the Admiralty to command a voyage to the north-west coast of America, and it was his tutor in navigation William Wales who he turned to when seeking crew. Wales recommended Edward Roberts, a pupil of Wales' from Christ's Hospital. Roberts, though well educated, was berthed at first on the main deck with the seamen, but was later given responsibility for the chronometers on board, and rose to the rank of midshipman – a move which did not go down well with the other midshipmen by all accounts.[23]

Vancouver's vessels for the American voyage were *Chatham* and *Discovery*, and eventually Edward Roberts was appointed assistant to Joseph Baker, who was the first lieutenant of *Discovery*, and on whom Vancouver heavily depended for his chart drawing skills. Vancouver was well pleased with Edward Roberts, both as a draughtsman and a calculator.[24]

From the musters, Roberts had been 18 years old when he joined *Discovery* as an AB on 7th January 1791, his promotion to midshipman was two years later, and in 1797 he became a lieutenant.[25]

The question of an astronomer to accompany the voyage had been dismissed by Vancouver, until just before he sailed in April 1791, when he changed his mind. The position was filled by William Gooch, who had been initially recommended and arrived in London the same month. Gooch was immediately sent to Greenwich for Maskelyne's approval, and was duly employed in the work at the observatory for assessment, eventually after two months, he was appointed by the Board of Longitude, at an annual salary of £400.[26]

Before Gooch sailed out to join Vancouver's voyage at Nootka in Canada, William Wales, ever the sagacious Yorkshireman, quickly advised him on spending his annuity – rather than sending it home to his parents, he should purchase items to trade with the natives he would encounter, and thus would increase his annuity by 'five thousand percent'.[27]

In November 1790 William Wales learned of the death of Larcum Kendall, a man who had gained his greatest respect over the years. In December of that year Mr Christie catalogued and sold at Kendall's house in Furnival's Inn Court, London, his Household Furniture and Effects. Lot 37 of that sale was a pocket Chronometer made by Kendall in 1786, which sold for 36 guineas, and was eventually presented to the Worshipful Company of Clockmakers, Guildhall, London, where it remains in their collection. Lot 39 at the sale was a very similar watch, signed by Kendall and dated 1776, it sold for 30 guineas.[28]

A timekeeper of the latter type appeared in a sale by Messrs Bonhams of New Bond Street, London in 2004, and their catalogue indicates that the watch could be the one sold as Lot 39 in 1790, and further speculates that it could have been either Kendall's own personal watch, or maybe commissioned by William Wales, 1776 being the year he took up his position at Christ's Hospital. Added to this watch's significance is the fact that the top plate was similar to that of K1, and it was signed 'Larcum Kendall', the only other timepieces signed in full by Kendall were K1, K2, and K3, all the others he signed merely 'L Kendall'. In the catalogue of the sale of William Wales' effects after his death there, appears as Lot 5, 'A pocket Time-piece by Kendall'.[29]

It was in the summer of 1792 that Mary Wales learned of the death of her sister-in-law Sarah Green at the age of 78, she was the widow of Mary's brother Rev John Green. Sarah lived in Rosamond Street, Clerkenwell, and was laid to rest in the same grave as her husband at Whitfield's Chapel in Tottenham Court Road, London. Sarah left her newest watch to her niece and god-daughter Sarah Wales.[30]

At the end of 1792 William Wales was saddened by the death of his friend Samuel Hearne, who had been suffering from ill health for some five years since his return from Hudson's Bay.

Hearne had kept journals during his exploration of the interior of Canada for copper deposits between 1769 and 1772, while in the employ of the Hudson's Bay Company. In 1782 Samuel Wegg had become Governor of the HBC, he had previously been chairman of a committee which aimed to manage the specimens of natural history, sent to the Royal Society in London by the HBC. In 1767 Thomas Pennant the naturalist had been elected a Fellow of the Royal Society, and he had a keen interest in the natural history specimens which were eventually sent to London. Ultimately it was Wegg, with Thomas Pennant the naturalist, and William Wales who worked to get Hearne's journal revised, edited and fit for publication.[31]

Shortly before the death of Samuel Hearne in London, he had signed a contract, witnessed by William Wales, allowing Wales to act to ensure its eventual publication. According to William Goldson writing the following year the manuscript was:

> ...purchased by Mr Wales, who intends committing it
> to the press.

Samuel Hearne's Journal was eventually published in 1795, by A. Strahan and T. Cadell..[32]

One event in 1793 reduced Wales' work-load, when Maskelyne decided that all calculations for the *Nautical Almanac* be ceased for the time being, as they had already been completed for the next ten years or more.[33]

The next year in 1794, Wales published an explanation of finding longitude by chronometer, appending his tables of *Equations to Equal Altitudes*. These equations had been computed while Wales was at Hudson's Bay, and first published in the 1773 Nautical Almanac, but they had of late been revised by Wales to present the calculation to a more accurate decimal part, rendering them more convenient. Wales had employed some of his pupils at Christ's Hospital to recalculate these during their leisure hours, the method used was that two boys would calculate the same computation, and the answers were then compared by Wales, much the same as Maskelyne had set the calculators of the *Nautical Almanac* to work.[34]

Wales finally acknowledged the expertise of his old rival Reuben Burrow. Burrow had died in Buxar, Hindustan in 1792, having been employed by the East India Company to train their corps of engineers in mathematics, and then as their chief surveyor.[35] In his work on finding longitude by the time-keeper method, we find Wales had included in a footnote:

> ...The late Mr. Reuben Burrow, who, whatever faults he might have, was certainly a very ingenious man, has recommended a piece of musquetto curtain, stretched in a frame, as a good shelter for the quicksilver......I have tried this mode of sheltering the quicksilver and found it answer the purpose well. [36]

There is evidence of the Arctic explorer John Ross being a pupil of William Wales,[37] Ross had entered the navy at the age of nine in 1786, and after some time in the merchant service completed his indentures in 1793, before entering the East India Company's service, he finally returned to the Navy as midshipman in 1799.[38] Wales had tutored Ross in astronomy, possibly sometime between 1793 and 1798.

Meanwhile George Gilpin, another of Wales' pupils, had been busy contributing to the world of science, and in 1791 he had been given custody of the warehouse which housed the instruments of both the Board of Longitude and the Royal Society.[39] In 1792 and 1794 there appeared in the *Philosophical Transactions of the Royal Society* papers by Charles Blagden, then Secretary to the Royal Society, and George Gilpin, who by 1794 had been Clerk to the Royal Society for some nine years. Gilpin was not a Fellow of the Royal Society, but his subjects must have surely qualified him as such – *Supplementary Report on the Best Method of Proportioning the Excise upon Spirituous Liquor,*[40] and *Tables for Reducing the Quantities by Weight, in Any Mixture of Pure Spirit and Water, to Those by Measure, And for Determining the Proportion, by Measure, of Each of the Two Substances in Such Mixtures.*[41]

A later paper written by Gilpin shows that he had also been working on the variations of the dip of the Magnetic Needle for twenty years, in the Royal Society Apartments in Somerset Place.[42]

The material gleaned on the subject of a biography, in whatever form that may be, is greatly enhanced when complimented by a portrait, and this is even better when images of other family members are discovered.

In July 1987 there appeared in one of the London salerooms, portraits of not only Mr William Wales, but also Mrs Wales (née Green). The catalogue page describes these:

John Russell, R.A.

Portraits of Mr. and Mrs. William Wales, long bust length: Mr. Wales facing right in a blue coat and white waistcoat and stock; Mrs Wales facing left wearing a brown dress with a white shawl draped over her shoulders and a bonnet tied at the front with a bow – the first signed and dated 1794, pastel, oval 23¼ x 17¼ in.

These pastels were made by Russell, himself an amateur astronomer, in gratitude for Mr. Wales's assistance in helping him to produce an accurate pastel of the moon.[43]

John Russell's interest in astronomy was encouraged in about 1784, when he met Sir William Herschell whose portrait he painted in 1794 – the same year he painted the images of William and Mary Wales (see Illustration No 5 for portrait of Mary Wales). When a young man, Russell had been struck by the moon's beauty, and he began drawing it, he drew it many times and produced the largest most accurate map of the moon ever before seen.[44]

In 1797 Russell eventually produced moon gores for a mechanical model of the moon, which he patented as the *Selenographia*, to demonstrate how it orbited the earth. His original painting of the moon at Radcliffe Observatory is about five feet square, and was completed in 1795.[45]

Russell was a prolific pastellist and also drew portraits of Sir Joseph Banks, and two of the Banks family, the one of Sir Joseph is depicted holding one of Russell's moon drawings.[46] He also drew the portrait of Mary Wales' cousin Savile Green of Leeds Pottery (date unknown), and in 1802, John Green, also of the Pottery, but no relation to Savile.[47]

John Russell, R.A. painted other husband and wife portraits, as well as William and Mary Wales, he did studies of Nevil Maskelyne and his wife Sophia, and Captain William Bligh and his wife Elizabeth. Bligh had sailed on *Resolution* as master on Cook's third voyage, and these two pastels now hang in the Captain Cook Memorial Museum in Whitby. The pair of Wales portraits were passed down through their family, their daughter Ann Hagley Eyre left them in her will to her nephew William Wales Stephens. They then appear to have been in the ownership of William Wales' brother John's descendants until they were sold at auction in 1987, they now belong to the Christ's Hospital School, Horsham, where they are displayed in square guilt frames in the Court Room.[48]

George Holroyd, whom Beaglehole tells us had reputedly walked to London with William Wales all those years ago, had a brother James, a ship's master.[49] James Holroyd died in 1795 and in his will he bequeathed:

> ...to James Wales son of my friend Willm Wales of Christ hospital Middlesex my encyclopedia together with as much money as will compleat the set and to John Wales son of the aforesaid William Wales all my Charts etc and other Instruments of Navigation that are worth his acceptance.......[50]

James Holroyd wrote his will in September 1790, when young John Wales was ten years old and his brother James Wales was seven. From this bequest, it seems that by the age of ten, young John who was showing an interest in a career at sea.

William Wales was by now a well respected Fellow of the Royal Society, and this enabled him to keep in touch with many of the other Fellows. One of these was Charles Hutton, who became Professor of Mathematics at the Royal Military Academy at Woolwich, initially he had opened a school in his home town of Newcastle upon Tyne before heading for London. A great friend of Maskelyne's, both Hutton and Wales worked as comparers for the Nautical Almanac, and in 1793 both were selected by a Board of Longitude technical panel, along with Banks, Maskelyne, and three of Maskelyne's past assistants – George Gilpin, Joseph Lindley, and John Crosley, and together with instrument and watch makers, to give evidence on chronometers made by Thomas Mudge.[51]

When William Wales was elected to the Royal Society, Charles Hutton was one of his proposers, the two had many parallels, both had fathers who had been colliery workers, and both had become mathematicians, working on mathematical tables, and with an interest in Conic Sections – both of course became teachers. Hutton had recommended Wales for membership of the Royal Society, and it is therefore no surprise to find Wales being made an Honorary Member of the Newcastle Literary and Philosophical Society of Newcastle-upon-Tyne, in 1795, of which Hutton had been one of the instigators.[52]

The work load of Wales was proving somewhat burdensome at this time, he was not in the best of health, and yet his expertise was in constant demand. For some years a sugar planter of Jamaica by the name of Ralph Walker, son of a Scottish farmer and former sailor in the West Indies trade, had been working on the problem of trying to solve the method of calculating the Longitude by the variation method. He had placed his resulting compass and reports of its trials before the Board of Longitude in June 1794, and went on to publish his *Treatise on Magnetism* which described his method of obtaining the variation, tables and results of trials.[53]

Nevil Maskelyne was unimpressed by Walker's invention, but the Board of Longitude had asked William Wales to carry out on-shore experiments. In March 1795 Wales had to report slow progress on his experiments due to ill health and inclement weather, however by June, Wales had reported on the apparatus as excellent, the Board bought one, and paid Walker £200 for his inventive skills.[54]

It seems that no sooner had Wales completed his report on Walker's compass that he was contacted by Maskelyne with another task. Following the discovery of Australia by Cook, the government decided to send out a fleet of ships in the mid 1780s, carrying convicts to build a colony out in New South Wales. Captain Arthur Phillip, R.N. would be governor, and Lt William Dawes of the Royal Marines would be sent as astronomer, on Maskelyne's recommendation. The First Fleet sailed out in May of 1787, and on arrival at Botany Bay the following year Phillips, unhappy with the position of Botany Bay, chose Port Jackson as mentioned by Cook, and so the city of Sydney was founded and established.[55]

Maskelyne had taken the opportunity of the government's assemblage of a fleet to ask that an astronomer be sent along, he was especially interested in the possible observation of a comet which was predicted to appear over New South Wales, and seized the opportunity by recommending Dawes. The results of this exercise had culminated in a Board of Longitude resolution in 1795, when Wales was handed five of Dawes' manuscripts of astronomical observations by Maskelyne, which had been made both at Port Jackson and on the Voyage. Wales' task was to complete Dawes' calculations and prepare them for publication.[56]

It was perhaps destiny that Wales' career was enhanced at this time by his appointed as Secretary to the Board of Longitude, a prestigious position which he was to hold until his death. The Board usually met at the Admiralty on a Saturday three times a year – March, June and November, with extraordinary meetings if needed. A secretary was first appointed by the Board in 1763, when John Ibbetson was selected, he held the post for nineteen years, to be replaced by Sir Harry Parker, Bart, an Admiralty clerk. Parker resigned in March 1795, when William Wales became the third secretary in December of that year.[57]

As secretary to the Board of Longitude, William Wales received a letter in 1796 from his old pupil George Vancouver, asking that the Board consider giving him monetary recompense for his voyage, when Vancouver had had to act as astronomer owing to the murder of William Gooch. Vancouver had greatly respected Wales some twenty years before on the voyage with Cook, and the letter, which was addressed to Wales, was written in a manner which suggested that he was still in awe of him.[58]

Vancouver had mapped the intricate west coast line of mainland Canada, this had been no mean achievement, and had put him into the same rank as Cook in marine surveying. Wales was directed to find out more about Vancouver's duties, and he ascertained that his work paralleled only that of Captains Cook and King. However the Board then had realized that unlike Cook and King, Vancouver's voyage had not been under their direct command, and thus they were under no obligation to grant Vancouver's request for recompense.[59]

Wales' life-long tendency to frugality was still evident in the Board of Longitude correspondence. In a letter to John Turner of Portsea, Wales had protested:

....When Gentlemen write about their own business; and are, at the same time, to lavish their enclosures, they ought to pay the postage of their letters. Your last letter cost 98d. A most wanton piece of profession! as it might all have been written on one side of half a sheet of paper. I am etc. W.W.[60]

By 1796 a sixth edition of Robertson's *Elements of Navigation* was published, again this edition had been revised by William Wales.[61]

At Christ's Hospital William Wales' teaching continued to make life-changing impacts on his pupils. He is described by one author as an 'urbane provincial' standing square on his Yorkshire background, who later in life resembled Mr Pickwick, he was a likeable man who read the classics.[62] Charles Lamb describes how when Wales had first entered Christ's Hospital, the King's boys had needed to be disciplined by this 'co-navigator of Cook', this 'excellent mathematician'. The sole aim of this hardy sailor had been to give the boys sailor habits, and although his teaching often demanded the laying on of the lash, he was patient and had a fund of humour, and a constant glee about him, which was enhanced by his north-country dialect. His general services to the school were of a high degree, and his method of teaching was carried on by the Mathematical School long after his death.[63]

One young lad who was a contemporary of Lamb and Coleridge was James Henry Leigh Hunt, a pupil at the school between 1791 and 1799. From essays of the time he spent there he apparently gained a great deal of enjoyment from the experience which he never forgot.

Leigh Hunt wrote of William Wales' plain and simple manners, and describes him as a heavy, large person with a benign countenance.[64] One of his Essays, *Seamen on Shore,* written some twenty years after he left his 'alma mater' is surely evidence of his recollections of his old mathematic teacher:

> ...When the Officer is superannuated or retires, he becomes, if intelligent and inquiring, one of the most agreeable old men in the world, equally welcome to the

silent for his card-playing, and to the conversational for his recollections. He is fond of astronomy and books of voyages, and is immortal with all who know him for having been round the world, or seen the Transit of Venus, or had one of his fingers carried off by a new Zealand hatchet, or a present of feathers from an Otaheitean beauty. If not elevated by his acquirements above some of his humbler tastes, he delights in a corner-cupboard holding his coco-nuts and punchbowl; has his summer-house castellated and planted with wooden cannon; and sets up the figure of his old ship, the Britannia or the Lovely Nancy, for a statue in the garden; where he stares eternally with red cheeks and round black eyes, as if in astonishment at its situation.............[65]

From the *Resolution* Journals, it is not evident that Wales lost a finger by a New Zealand hatchet as Leigh Hunt indicates, but he was involved in chopping all those trees down at Dusky Bay, when this could indeed have happened, and he was not the sort of person to either write about the incident, nor allow it hold up his important work, the ship did of course carry a surgeon in case of such accidents.

In 1796, Lancelot Pepys Stephens was appointed Under-Master at Christ's Hospital, he was a past pupil and exhibitioner. Lancelot had gained his Bachelor of Arts and Masters degrees at Pembroke College, Cambridge, and had been Assistant Master at a school at Clapham for the past nine years.[66]

Another past pupil had also gained a new appointment from the Governors of Christ's Hospital, and on 28th November, 1796, the front page of the *Times* announced notices from the two, one beneath the other. The higher notice showed the appointment of A.W. Trollope to the vicarage of Ugley in Essex, for which the Governors of Christ's Hospital held the advowson, and the lower notice of L.P. Steven's recent appointment, showed the signature to be 'R.P. STEPHENS', in error:[67]

To the Right Worshipful the PRESIDENT, the Worshipful the TREASURER, and GOVERNORS of CHRIST'S HOSPITAL.

THE Rev. ARTHUR WILLIAM TROLLOPE

returns his grateful acknowledgements for their unanimous lection of him to the VICARAGE of UGLEY, with the CURACY OF BARDEN, and trusts his future conduct will justify this flattering mark of their approbation.

To the Right Worshipful the PRESIDENT, TREASURER, and GOVERNORS of CHRIST's HOSPITAL

MY LORDS AND GENTLEMEN,

I Return you my thanks for having appointed me to the Office of UNDER GRAMMAR-MASTER to Christ's Hospital ; and I hope to prove my gratitude by faithfully discharging the duties of the situation in which your goodness has placed me. I am, My Lords and Gentlemen,

Yours obliged humble Servant,

Clapton, Nov. 26, 1796. R.P. STEPHENS.

By 1797 Samuel Taylor Coleridge had left University after abandoning his course, enlisted in the Army from which he was discharged as 'insane', had then married, and was fast making his name as a poet, being in the company of Robert Southey and William and Dorothy Wordsworth. In November 1797 Coleridge was out walking with William Wordsworth and his sister Dorothy, when it was mooted that perhaps a ballad could be written and sold – and the *Ancient Mariner* was born.[68]

The fact that William Wales had taught Coleridge one afternoon each week over four years while at Christ's Hospital, has caused some authors to speculate that it was his old tutor's tales, and teachings, that had inspired Coleridge to write his *Rime of the Ancient Mariner*. It is most likely that Wales' huge library of books was at Coleridge's disposal, tomes on voyages of discovery, on astronomy, poetry, classical mythology, and not least Wales' own journal of his voyage with Captain Cook – all combined to tell the tale of an adventure which transports the reader into a world of total imagination, illustrating the contrasts of life and death, of the beautiful and the frightful, and of the power of the sea, and its influence over the fate of mankind. Wordsworth revealed that Coleridge called his Mariner the 'Old Navigator', a term which he could equally have used when describing his old tutor.[69]

The personal journal written by William Wales during the second voyage of Captain Cook, contains so many parallels with the lines of the *Rime of the Ancient Mariner,* that it is almost as though Coleridge relied heavily on Wales' writings when he composed the poem. In fact Wales' journal appeared for sale in 1920 at the Museum Bookstore, 45 Museum Street in London, WC1, the shop owned by Leon Kashnor, the advertising leaflet goes to some lengths to describe:

> ...an hitherto unknown volume consisting of 374 large folio pages. The Original Journal kept by Wm Wales on the Second Voyage of Captain J. Cook to Australasia. The fibre and soul of an original explorer; not, indeed, merely a book, but a living, palpitating page of life, the life of the sun-lit spaces of the Southern Seas, when all the world was young and uncharted seas washed the dreamlands of statesmen and philosophers........[70]

The value of the manuscript Journal is recorded in the same narrative:

> ...There were other Journals kept on the *Resolution,* for Wales mentions something of it in one or two places; but it is very doubtful if anyone else had the ardent passion for certainty, truthfulness and detail which William Wales exhibits from the moment he sets out...

> ...On the whole it may be safely asserted that this is the most valuable manuscript concerning Australasia ever offered for sale. It is not a page from a log, but a pretty complete record of the whole voyage, incorporating all that a ship's journal would, and at the same time being written by the leading officer of the expedition.

> It is inevitable that William Wales sketches his own character in this lengthy Journal, and incidentally gives us pictures of the arguments taking place from time to time. Cook stands here, not as a finished explorer or man of imagination, but as an experienced sailor, harsh at times but easily led by those of superior education and of sufficient character.

> We get to know these people in a way that is impossible from the ridiculous interference of the editor of the printed account, and there is sufficient of grace in the manner of writing to enable us to visualize the actual scenes that meant so much to the Empire.....[71]

The manuscript journal of William Wales was purchased in 1922 from the Museum Bookstore in London, by the Mitchell library in Sydney, Australia.[72] This Library was developed as a direct result of the death of David Scott Mitchell, a bibliophile, who on obtaining the *First Fleet* Journals in 1887, became an obsessive collector of Australiana and left in his will his vast book collection, and seventy thousand pounds, to the Trustees of the Public Library on condition his collection be housed separate from the general library, and would be known as the *Mitchell Library*.[73]

The new addition to the Library was reported in *The Brisbane Courier* on 3rd November 1922.[74]:

> ## AN HISTORIC JOURNAL
>
> ---
>
> LONDON, November 1.
> The Agent General for New South Wales (Sir Timothy Coughlan) has purchased for the Mitchell Library the original journal kept by William Wales, the official astronomer on Cook's second voyage to Australia. The journal, on which the publication of narratives of Cook's voyages was partially based, covers the period from June, 1772, to October, 1784.(sic)[75]

The fact that the grandson of Samuel Taylor Coleridge, died less than seven months before the personal journal of William Wales was advertised for sale, may have some significance. Ernest Hartley Coleridge published his grandfather's letters, he died on 19th February 1920.

A further fact of possible significance is that Christ's Hospital sent some of their old and rare books to Sotheby's sale in 1920, which had been donated by past benefactors. *The Athenoeum* reported that the school was not parting with its 'real association volumes', and the only one disposed of which was by an *alumnus* was by Camden – but then William Wales perhaps would not be defined as an alumnus.[76]

J C Beaglehole describes Wales' Journal as still extant at the Mitchell Library in Sydney, Australia. One of the *Civilians' Journals* of the voyage with Cook, it is a rather battered folio of 376 closely written pages, and not complete. Bound in at the end of the journal is a rather puzzling plan of a town, the drawing shows it to be fortified and has an anchorage, Beaglehole goes on to reflect on the integrity of Wales, his skills in scientific observation, and his exactitude, not only did he excel in his scientific recording in his Journal, but also had an appreciation of poetry and natural scenery, and described his fellow mankind with talent and at length. Beaglehole sums up his examination of this manuscript:

> ...To find Wales's journal is to find the explanation of a great deal.[77]

Of the puzzling plan of a fortified town which is bound with Wales' Journal, this has been identified as a possible depiction of the bombardment of Algiers in 1816. The cartographer remains a mystery.[78]

The Admiralty copy of Wales' manuscript Journal is entitled simply *Log of the Resolution,* and is held in the Records of the Board of Longitude.[79]

In 1797 William and Mary Wales' eldest child Sarah, now over twenty one years of age, married Reverend Arthur William Trollope at her parish church, Christ Church, Newgate Street, London, by licence. Rev Trollope was still of the parish of Ugley in Essex.[80] Witnesses at the wedding were Lancelot Pepys Stephens and William Wales.[81] Having entered Christ's Hospital School at the tender age of seven, in 1775 Arthur Trollope had left to go to Cambridge University twelve years later where he was no mean scholar, gaining his B.A., then his M.A., and then his Doctorate, winning numerous prizes and medals.[82]

Joseph Dymond died at Blyth, Nottinghamshire in 1796 at the age of 50, his grave stone in the form of a large monolith survives in the churchyard.[83] The memorial appeared on a 'Monumental structure at risk' register in 2005, when the writer visited it and saw vegetation sprouting from its base.

At the end of August 1798 came news of the Wales' first grandchild, a son was born to Dr A. W. Trollope and his wife Sarah, née Wales, at Ugley in Essex.[84] The child was named William Arthur Trollope, and who would go on to be admitted a pupil at Christ's Hospital in 1807,[85] and after going on to study at Pembroke College, Cambridge, would eventually become a master at Christ's Hospital, like his father and grandfather, whom he recorded in his *History of Christ's Hospital*, which he wrote in 1834.[86]

The book by William Wales, which was handed to John Bonnycastle by Reuben Burrow before Burrow's death, was eventually reviewed by Bonnycastle, and prepared for publication as advised by Burrow. It was probably the latter half of 1798 when Bonnycastle, on the way to London with his review to arrange publication, met William Wales, who he reported was in a poor state of health, appearing to be in the last stages of consumption. Bonnycastle was so shocked, that immediately he arrived in London he burnt the manuscript of his review, not wishing to hurt Wales' feelings, when he was obviously so ill, and so near death.[87]

In December 1798 William Wales died, and was buried in the south cloister of Christ's Hospital. By tradition the coffin was carried by torchlight, while the procession of boys sang a dirge. This practice was eventually discontinued, and by the time W.A. Trollope wrote his *History of Christ's Hospital*, funerals were carried out in broad daylight.[88]

Records show that the winters of the 1780s and 1790 were exceptionally severe, but the season of 1798-99 had been particularly bad in London from late December until early January, cold weather had plagued Wales throughout his life.[89]

In 1902 when the school was relocated to Horsham in Sussex, and the old buildings in Newgate Street, London, were to be demolished, the Governors purchased a plot at Ilford Cemetery to receive the remains of the Newgate Street burials, where they were duly reinterred in Grave No 924, Square 49.[90] There was a wall surrounding the grave area, but this was later demolished.[91]

Wales' memorial perhaps lies partially in the *Rime of the Ancient Mariner*, which was published the same year as his death, and partially in the lives of all other mariners, whose lives were made that much safer by his work, his writings, and his teachings on his beloved subject of navigation. Just prior to his death, Wales had prepared the *Requisite Tables*, the third edition which was published in 1802.[92] His obituary in *Gents Magazine*[93] includes his positions as a Fellow of the Royal Society, Master of the Mathematical School at Christ's Hospital, and Secretary to the Board of Longitude, as well as listing a great many of his published works.

An obituary appeared in the Monthly Magazine and British Register:

William Wales, esq. F.R.S. master of the mathematical school, Christ's-hospital, and secretary to the board of longitude. This profound mathematician sailed round the world with Capt Cook, and his essential services are recorded in the journals of that celebrated navigator. He was one of the best mathematicians of the age, peculiarly qualified for the instruction of youth by his abilities and his temper, which he commanded with singular judgment.[94]

Endnotes

1   Samuel Taylor Coleridge, (1772-1834). *The Rime of the Ancient Mariner.*

2   Robertson, J, 1786. *The elements of Navigation, containing the theory and practice. With the necessary tables. To which is added A treatise of marine fortifications.* London, C. Nourse. 2 volumes.

3   *The Monthly Review or Literary Journal* London. 1786., Vol. 75. p.355.

4   Knowles, John, 1831. *The Life and Writings of Henry Fuseli.* Colburn & Bentley.

5   Mackaness, George, 1931. *The Life of Vice-Admiral William Bligh.* London, Angus & Robertson.

6   Ibid.

7   Letter from William Wales to Joseph Banks dated 8th August 1787. (Webster collection).

8   Alexander, Caroline, 2003. *The Bounty.* London, Harper Collins. p.417.

9   Obituary of Dr Francis Hayward, M.D. in Cave, E., 1831. *The Gentleman's Magazine and Historical Chronicle*, Vol 101, Part 1. p.469.

10 Personal communication, Cliff Thornton.

11 Matthew, H C G & Harrison, B (Eds). 2004. *Oxford Dictionary of National Biography.* Oxford, Oxford University Press.

12 Wales, William (Ed)., 1788. *Astronomical Observations, Made in the Voyages which were undertaken by Order of His Present Majesty, for making Discoveries in the Southern Hemisphere, and performed by Commodore Byron, Captain Wallis, Captain Carteret and Captain Cook, in the Dolphin, Tamer, Swallow, and Endeavour. Drawn up and published by Order of the Commissioners of Longitude, From the journals*

which were kept by the several Commanders, and from the
papers of Mr Charles Green, formerly Assistant at the Royal
Observatory. London, C. Buckton & P. Elmsley.

13 Hawkesworth, Dr John, 1773. *An Account of the Voyages
undertaken by the order of His Present Majesty for making
discoveries in the southern hemisphere, and successively
performed by Commodore Byron, Captain Wallis, Captain
Carteret, and Captain Cook in the Dolphin, the Swallow, and
the Endeavour. Drawn up from the journals which were kept
by the several Commanders, and from the papers of J Banks.*
London, W Strahan & T Cadell.

14 RGO Archives, Cambridge. Ref: 4/4/187. Letter dated 4th
May 1787 from John Harrison to W Wales, advising that he
no longer has any record of the observations he made as purser
on HMS Dolphin of the eclipse observed from Port Royal,
Tahiti on 25th July 1767.

15 Wallis, Helen (Ed), 1965. *Carteret's Voyage Round the World
1766-1769.* London, Cambridge University Press for The
Hakluyt Society.

16 Smeaton, John,1789. *Description of an Improvement in the
Application of the Quadrant of Altitude to a Celestial Globe,
for the Resolution of Problems Dependant on Azimuth and
Altitude.* Philosophical Transactions of the Royal Society, Vol
79.

17 Matthew, H C G & Harrison, B (Eds), 2004. *Oxford
Dictionary of National Biography.* Oxford, Oxford University
Press.

18 Venn, J & J A, 1883-1958. *Alumni Cantabrigiensis.*
Cambridge, Cambridge University Press.

19 Peter Robb, 2011. *Sex and Sensibility.* Oxford University
Press, India. p.37.

20 Mrs Mary Wales Fenton. *Memoir of Mrs Abigail Manners.* (by
her daughter). Methodist New Connexion Magazine, October
1848. p.439.

21 Letter from William Wales to Jesse Ramsden dated 16th
March, 1781. Royal Society MM.7.25

22 Coleman, E C, 2000. *Captain Vancouver North-West Navigator*. Whitby, Caedmon.

23 ibid.

24 Kaye Lamb, K, 1984. *Voyage of George Vancouver*. London, Hakluyt Society.

25 Website of John Robson. www.pages.quicksilver.net.nz

26 Howse, Derek, 1989. *Nevil Maskelyne, the Seaman's Astronomer*. Cambridge, Cambridge University Press.

27 Dening, Greg, 1995. *The Death of William Gooch*. Melbourne University Press. p.113.

28 Bonhams Catalogue, 23rd November 2004. *Fine Watches and Wristwatches*. London.

29 ibid.

30 Will of Sarah Green, PRO Probate Records. Ref. PROB 11/1220.

31 Lindsay, Debra (Ed), 1991. *The Modern Beginnings of Subarctic Ornithology*. The Manitoba Record Society Publications, Vol. 10.

32 Hearne, Samuel, 1795. *A Journey from Prince of Wales's Fort in Hudson's Bay, to the Northern Ocean. undertaken by order of the Hudson's Bay Company, for the Discovery of Copper Mines, a North West Passage, &c*. London, A. Strahan and T. Cadell.

33 Howse, D, 1989. *Nevil Maskelyne – the seaman's astronomer*. Cambridge University Press.

34 Wales, W, 1794. *The method of finding the Longitude at Sea by Time-Keepers: to which are added, Tables of Equations to Equal Altitudes*. London.

35 Matthew, H C G & Harrison, B (Eds), 2004. *Oxford Dictionary of National Biography*. Oxford, Oxford University Press.

36 Wales, W, 1794. *The method of finding the Longitude at Sea by Time-Keepers: to which are added, Tables of Equations to Equal Altitudes*. London.

37 Levere, Trevor H, 2004. *Science & the Canadian Arctic – a Century of Exploration 1818-1918* Cambridge, Cambridge University Press.

38 Ross, Maurice James, 1994. *Polar Pioneers: John Ross & James Clark Ross*. McGill-Queen's University Press.

39 Howse, F. & Hutchinson, B., 1969. *The Clocks & Watches of Captain James Cook 1769-1969*. London, The Antiquarian Horology Society.

40 Philosophical Transactions of the Royal Society Vol 82, 1792.

41 Philosophical Transactions of the Royal Society Vol 84, 1794.

42 Philosophical Transactions of the Royal Society Vol 96, 1806.

43 Christie's Auction Catalogue, 14th July 1987.

44 Matthew, Colin, (Ed), 2004. *The Oxford Dictionary of National Biography*. Oxford University Press.

45 Website of Melbourne Observatory: www.melbourneobservatory.com/18thCentury.htm.

46 Smith, E, 1911. *The Life of Sir Joseph Banks*. London, Bodley Head.

47 Griffin, John D, 2005. *The Leeds Pottery 1770-1881,* The Leeds Art Collection Fund.

48 Wales, Wendy, *A Tale of Two Portraits*. Cook's Log, the Journal of the Captain Cook Society, 2010; vol. 33; No.1; p.18.

49 National Archives Ref ADM346/15/8/ James Holroyd, master of *HMS Juno* 1770-1772 England to Falkland Islands, including South America, E Coast.

50 Will of James Holroyd, PRO Probate Records. Ref PROB 11/1267.

51 Howse, D, 1989. *Nevil Maskelyne – the seaman's astronomer*. Cambridge University Press.

52 Personal Communication, The Literary & Philosophical Society of Newcastle-upon-Tyne.

53 May, W E, 1987. *The Gentleman of Jamaica (Ralph Walker)*. The Mariner's Mirror. Vol. 73; No.2; p 160.

54 ibid.

55 Howse, D, 1989. *Nevil Maskelyne – the seaman's astronomer.* Cambridge University Press.

56 Morrison, Doug & Barko, I. *Dagelet and Dawes: Their Meeting, Their Instruments and the First Scientific Experiments on Australian Soil.* Historical Records of Australian Science, 2009, 20. pp 1-40.

57 Howse, D, 1989. *Nevil Maskelyne – the seaman's astronomer.* Cambridge University Press.

58 Kaye Lamb, K, 1984. *Voyage of George Vancouver.* London, Hakluyt Society.

59 ibid.

60 Board of Longitude Papers, Ref 14/52 p.396r

61 Robertson, J, 1796. *The Elements of Navigation containing the Theory and Practice with the necessary Tables and Compendiums for finding the Latitude and Longitude at Sea, to which is added a Treatise of Marine Fortification.* London. F. Wingrave. Sixth Edition

62 Moorhead, Alan, 1966. *The Fatal Impact.* London, Hamish Hamilton.

63 Johnson, R Brimley, 1896. *Christ's Hospital: Recollections of Lamb, Coleridge and Leigh Hunt.* London, George Allen.

64 ibid.

65 Leigh Hunt, 1906. *Essays and Sketches.* London, Oxford University Press. The World's Classics edition.

66 Venn, J & J A, 1883-1958. *Alumni Cantabrigiensis.* Cambridge, Cambridge University Press.

67 *The Times* Newspaper, Nov. 24, 1796.

68 Watters, Reginald, 1971. *Coleridge.* London, Evans Brothers Ltd.

69 Smith, Bernard, 1992. *Imagining the Pacific.* Melbourne, Melbourne University Press.

70 *Captain James Cook and Australasia.* an advertising leaflet dated 11th September 1920. Copy stamped Public Library of Victoria.

71   ibid.

72   Personal communication, Bill Whelen.

73   Fletcher, Brian H, 2007. *Magnificent Obsession: The Story of the Mitchell Library.* NSW. Allen and Unwin.

74   Website of the National Library of Australia: http://trove.nla.gov.au/ndp/del/article/20581480

75   The period of the Journal is from June 1772 to October 1774.

76   Blunden, Edmund, 1923. *Christ's Hospital, a Retrospective.* London, Christophers. p.191.

77   Beaglehole, J C (Ed), 1969. *The Journals of Captain James Cook on His Voyages of Discovery. II. The Voyage of Resolution and Adventure 1772-1775,* Cambridge. Cambridge University Press.

78   Personal communication, Cliff Thornton.

79   RGO, Department of Manuscripts, University of Cambridge. Board of Longitude Papers. RGO 14/58.

80   Faculty dated 27th July 1797.

81   Guildhall Library, London. Copy of the Parish Registers of Christ Church, Newgate Street, London.

82   Dictionary of National Biography.

83   Listed Buildings website: http://www.britishlistedbuildings.co.uk/en-416956-memorial-to-joseph-dymond-in-church-yard

84   Parish Registers of Ugley, Essex, Baptisms.

85   Guildhall Library, London. Christ's Hospital Admissions Register Manuscript 12818A/80. pp.156/7. Minute dated 1807.

86   Trollope, W A, 1834. *A History of the Royal Foundation of Christ's Hospital.* London, William Pickering.

87   Knowles, John, 1831. *The Life of Writings of Henry Fuseli.* Colburn & Bentley. p.323.

88   Allan, G A T, 1949. *Christ's Hospital.* London, Ian Allan Ltd.

89   Website: http://www.hollinsclough.org.uk/weather.htm.

90   Corporation of London: Burial Registers of Little Ilford Cemetery, Manor Park, London.

91   Corporation of London: Christ's Hospital correspondence, dated 20th July 1962.

92   Howse, D, 1989. *Nevil Maskelyne – the seaman's astronomer.* Cambridge University Press.

93   *The Gentleman's Magazine*, vol.84. p.1155.

94   *Monthly magazine and British register*, 1799. London. Vol. 7; Pt. 1; p.75.

16

THE LEGACY

"... Many are the living witnesses to the success of his instructions; while it will be readily acknowledged, that by his energies the Royal Mathematical School of Christ's Hospital was first seen to realize the objects of its foundation, and gave the promise of becoming one of the first naval seminaries in the world."[1]

The schoolmasters of the eighteenth century had many roles to play, and their associates were often called on to advise on their own particular branch of expertise. When William Vincent, headmaster of Westminster School in London wrote his work on the *Navigation of the Ancients*[2] he had approached William Wales on the subject of the latitude of Meroè, and when this was published after Wales' death, Dr Vincent wrote a tribute to his memory, stating that he could vouch for the truth of this eminent mathematician and astronomer, and he had transcribed his remarks with pleasure. Vincent added that he had been given a calculation by Mr Wales just a few days before his death. He personally regretted Wales' passing, being 'deprived of a most worthy friend and truly valuable coadjutor'. Wales wrote a dissertation on the *Achronical Rising of the Pleiades*, which was appended to Vincent's work.[3]

It was George Gilpin who succeeded William Wales as Secretary to the Board of Longitude. Gilpin was also at this time Clerk to the Royal Society, with charge of the instruments of both bodies, his steady dedication to this work was appreciated by the members. J & W Cary, globe-maker, of the Strand in London produced a pair of twelve inch globes, one terrestrial and one celestial. The terrestrial showed the discoveries by McKenzie, Hearne, Vancouver, Cook and La Pérouse and the sea route of Captain Phipps to Spitzbergen. The celestial globe showing constellations with about 3500 stars, and was based on the work of 'George Gilpin of the Royal Society'.[4]

Gilpin had assisted when Joseph Banks published tables to prove that John Arnold's watches were superior to Thomas Earnshaw's, in 1804.[5] In 1806 Gilpin published *On the Variation & Dip of the Magnetic Needle*,[6] and had been working with Henry Cavendish on the analysis of water. On Cavendish's death in 1810 Joseph Banks wrote to William Scoresby apologizing for providing him with the wrong apparatus to measure sea temperature, the reason for this had been due to the death of Henry Cavendish, and also the death of George Gilpin at the age of 56 later the same year. Banks describes the two as:

> ...the loss of these two admirable men, for such they were, both of them, made me at the time too negligent of & indeed unfit for my usual pursuits. I find however that the instrument is now Ready for Delivery, as I saw it a few days before I left town & gave then the final directions to Mr Carey, instrument maker in the Strand to finish it for me....[7]

William Wales had signed his will on 6th October 1798, and thereby directed that all his books, instruments, the clock from the observatory, his watch, and all other effects, which would not be of immediate use to his wife and dependent family, be sold, and the proceeds be used to purchase securities, the interest of which together with interest from other sums belonging to him, he left to his wife for the term of her natural life. On Mary's death the estate, was then to be divided equally between his five children, Sarah, Ann Hagley, Mary Judith, and sons John and James, or their heirs. William and Joshua had not survived their father. Mary Wales was also to have any stock due to William Wales at his death in the books of the Worshipful Company of Stationers of London, with any due dividends, and the residue of his estate not covered previously in his will, to be disposed of as she wished. Executors of the will were wife Mary Wales, son in law Rev Arthur William Trollope, and Ann Hagley Wales.[8]

For five days during March 1799 in London, at the House of Leigh & Sotheby in York Street, Covent Garden, the sale took place of the *Valuable Mathematical Library of the late Mr William Wales, F.R.S. Master of the Royal Mathematical School, Christ's Hospital. Including likewise a good Collection of Books, in History, Voyages and Travels, Poetry, Belles Lettres, Miscellanies, &c. Also his Mathematical Instruments and Maps. With some Original Drawings by Hodges.* According to the copy inspected, the price of the catalogue was 6d. [9]

At the beginning of the sale, Leigh & Sotheby disposed of four medals, followed by the pocket time-piece made by Larcum Kendall, which according to the hand-written margin notes in the copy of the Catalogue inspected, raised £20.9s.d. Sale of the instruments and maps then followed, these included a 'Russell's Moon' made by Wales' portrait painter, and which sold for £1.5s. There then followed the sale of Wales' 'Drawings and Prints', a large proportion being executed by his friend William Hodges. Among the prints is one of the *Death of Captain Cook* [10]

Wales' total library was disposed of in one thousand, one hundred, and forty one lots, and by far the largest category of books was Mathematics, which was sold in over 200 lots, closely followed by books on Voyages and Astronomy. Navigation was another major category, and there were books on horology, engineering, physics, philosophy, many on geography and travel, and of course, maps. But Wales' library catalogue reveals his other interests, in history, politics, religion, demography, poetry, drama, a copy of Gay's *Beggar's Opera,* with music, and there were satirical novels, and books on games including cards, backgammon and chess. Books of reference included England's Gazetteer by Whatley, an Atlas, Nugent's Pocket Dictionary – French and English, and Johnson's Dictionary in two volumes [11]

Many periodicals are listed in the catalogue of William Wales' library sale, the pages to which Wales had so often contributed. There were copies of *The Annual Register, The Gentleman's Magazine, The Ladies' Diary, The Gentleman and Ladies' Palladium, The London Review of English and Foreign Literature, The Monthly Review, The Gentleman's Diary, The Critical Review,* and not least the Royal Society's *Philosophical Transactions.* There were multiple copies of *Nautical Almanac* and *Requisite Tables.* The *Gentleman's Magazines* alone, as Lot number 1046, ran to 85 volumes. and covered the years from its launch in 1731, four year's before Wales' birth, to 1798. There were also over 60 lots which were entered as *Tracts*, these were leaflets, often of many pages and on diverse subjects. Finally there was one instructing how to make ones will, and how it disposes of a person's estate.[12]

The catalogue of the sale of Wales' Library was used as a source of information in the distinguished book by Professor E.G.R. Taylor *The Mathematical Practitioners of Hanoverian England 1714-1840,* published in 1966 by the Cambridge University Press. This volume provides a comprehensive cross-reference to the lives, work, and interactions of the many mathematicians, astronomers, surveyors, instrument makers, and teachers who were actively employed during this important period in the history of mathematics.

In 1992, a brass-bound mahogany chiming bracket clock by Ellicott of London, which had once belonged to William Wales and passed down through the family, appeared in an auction by *Sotheby's's*, it still retained its original bracket and its value was estimated at between £10,000 and £15,000.[13]

On the death of William Wales the Governors of Christ's Hospital wrote to Mr John Davis of 31 Paradise Row, Rotherhithe, asking him to instruct the boys in the Mathematical School until a successor was appointed. Davis had apparently previously covered for the absence of a master, and he was assured a replacement would be found within the month.[14]

William Wales was eventually succeeded at Christ's Hospital Royal Mathematical School by William Dawes, astronomer with the 'First Fleet' to Botany Bay, returning to England in 1792, and then through the influence of William Wilberforce, had become Governor of Sierra Leone.[15]

It was William Dawes' observations in Australia that Wales had been given to work on by Maskelyne in 1795, and had still been working on when he died. This created an uncomfortable situation for Mary Wales and her family, now that Dawes, as the new Master of the RMS, resided within the Wales' household at Christ's Hospital. Dawes seemed to think that by this time William Wales should have done more work on them, however it was possibly because her husband had not been paid for any work he had carried out, that Mary had acted rather offhand towards Dawes' requests to retrieve them, he did nevertheless take his journals. Later that year Dawes had told Maskelyne that he wished to pass his journals on to George Gilpin, as clerk to the Royal Society, for safe-keeping. A request which the Astronomer Royal refused, the whereabouts of these Journals remains a mystery.[16]

Soon after the death of William Wales, the Upper Grammar Master James Boyer retired to the living of Gainscolne, and Boyer's position at Christ's Hospital was taken by Rev Arthur William Trollope,[17] husband of Wales' eldest daughter Sarah, who would then take up residence at Christ's Hospital with her husband in premises with which they were both already familiar. Meanwhile Sarah's mother Mary Wales, and her surviving unmarried children Ann Hagley, aged 28; Mary Judith, now 20; John, aged 18; and 15 year old James; would have been required to move from their home within the confines of the school.[18]

The Treasurer and Governor's of Christ's Hospital then received a petition from Mary Wales, asking for support:

..The humble Petition of Mary Wales, Widow. Representeth That her late Husband William Wales, was Master of your Mathematical School upwards of three and twenty years. That his unremitting attention and integrity in the discharge of the duties of that arduous office are well known to many of the Governors, & to every person who was acquainted with him. That by his death your Petitioner is left at an advanced age in very contracted circumstances with four Children without provision. That therefore she humbly solicits the assistance of the Governors, of which she will ever return the most grateful remembrance. Mary Wales..........

In consideration of the able and faithful service given to the school by William Wales over many years, the Treasurer moved that Mary be paid eighty pounds per annum, and this was carried unanimously.[19]

In the June of 1799, Mary Wales and her family had more sad news to bear, when they learned of the death in Leeds of Mary's brother Joshua Green, at the age of seventy nine, he left a wife Judith but had no issue. In his will he left Mary an annuity of £15 to be paid quarterly, and on the death of the survivor of his wife or Mary Wales, Mary's surviving children were to inherit equal portions of six hundred pounds from Joshua's estate. Judith survived Joshua by nearly ten years.[20]

By the end of the 18th century Mary Wales and her family had moved to Mare Street in Hackney, where they rented a house belonging to Thomas Mattravers.[21] In the local parish church of St John-at-Hackney, which had only recently been completed, Anne Hagley Wales married William Eyre almost one year after her father's death, on 14th December, 1799.[22] They were married by Rev Arthur William Trollope, and one of the witnesses was Mary Judith Wales.

Anne Hagley and William Eyre lived at Upper Thames Street after their marriage, but by the time of William's death in 1836, he was 'of Kingsland Place' and the Sun Fire Office Records in the Guildhall Library indicate he was living at 6 Kingsland Place in 1827. Kingsland was in Hackney, the place of their marriage.

On 16th May, 1812 Mary Judith Wales, was also of the parish of St John, Hackney when she married Rev Lancelot Pepys Stephens, by licence, at St Botolph's church, Aldersgate, London, which was the parish church of the bridegroom.[23]

L. P. Stephens was Under Grammar Master at Christ's Hospital and he had been ordained a priest in 1798.[24] After fourteen year's absence, Mary Judith would again go to live at Christ's Hospital where she had been brought up. She was now 34 years of age. Her eldest sister Sarah already lived there as the wife of the head, Rev Arthur William Trollope, who had performed the marriage ceremony of Mary Judith and Lancelot. Mary Wales, mother of Sarah and Mary Judith, would then be 72 years of age, and it appears she left Mare Street in Hackney in 1813[25] – it could be that she went to live with one of her daughters – she could even have returned to live at Christ's Hospital at this time.

William Wales is remembered with fondness by the staff and pupils of Christ's Hospital, now at Horsham in Sussex, where the writer learned that the School will be eternally grateful to him for saving the school from the Gordon Rioters.[26] In this context Wales' old pupil Coleridge, on recalling with regret his scorning of mathematics, wrote:

> ...what bitter neglect, and in the conscience of such glorious opportunities, both at School under the Janus Mathematician, Wales, the companion of Cook in his circumnavigation, and at Jesus College, under that excellent Mathematical Tutor, Newton, all neglected, with still greater remorse....[27]

Janus, the two headed Roman god of door-keeping, possibly Coleridge equated him with Wales who had famously stood at the gates of Christ's Hospital, and defended it from the Rioters in 1780.

In the Christ's Hospital museum a well-worn wooden armchair is displayed, together with a brass plaque declaring that it is the 'Chair used by William Wales, F.R.S.' (see Illustration No 10) In the Court Room hang the portraits of William Wales and Mary Wales by John Russell, while in the quadrangle cloisters there is a white marble tablet which was perhaps relocated from the cloisters at Newgate Street, London when the school moved in 1902[28]. (see Illustration No 15)

It was a tribute to Wales' memory years later when, in September 1837, there appeared a letter in the Staffordshire Advertiser to the Editor:

Sir,

A Friend has just placed in my hands the STAFFORDSHIRE EXAMINER of September 9th, containing a scurrilous and libellous attack upon my father, which I will not at present notice, any further than to disabuse the public mind of the abominable and direct lies contained therein. It is stated, that after promotion from "the forecastle of a gun brig," to the "rank of midshipman," he was unable to pass the ordeal for further progress in the Navy, and was "translated to the office of chief butler of the Earl of Bradford's pantry"!! The following brief statement will, in the eyes of a discerning public, directly refute the above impudent falsehoods.

My Father was educated at Christ's Hospital, and there obtained a Classical and Mathematical education; the latter under the celebrated William Wales and under him obtained high honors. He was a contemporary and associate with Coleridge, Charles Lamb, and other eminent men educated in that establishment. After having passed a three days' rigid examination at the Trinity House, as to his attainments in Mathematics and Astronomy, he entered as Midshipman in the Honorable East India Company's Service where he acquitted himself with great credit. The only reason of his leaving that service in 1796 was a dislike to a seafaring life, for he was offered a lucrative and honourable promotion had he chosen to remain therein. Since that time he, for several years, maintained his rank in the most respectable society, as a Surveyor and

Engineer in London, and with unblemished reputation. – At an advanced period of his life, in the year 1820, he accepted of the situation of agent and confidential adviser to the late Earl of Bradford, and has the honor as well as happiness to enjoy the most unlimited confidence of the present Earl.

To those Friends of my Father who have known him from the earlier period of his life, this refutation is altogether unnecessary.

I am, sir, your very obedient Servant,

PETER POTTER, Jun.

Gorway House, Walsall, September 21, 1837.[29]

In 1828 the Board of Longitude finally disbanded. It had paid John Harrison his final reward for inventing the Time-keeper, on 3rd July 1773, and in the fifty seven years afterwards it had funded the publishing of various volumes of Tables to assist navigation, and had paid rewards to various nautical observers, who had been able to fix the latitude and longitude of points around the world. To instrument makers, and of course makers of time-pieces for its experiments, the Board had paid rewards, also for work on the improvement of its instruments and watches. In 1820 the ship's companies of the *Hecla* and *Griper* had been rewarded £5000 for reaching 110° W within the Arctic Circle. The Board's instruments were given to the Hydrographer of the Navy, the Royal Society was given the books and records, while the Admiralty took over responsibility for the *Nautical Almanac*.[30]

On 7th February, 1811 Sir Nevil Maskelyne died at the Royal Observatory in Greenwich, he was 78 years of age. He had been Astronomer Royal for 46 years and worked to the last. Just two days before his death, his daughter Margaret wrote of his illness, and advised that work on the Nautical Almanac must be ceased for the present. He was succeeded as Astronomer Royal by John Pond, past pupil of William Wales, and with the approval of Sir Joseph Banks.[31]

Sir Nevil Maskelyne had attended nearly all the meetings of the Board of Longitude over the 46 years of his membership, being the most significant and influential person in its history, and for most of those years he was in contact with William Wales, and family members George Gilpin, Charles Green and John Wales.

Maskelyne has not always been afforded the reputation he deserves, according to his biographer. On the contrary he has been described by many authors as a jealous contender of the longitude prize, who did his best to stem John Harrison and other's claims to the award. Derek Howse defends Maskelyne as a fair member of the Board of Longitude, who never abused his position in public service to gain personal reward. He was a conscientious employer, who always looked after, not only those he had responsibilities for, but also those who were worse off than himself. He worked hard on the development of astronomy and navigation, and thus greatly respected the hard work of others in the same field, nurturing the careers of many of his assistants, computers, and comparers, of which William Wales was no exception.[32]

On Maskelyne's death, as with William Wales', his library was sold by Leigh and Sotheby. The sale lasted three days, and the 757 lots realized £451.18s.d.

The Hudson's Bay Company still keeps the memory of William Wales in their historical literature. Some years ago there appeared a comic book produced by the Company, entitled 'Tales from the Bay', in which *The Transit of William*

Wales over ten pages, aimed to tell the story of the Royal Society's quest to prove Newton's theory of gravity. The comic incorporates several posers for the reader to solve.[33]

The East India Company recorded William Wales in their annals when, on the promotion of his nephew Captain John Wales, they recorded:[34] albeit erroneously mistaking his uncle for his father, and the detail of the Cook voyages:

> .....In 1809, the court of Directors established a Marine Survey Department in Bengal, and Captain Wales, of the Marine, was appointed the first Surveyor-General. He as an officer of rare professional and scientific attainments. His father, Mr John Wales, accompanied the great circumnavigator, Captain Cook, in the capacity of astronomer, in his first and second voyages, and was afterwards elected Master of Christ's Hospital; from him the son imbibed that taste for astronomy which gained him a considerable reputation in India, while his acquirements in the sister science of marine surveying, were the means of raising him to his present eminence.....[35]

A minor planet was discovered in December 1998 by the Kitt Peak National Observatory, 56 miles south-west of Tucson, Az in the Sonoran Desert. In honour of the two Hudson's Bay transit observers it was named *Walesdymond* by *Peter Jedicke*.[36]

In 1968 Canada celebrated the two hundredth anniversary of the 'first fixed point Meteorological Reading undertaken by an established scientist', with a commemorative stamp depicting a map and instruments, a Cole First Day Cover produced at the same time shows William Wales, scientist, astronomer, explorer, in front of a map of eastern Canada.

In 1974 the New Hebrides[37] produced a strip of three postage stamps to commemorate the bicentenary of the discovery of the islands. The first in the strip shows Captain J. Cook with a map of the island of *Tanna*, the middle stamp depicts William Wales, beach landing, with the tent observatories in the background, and the third shows Wm Hodges busy sketching on shore. These show drawings of each, as depicted from their portraits.

When in March 2008, the writer sailed into Dusky Sound, in what is now the National Park World Heritage Site of *Fiordland,* which encompasses three and a half million acres in the south western corner of New Zealand's South Island, the scene appeared to be almost as described by William Wales some two hundred and thirty five years previously. A heavy mist hung over the water searching the bays, encircling the islands and clinging to the steep cliffs – the silence was almost deafening, it was as though this landscape was frozen in a time warp, and not changed since Cook had first briefly taken *Endeavour* there on the first voyage – the first recorded European visit to this paradise. Here the weather has great influence, the westerly winds bring moisture and rain in summer, and snow in winter.

The lecturer on board the ship[38] told of Dusky's mysterious cloudy form, its swampy flat lands of moss, ferns, and fungi, and its trees of beech, of pine and of tree ferns washed by an annual rainfall of some eight metres. So wet that no bees survive here – the flowers of yellow or white are pollinated by moths. Birds include crested penguins, skua, and mollymawks or gulls, and the royal albatross with wingspan of some two metres. There are parrots here, kaka, kea, and the kiwi. We were told of the takah, flightless and indigenous bird of the rail family, this had not been seen for some fifty years, before reappearing again, only 86 had been left in the world, but eggs were now to be found on Stewart Island, so perhaps their future is to be viewed more optimistically than of late.

Our departure from Dusky via Acheron Passage was witnessed by the peak of *Mount Wales* appearing through the mist on Resolution Island, one of just a few places[39] named after William Wales, and his contemporaries.

To the north in Milford Sound, jade occurs, and black coral is found in the fiords, and even gold. There is a hydro-electric plant, and 500 miles of walking tracks. This place supports bottlenose dolphins, fur seals, lizards, skinks, rats, and bats, – such a magical place, there is little wonder the *Resolution* stayed for five weeks, and that it was chosen for those scenes of Tolkein's 'Middle Earth' by the film makers of *Lord of the Rings*.

Endnotes

1   Trollope, W A, 1834. *A History of the Royal Foundation of Christ's Hospital*. London, William Pickering. (On writing of his Grandfather, William Wales).

2   Vincent, William, 1800. *The Periplus of the Erythrean Sea, containing An Account of The Navigation of the Ancients with Dissertations*. London, Cadell and Davies.

3   *The Gentleman's Magazine*, vol.84; p.1155.

4   Website of Christies: http://www.christies.com

5   Howse, Derek, 1989. *Nevil Maskelyne, the Seaman's Astronomer*. Cambridge, Cambridge University Press.

6   Taylor, E G R, 1966. *The Mathematical Practitioners of Hanoverian England 1714-1840*. Cambridge, Cambridge University Press. p.262.

7   Stamp, Tom and Cordelia, 1975. *William Scoresby, Arctic Scientist*. Whitby, Caedmon Press.

8   Will of William Wales, PRO Probate Records. Ref. PROB 11/1318.

9   *A Catalogue of the valuable Mathematical library of the late William Wales F.R.S.* 1799. Leigh and Sotheby. Copy in the Graves Collection, University College of London Library.

10 ibid.

11 ibid.

12 *Catalogue of the valuable Mathematical library of the late William Wales F.R.S.* 1799. Leigh and Sotheby. Copy in the Graves Collection, University College of London Library.

13 *Clocks. The magazine for horological collectors and restorers.* December 1992. p.49.

14 Guildhall Library, London. Christ's Hospital Manuscripts, Letter Books, 12828/7. p.374..

15 Howse, F & Hutchinson, B, 1969. *The Clocks & Watches of Captain James Cook 1769-1969.* London, The Antiquarian Horology Society.

16 Morrison, Doug & Barko, I. *Dagelet and Dawes: Their Meeting, Their Instrumnts and the First Scientific Experiments on Australian Soil.* Historical Records of Australian Science, 2009, 20. p. 1-40.

17 Guildhall Library, London. Christ's Hospital Manuscripts Minute Books, 12806/13/283.

18 Personal communication, Archivist of Christ's Hospital, Horsham., Sussex.

19 Guildhall Library, London. Christ's Hospital Manuscripts, Court Minute Books, 12806/13. p.274.

20 Griffin, John D, 2005. *The Leeds Pottery 1770-1881.* Leeds, The Leeds Art Collections Fund.

21 London Metropolitan Archives: London Land Tax Records.

22 Parish Registers of St John-at-Hackney, London, Marriages.

23 Parish Registers of St Botolph, Aldersgate, London, Marriages.

24 Venn, J & J A, 1883-1958. *Alumni Cantabrigiensis.* Cambridge, Cambridge University Press.

25 London Metropolitan Archives: London Land Tax Records.

26 Personal visit by the author in May, 2007. Although this tablet records his age at death as 65, rather than 64, it does make the date of Wales' birth passed down through the family more credible.

27 British Library. Handwritten note on the fly-leaf of S.T. Coleridge's copy of William Law's edition of the works of Jacob Behmen Vol, 1.

28 Personal communication, Archivist of Christ's Hospital. Horsham, Sussex.

29 *The Staffordshire Advertiser,* Saturday 23rd September 1837. p.2.

30 Howse, Derek, November 1998. *Britain's Board of Longitude: The Finances, 1714-1828.* Mariner's Mirror, Vol. 84, No. 4. pp 400-417.

31 Howse, D, 1989. *Nevil Maskelyne – the seaman's astronomer.* Cambridge University Press.

32 ibid.

33 Boyd, Ron, Kasman, Ron., Waley, James. 1995. *Tales from the Bay – William Wales.* Hudson's Bay Company.

34 There are errors in this notice, Captain John Wales' uncle should read "Mr William Wales", and the detail about the Cook voyage should read "....in his second voyage" only.

35 Lowe, Charles Rathbone, 1877. *History of the Indian Navy (1613-1863).* London, Richard Bentley.

36 Website: http://rasc.ca/sites/default/files/transit.pdf. Broughton, Peter. *Historic Transits of Venus from a Canadian Perspective.* Minor Planet No. 15045; Name Reference 49101; Discoverer Spacewatch.

37 Now called Vanuatu.

38 Jon Von Tunselman of Fiordland National Park.

39 See *Appendix VIII.*

17

IN CONCLUSION

... To Mr. Wales I was known only by the courtesy of literature, but such was his love of science, that I never consulted him without receiving every assistance that it was in his power to give. I insert that as his last favour, and not without a tribute of gratitude to the memory of a man, who was as excellent in private life, as an husband and father, as he was eminent in the science he professed, the friend and companion of the illustrious Cook.[1]

The following account of William Wales' family after his death in 1798 tells of the surviving members variously rising and falling in fortune, some emigrated to the other side of the world, many stayed. Like all families their history never fails to surprise.

THE WIFE OF WILLIAM WALES

MARY WALES (1740-1827)

Mary Wales survived her husband by some 28 years. Widowhood saw her and the family's enforced move from the Master's house within the confines of Christ's Hospital school, which had been their home for over 20 years, to Hackney in London. Her two spinster daughters later married at St John's Church, Hackney, Anne Hagley in 1799, and Mary Judith in 1812. Mary Wales died on 29th January 1827, at the home of Mary Judith and her son-in-law, of the Vicarage, Clavering in Essex where her son-in-law was incumbent, she was 86 years old. Mary is buried at Clavering and in the church is a marble memorial. (see Illustration No 14)

Her two sons, John and James, were mentioned in their father's will[2] in 1798, but Mary was to learn of the deaths of her two surviving sons in India during her lifetime. In her will she declares the kindness and affection shown to her by Mary Judith and her son-in-law, this indicates that perhaps she had lived with them for some time before her death. She bequeaths her estate to her three daughters, with a special amount to be held in trust for her two grandsons, the sons of Mary Judith and Lancelot Pepys Stephens for their 'advancement in the world'.[3]

THE CHILDREN OF WILLIAM & MARY WALES

Of the seven children born to William and Mary Wales it is apparent from their father's will that five survived him.[4] The eldest son William had died while studying at Cambridge in 1789 aged just 21, and their second son Joshua, baptized at Christ Church, Newgate Street in 1776, is not mentioned in his father's will, The couple had another two sons, John born 1780 and James born 1783, both died in India, and only the three girls survived their mother.

SARAH WALES (C1767-1849)

Sarah had married Arthur William Trollope in 1797, having lived with her parents at Christ's Hospital, she moved to Ugley in Essex where her new husband was vicar, only to move back to Christ's Hospital two years later when her husband was appointed Headmaster there.[5] On her husband's death in 1827, she would again move from Christ's Hospital. In 1841 she was living with her son Edward and his wife Catherine, at 59 Dougherty Street, London, and she died of 'old age' aged 82, on 28th August 1849 at 24 John Street, Bedford Row, Holborn, the home of her daughter Sarah Daniel.[6]

Sarah Trollope was buried in the vaults at Christ's Hospital, and a plaque erected to her memory.[7] The vaults had been dug in 1834, for interment of officers of the Hospital and their families, replacing the 'lesser playground' and surrounding cloisters for burials, which had been used since the foundation of the old Grey Friars Monastery. The vault was of two chambers, one which was used to bury the remains of bodies found when the vault was dug – this was then bricked up, and the outer chamber then used for new coffins to be laid. This outer chamber was constructed with adequate ventilation so that disagreeable odours were prevented. Sarah's coffin was the sixth to be buried there since its construction, and all the coffins there were lined with lead. Such care was taken with these interments, that her son George Trollope was surprised when a letter appeared in *The Times* by a person with the pseudonym *Veritas* complaining that the opening of the vault had been done with 'scandalous negligence'. George immediately replied at length, describing the process of opening the vault and the placing of the coffins there, assuring the readers that he alone was responsible with these charges, and if the charges were true, then the governors of the hospital would have sufficient cause for withdrawing their confidence in him, but as there were no grounds for the accusations, he suggested the letter was a 'scandalous libel'.[8]

ARTHUR WILLIAM TROLLOPE (1768-1827) educated at Christ's Hospital, he was the son of Thomas Trollope, a London wine merchant. His great grandfather was Sir Thomas Trollope (c1667-1729) 3rd Baron Casewick and Sherriff of Lincolnshire, the family descendants also included the author Anthony Trollope (1815-1882).

Arthur William Trollope, M.A., D.D., had been a prize-winning classical scholar of Pembroke College, Cambridge, before taking up his position as vicar of Ugley in Essex. In 1799 he was appointed Headmaster of Christ's Hospital, a position he held until his retirement 28 years later, to his living of Colne Engaine in Essex in 1827, and it was here, two months after retiring, that he died, aged 59 years.[9]

Trollope was a contemporary of S.T. Coleridge and had been a fellow-pupil with him at Christ's Hospital, and Coleridge wrote a latin Ode entitled 'Honos alit artes', and the text of a Latin ode upon the occasion of Trollope's Honour, the second Chancellor's Classical Medal.[10]

A portrait of AW Trollope was included in his son's book on the History of Christ's Hospital.[11] The portrait is attributed to James Tannock, R.A.[12]

Sarah (nee Wales) and Arthur W Trollope had seven children:

William Arthur Trollope (1798-1863) was the first grandchild of William and Mary Wales, and the only one to be born before William Wales' death. W.A Trollope was educated at Christ's Hospital,[13] and entered Pembroke College, Cambridge in 1817, gaining his M.A. in 1824. In 1822 he was appointed one of the Classical Masters at Christ's Hospital, where he remained until 1834.[14]

One of his pupils described him as of neuter gender, and thought because his articulation was jumbled, and he rolled his words one into another before they took sound, he must have been paralyzed at some time. He dragged his leg after him 'as a Scotchman would a haddock'.[15]

He wrote *History of the Royal Foundation of Christ's Hospital* which was published in 1834, in which the Tannock portrait of his father A.W. Trollope appears.[16]

In 1825 W. A. Trollope married Sarah Clarke (c1800-1858) at East Bergholt, Suffolk. Sarah's brother was Rev William

Branwhite Clarke, a geologist, who was the first man to find gold in Australia.[17]

On leaving Christ's Hospital W. A. Trollope held a number of livings, but with a large family to support, and on the advise of his brother-in-law W. B. Clarke, he and Sarah, and their ten children sailed for Australia on the *John Munn*, and they eventually settled in Tasmania. During the 5 month passage to Australia, Trollope wrote a diary of the voyage, which is now deposited in the National Library of Australia.[18]

Sometime, perhaps toward the end of his life, Trollope found time to write a brief Autobiography which remains unpublished. In it he attempts to explain why his life had taken the course it did, how he was cheated out of his royalties for his published works, how his infirmity affected his career, and how in the end he was forced to leave the country of his birth, only to face more disappointments, trials and troubles abroad.[19]

W. A. Trollope died in 1863 at he age of 65, and is buried at St Mary's Church, Green Ponds, Kempton, Tasmania, where he was minister of the parish. His wife Sarah had died five years earlier aged 58, in Hobart, Tasmania.

Children of W. A. Trollope and Sarah (nee Clarke) were William Trollope (1826-1878); Arthur William Trollope (1827-1828); Henry Barne Trollope (1827-1828); Henry Barne Trollope (1828-1829); Sarah Trollope (1830-1849); George Leonard Trollope (1831- ?); Emily Maria Trollope (1832-1880); Mary Harriet Trollope (c1833–1907); Edward Frederick Trollope (1834-1910); Lumley John Trollope (c1834-1929); Charlotte Eliza Trollope (1837-1931); and Sophia Trollope (1848-1849).

Rev Arthur Trollope (1799-1848) was educated by his father, but not under the foundation of Christ's Hospital. He went to Pembroke Hall, Cambridge and gained his B.A.[20] and M.A. He lodged at St Botolph, Aldersgate London, and for 21 years until his death he was curate of the united parishes of St Mary-le-Bow, St Pancras, Cheapside, Soper-lane and All-Hallows, Honey Lane churches, London.[21] He died unmarried.in 1848 in his 49th year.

Jervoise Trollope (1801-1804) was baptised at Christ Church, Newgate Street, London,[22] and buried in the Cloisters at Christ's Hospital on 6th January 1804.[23]

George Trollope (1802-1864) was educated at Christ's Hospital 1809-1817.[24] On his discharge he was taken into the Counting House of Christ's Hospital school as apprentice,[25] and rose to Chief Clerk, he worked there until his death at Christ's Hospital. He married Alicia Wilby (1808-1887) in 1838. They had two daughters, Alice Jane Trollope (1841-1924), who remained unmarried, and Mary Ann Sybil Trollope (1842-1932), who married Rev William Mayou Daniel.

After George's death his wife, and daughter Alice Jane, lived at Reigate in Surrey until their deaths.

Edward Trollope (1803-1847) became a solicitor in London. He married twice, first Mary Ann Wilby (1801-1834) in 1833, and they had a son Edward Walker Trollope (1834-1838), and second, Catherine Daniel (1802-1866) in 1840, at Burton-on-Trent, Staffordshire, and by Catherine, had a daughter Catherine Sarah Trollope (1841-1925), who married Rev Charles Andrew Daniel (1841-1911) in 1867 in Derby. They had one daughter who remained unmarried.

Amelia Trollope (1806-?) was baptised at Christ Church, Newgate Street, London. The date of her death is unknown.

Sarah Trollope (1808-1878) married William Thomas Shave Daniel (1806-1891), in 1840 at St Pancras, London. W. T. S. Daniel Q.C. was a law reformer, and an eminent judge of the County Courts.[26] Sarah was his second wife, and together they had one son Arthur William Trollope Daniel (1841-1873), who became a barrister at Lincolns Inn. A. W. T. Daniel was also a world-class sportsman, who captained the Harrow cricket and football XIs, and was a Middlesex batsman and wicket-keeper.[27]

ANNE HAGLEY WALES (c1770-1853)

Anne Hagley Wales was born at Clerkenwell, London.[28] Anne married William Eyre in 1799, the year following her father's death, at the church of St John at Hackney. Anne was widowed in 1836, and in 1841 she was living in Lambeth, Surrey, her 5 year old grandson George, son of her late son George Eyre, was living with her. Ten years later she was in Leicester visiting her nephews, William Wales Stephens and Arthur Lancelot Stephens, with her sister Mary Judith Stephens and Mary Clare, the sister of Arthur William Trollope. In her will she bequeathed the portraits of her mother and father to her nephew William Wales Stephens.[29] When she died her abode was Berwick Field, Croydon, she was 83, and buried in West Norwood Cemetery, London.[30]

WILLIAM EYRE (1769-1836). Was a wine merchant of Great St Helen's in London. William was born in the Penistone area of Yorkshire, the son of James Eyre and Mary Smith. The Eyre family were of Derbyshire, and inspired Charlotte Bronte to name her famous character *Jane Eyre.*[31] William Eyre was also related to the Eyre Jackson family of Tullydoey, Co Armagh, Ireland, who made a fortune as linen drapers and bleachers.[32] James Eyre Jackson of Tullydoey, was a Justice of the Peace, nephew of William Eyre, and one of the executors named in Anne Hagley's Eyre's will.

William Eyre and Anne Hagley had at least four children:

William Eyre (1801-1802). William was baptised at the church of St Michael Crooked Lane,[33] London, and he was buried, aged one year, at St Margaret Lothbury, London, when he was described as from Crooked Lane.[34]

James Eyre (1802-?) James was baptized at the church of All Saints, Edmonton, London, when his father was described as a 'Gentleman from Church Street'.[35] It appears that James died young. When Anne wrote her will she wished to be buried with her husband and children, and in June 1836, after her son George died in Australia, there appeared a notice in the *London Standard*:

> ...Nov 6. 1835, at Perth, Swan river, George, only surviving son of the late William Eyre Esq of Kingsland.[36]

Benjamin Eyre (1804-1805)[37] Benjamin died aged seven months and was buried at St Margarets church, Lothbury, London, when he was described as 'from Edmonton'.[38]

George Eyre (c1808-1835) died and was buried in Perth, Australia in 1835.

In 1829 George Eyre had written to the Colonial Office enquiring about land in Australia, describing himself as an 'agriculturalist'. He arrived in Australia in 1830, and during the voyage he had met, and fallen in love with Catherine Bamber, the daughter of a shipowner from Liverpool, but when Catherine's father disapproved of them marrying, they eloped and married at Freemantle, spending their honeymoon in a tent. This is recorded as the first ever elopement in Western Australia.[39]

George's career varied from auctioneer to fisherman, then in 1835 he was involved in a fight with a fellow drinker in Perth, he fell on a barrel and died of a ruptured bowel, he was buried in Perth, the year before his father's death.[40]

George's wife Catherine returned to England with their two sons, William James and George. In 1841 George junior was living with his grandmother Anne Hagley Eyre, and in 1851 Catherine and her sons were living in Bermondsey, London, where Catherine was an 'annuitant', with the two boys working as Clerks. Then in 1858 William James, and George with his wife and family, arrived back in Australia, where they farmed and raised families.

MARY JUDITH WALES (1778-1865)

Mary Judith Wales was born at Christ's Hospital, and in 1812 married Lancelot Pepys Stephens, by licence, the ceremony was performed by her brother-in-law Arthur William Trollope at the church of St Botolph's Without, Aldersgate, London, at the same church as her uncle Charles Green had married Elizabeth Long in 1768. When she married, Mary Judith was of the parish of St John Hackney, and L P Stephens was Under Grammar Master at Christ's Hospital, so Mary Judith would once more, and for the next five years, be living within the confines of Christ's Hospital where she was brought up. After her husband passed away in 1833 at Clavering, Essex, his effects were sold,[41] and Mary Judith moved to Bromley College which was founded in 1666 by Bishop Warner of Rochester, to provide 19 poor widows and loyal clergymen with housing. Mary Judith Stephens died there in 1865, aged 87.

LANCELOT PEPYS STEPHENS (1766-1833), a past pupil of Christ's Hospital, he was the son of Lancelot Stephens and Mary West Bridell.[42] Mary died in 1768 leaving three children, her son Lancelot Pepys was 2 years old. Their father Lancelot was a coffee man, and owned Tom's Coffee House in Devereux Court, off the Strand in London, his father had pre-deceased his grandfather, who was a considerable property owner.[43] Their grandfather re-wrote his will after Lancelot Pepys Stephens' father's death, and it was his two uncles who profited from this.[44] But their brother Lancelot's wife was pregnant with young Lancelot when her husband died and she petitioned the Lord High Chancellor that her husband's brothers had been wrongly possessed of her late husband's heirs entitlement to a share of their grandfather's estate.[45] Despite a lengthy legal dispute Lancelot Pepys Stephens' father never profited from the family's fortune.

It was due to Lancelot Pepys Stephens' mother's early death, that he was granted admission to Christ's Hospital, and then to Pembroke College, Cambridge where he gained his B.A. and M.A. From 1787 to 1796 he was assistant master at a school in Clapton before being ordained, and taking up his position of Under Grammar Master at Christ's Hospital.[46]

Charles Lamb wrote that he was the kindest of boys and men.

James Leigh Hunt described him as:

> ...short and fat with a handsome, cordial face. You loved him as you looked at him; and seemed as if you should love him the more the fatter he became. I stammered when I was at that time of life : which was an infirmity that used to get me into terrible trouble with the master. Stevens used to say, on the other hand, "Here comes our little black-haired friend, who stammers so. Now let us see what we can do for him."

The consequence was, I did not hesitate half so much as with the other. When I did, it was out of impatience to please him.

Such of us were not liked the better by the master as were in favour with his wife. She was a sprightly, good-looking woman, with black eyes; and was beheld with transport by the boys, whenever she appeared at the school-door. Her husband's name, uttered in a mingled tone of good-nature and imperativeness, brought him down from his seat with smiling haste. Sometimes he did not return. On entering the school one day, he found a boy eating cherries, "Where did you get those cherries?" exclaimed he, thinking the boy had nothing to say for himself: "Mrs Boyer gave them me, sir." He turned away, scowling with disappointment.[47]

According to his nephew, Stephens had been the faithful Under Grammar Master at Christ's Hospital school for over twenty years, and:

...His name will long be remembered with affection by those who, in passing through the school, had been partially under his charge. In Communicating his instructions the sternness of the preceptor was forgotten in the indulgence of the parent ; and, while his mildness of manners and gentleness of discipline will not be forgotten by the objects of his care, his openness of disposition, benevolence of spirit, and warmth of friendship have endeared him to the hearts of all who know him. He has been followed into his retirement by the best wishes of his friends and pupils; and may he long survive in the enjoyment of the happy consciousness of a useful and well spent life! [48]

A past pupil was Tom Barnes, editor of the Times, confirmed years later that the names of L.P. Stephens and Arthur Wm Trollope were still well remembered by both septuagenarians and octogenarians.[49]

Lancelot Pepys Stephens retired to the living of Clavering with Langley in Essex of which Christ's Hospital held the advowson, and here he was able to contribute to the schooling of the children. He opened two rooms for the school in the workhouse there, where he taught children until 1826. He then opened a separate school for 81 girls during the week, and taught the boys there on Sundays, but after a dispute with the workhouse authorities he was forced to carry on his teaching back in the church.[50]

From the parish registers is a record of him 'beating the bounds' in 1823, when he led a group of 30 parishioners around the boundaries of Clavering, the details of which are recorded in the parish registers of that place.[51]

Lancelot Pepys Stephens died in 1834 and a memorial to the memory of both he and his sister is to be found on the wall in Clavering Church:

To the Memory of the
Revd. LANCELOT PEPPYS STEPHENS A.M.
LATE VICAR OF THIS PARISH
AND FOR MANY YEARS ONE OF THE
CLASSICAL MASTERS OF CHRIST'S HOSPITAL
WHO DIED JANUARY 7TH 1834
IN THE 67TH YEAR OF HIS AGE
ALSO
ELIZABETH CATHERINE STEPHENS
SISTER OF THE ABOVE
WHO DIED AUGUST 12TH 1831
IN THE 70TH YEAR OF HER AGE

The sale of his effects after his death, reveal that Rev Stephens owned a library of 750 books, which included scientific and literary works, valuable classical works and rare volumes of divinity.[52]

Lancelot Pepys Stephens and Mary Judith had three sons:

Lancelot Stephens (1814-1815) the eldest, died at the age of 6 months.

William Wales Stephens (1815-1882), was born at Christ's Hospital, London.

In the 1841 Census he is living at Friar Lane in Leicester with his brother Arthur, when they are both described as 'Chemists', the circumstances of which are laid out in a newspaper of 1840[53]:

*To the Nobility, Gentry, clergy and Inhabitants of
Leicester and its Vicinity.*

In consequence of the decease of my late son, Mr. James Dulley,
sometime Chemist and Druggist, of the Hotel-street, in this
town, I, as executor to my said son have this day disposed of
the Stock-in-trade, Good-will, &c., of the said business, to Mr.
W.W. STEPHENS; who having lived as assistant with my son
during the whole of his occupation of it, I trust will continue
to give satisfaction, and receive a continuance of that support
which was awarded to my son.

(Signed) DAVID DULLEY, Executor.

Wellington-street, Leicester,

19th Sept., 1840.

WILLIAM WALES STEPHENS,

HAVING purchased of the Executor the entire STOCK, and
entered upon the Old Established Business late in the occupation
of Mr James Dulley (successor to Mr. Masters),

CHEMIST AND DRUGGIST

Begs leave to solicit of his Friends and the Public in general
a continuance of that support so liberally bestowed on his
predecessors.

W.W.S. having been apprenticed to, and received the education
of, a Surgeon, as well as having been in the business of a Chemist
and Druggist for the last ten years, in houses of respectability
in London and the country, trusts to be enabled to deserve
the confidence of the public by accuracy in the dispensing of
any Physicians' or Surgeons' Prescriptions, in family recipes
submitted to his care.

W.W.S. begs leave particularly to state that every Drug or
chemical used by him is warranted to be of the purest quality.

From Anne Hagley Eyre's will, her nephew William Wales Stephens inherited the portraits of William and Mary Wales by John Russell.[54] By 1861 he was back in London, and manager of a public house in St. Anne's Westminster, in 1866 he had the Duke of Clarence public house at 61 Hackney Road in London, but unfortunately went bankrupt,[55] so in the 1871 census he is a surgeon's assistant in the Kensington district of London. He died of heart disease in 1882 aged 67, when he lived in Bloomsbury, London, he was unmarried and described as a 'Dispenser sub-med'.

Arthur Lancelot Stephens (1817-1875), was born at Christ's Hospital, London, and had been educated at St Paul's School in London.[56] He was with his brother in Leicester as a chemist in both the 1841 and 1851 census. He could not be located from the 1861 and 1871 census returns, but when he died in 1875, he was in Charing Cross Hospital, Agar Street, London and described as a chemist, so was perhaps working at the hospital when he died, aged 58, of kidney disease. He was a bachelor.

JOHN WALES (1780-1803)

Mary Wales had petitioned Christ's Hospital for financial support for herself and four of her children[57] in 1799 on the death of her husband. However there is evidence that their son John, and possibly also his brother James were in India at this time.

In 1798 the year of his father's death, John visited Richard Blechynden, who had been tutored in astronomy and mathematics by William Wales, and was a great friend of John's cousin John Wales, of the Hon East India Compay. Blechynden tells of John Wales, son of Mary, being fifth mate on the vessel *Thetis* in 1798, and of him revealing that his brother William Wales had died of venereal disease while at Cambridge University.[58]

John Wales died and was buried 23.8.1803 in Calcutta, West Bengal, India.[59] He was an officer on the ship *Lushington* in the East India Company Service.[60]

On 26th July 1804, his mother Mary Wales received £300 probate from John's estate.[61]

JAMES WALES (1783-1801)

James went to India as had his brother John. Richard Blechynden knew them both, and tells of young James borrowing some money from him, which he regretted as James had died of hepatitis before the loan was repaid.[62]

James pre-deceased his brother John by two years, and was buried also in Calcutta, Bengal, India on 26th August 1801.[63]

THE FAMILY OF MARY WALES (née GREEN)

PARENTS
JOSHUA GREEN (1687(?)-1749)
ANN GREEN (dates unknown)

Mary Green's parents were Joshua and Ann Green, details of their marriage has proved elusive, and this has also been the case when searching for the origins of the second baptismal name of Mary's second daughter, Anne Hagley Wales.

It is thought that Joshua Green senior was born at Hemsworth in 1687. Hemsworth is less than 3 miles from Wragby. The first evidence of a child of Joshua Green appears in 1720 at Wath on Dearne with the baptism of Joshua Green junior, followed by four at nearby Wentworth, William in 1727/8, Charles in 1734, Elizabeth in 1737 and Mary in 1740/1.

In Joshua Green senior's will, written in November 1735, when his abode is given as Barrow, near Wentworth, and his occupation was a butcher, the order of the children given is John, Ann, Joshua, William and Charles – Elizabeth and Mary had yet to be born.[64]

THE SIBLINGS OF MARY GREEN

REV JOHN GREEN (C1719-1774)

After Rev John Green's death 1774 and his wife Sarah in 1792, and all their family having pre-deceased them, they left the bulk of their estate to their niece Rhoda Green, daughter of John's brother William Green.

ANN GREEN (C1719- ?)

Ann is mentioned next after John in their father's will of 1735,[65] it is not known what happened to Ann in later life.

JOSHUA GREEN (1720-1799)

Joshua married twice, but died in Leeds without issue. He had been a founding partner in the Leeds Pottery, and this business had also employed other members of the family, notably his cousin Savile Green who was son of his father's brother John who had married Catherine Savile, sister of the first Earl of Mexborough. Savile Green eventually married Rhoda Green, the daughter of his own cousin William.[66]

WILLIAM GREEN (1728- ?)

William Green married Ann Rhodes in 1751 at Wath on Dearne, and they had four children. A daughter Rhoda who married Savile Green of Leeds Pottery; William, who it is thought went down to London; Ebenezer, who was a liquor merchant in Leeds[67] before eventually being employed by the Leeds Pottery;[68] and Lydia Green, who married George Gilpin, the servant who accompanied William Wales on

Cook's Voyage. George and Lydia Gilpin had two sons, George and Ebenezer, and three daughters.

George Gilpin died in 1810, when his son George was considered by the Royal Society as his successor, but they found he was already employed as a clerk in the Navy Office. His youngest son Ebenezer did not succeed, as he had only just left school when his father died.[69]

George Gilpin junior died the year after his father in 1811, aged 29, and the younger son Ebenezer died in 1819 aged 24. Their mother Lydia died in 1827, all four were buried in the church of St Mary le Strand.[70] On the death of their father at least one of the Gilpin's daughters was placed at Miss Pawsey's school at Ampthill, in 1811, with the approval of Queen Charlotte,[71] this was the royal embroidery school, established to provide embroidery for the royal household, and provide employment for the daughters of professional gentlemen. Lydia Green and her family lived in a rented house in Union Street, St Pancras, Camden between 1813 and 1822.[72]

The three Misses Gilpin had all moved to Birmingham by 1841, where Lydia was a schoolmistress.[73] In 1851 the three sisters were still living together, at Weston super Mare in Somerset, all unmarried. In1861 Lydia was described as an *Owner of Houses,* and Mary Ann had been blind for three years. All the sisters died unmarried.

CHARLES GREEN (1735-1771)

Charles Green had married Elizabeth Long in London, before setting out on the voyage with Captain Cook on *Endeavour*, he had died during the voyage.

ELIZABETH GREEN (1737- ?)

Elizabeth was living at Darfield in Yorkshire when she married Jonas Taylor, a clothier, at Calverley, near Leeds, in Yorkshire. Jonas and Elizabeth Taylor had a son William who was born at Greenwich, near London. William was employed by, and eventually took over the management of the Leeds Pottery.[74]

THE FAMILY OF WILLIAM WALES' BROTHER JOHN

John Wales was the only brother of William, he lived in Warmfield, Yorkshire, while his brother sailed the world and enjoyed fame and adventure. They had a sister Sarah who died unmarried.

The early death of John's wife Mary had left him with three daughters and one son to raise.

Evidence from the Warmfield burial registers suggests that William Wales had eventually gained his brother employment, through Sir Nevil Maskelyne, as a Board of Longitude Calculator.

John and Mary Wales had four children:

MARY WALES (1765-1824)

Mary married Richard Womack at Warmfield. Richard was a collier, and brother to her sister Sarah's husband. They had 6 children.

JOHN WALES (1766-1810)

It was a quirk of fate that first led to the details of the life of John and Mary's only son John.[75] The writer was told of a large gravestone in Kirkthorpe churchyard in Yorkshire, carved with the names of John and Mary Wales and their son, and mention of the Hon. East India Company. This prompted further investigation of an entry in the Cambridge Alumnii volumes, just below that of William Wales' son William, who had died while studying there. The entry told of another William Wales, whose father John, was a Captain who had served in the H.E.I.C.S.

The stone lies horizontal on the ground to the south of Kirkthorpe church, (see Ilustration No 12) and reads:

> Here
> Lieth the bodies of MARY WALES,
> died the 21 December 1769 aged 28
> Years and JOHN WALES died 28
> April 1787 aged 51 years.
> This Stone was put on their ashes
> by their only Son Lt. John Wales
> after an Absence of 22 years from his
> Native Country out of respect to the
> Remains to the Authors of his
> Being; in the Year 1801.
>
> After a short Illness
> On the 15th January 1810, died at
> Calcutta
> Capt John Wales
> Of the Honble. East India Company
> Bombay Marine,
> only Son of the above
> John and Mary Wales
> Aged 43 Years
> He would gladly have mingled his ashes
> With His Parents
> But Providence determined otherwise
> Faithful to All; in Duty firm but Kind
> Human, yet Valiant; Active yet Resign'd
> 1811.

Family papers indicate that John had been apprenticed to a surgeon as a youth, which he disliked intensely, this hatred caused him to break his indenture and run away to sea at the age of 12.[76]

John's niece wrote of her uncle entering the East India Company's service as a Midshipman, and so distinguished himself during the Tippo Saib wars, that he became a Captain at the age of 19. He was a hard taskmaster, and would in no way allow swearing or drunkenness aboard his ship.[77]

Capt John Wales was a great friend of Richard Blechynden, who, as part of his education, had been tutored by William Wales at Christ's Hospital.[78] This friendship could indicate that Capt John Wales was also tutored by his uncle William before heading for a career in surveying. John was 9 years old when his Uncle took the position of head of the Royal Mathematical School in Christ's Hospital, and four years later young John volunteered for service with the Hon. East India Company, quickly rising through the ranks of its navy, the *Bombay Marine*.[79] John was made a Captain in 1803, and in 1808 the Directors appointed him Surveyor General of India, stationed at Fort William he was responsible for all the marine surveys in the eastern waters.[80]

John Wales died in 1810 after a long illness, and was buried at Calcutta.[81]

In 1802 John had married Maria Catherine Dixon at St Mary le Bone, London. Maria Catherine was the daughter of a wealthy London merchant, Marcus Dixon.[82] Her sister Elizabeth Morris Dixon married Archibald Blair, another surveyor of the Hon. East India Company, a colleague of Captain John, and a member of the illustrious Blair family of Windyedge, Scotland.[83]

Captain John Wales and Maria Catherine had the following family:

Rev William Wales (1804-1889) Born in India, William was entered into Christ's Hospital in 1810 after his father's death,[84] and then in 1817 he was transferred to Mill Hill School in London.[85] He entered St Catharine's College at Cambridge in 1823 under the Skerne Foundation, sanctioned due to his father being a native Yorkshireman.[86] On gaining his B.A. degree he was ordained a priest.[87]

Rev William Wales was the vicar of All Saints, Northampton for twenty seven years, during which time he was appointed Chancellor of the diocese of Peterborough. In 1859 he became the Rector of Uppingham in Rutland, where he found the church in a sorry state, and set about seeing to its restoration in the Victorian style, he was a contemporary of Edward Thring, the famous head of Uppingham School. [88]

Retiring in 1879, Rev William Wales moved to Great Houghton in Northamptonshire, and from there he then moved to Leamington Spa, where he died. He is buried at Great Houghton.[89]

Rev William Wales first married Frances Haslope, whose niece Mary Ethel Louisa Haslope married George Brooks Percy Spooner Lillingston of Ferriby in Yorkshire, a family who were linked to William Wilberforce and George Vancouver among others.[90]

Frances died at the age of 40, suddenly in 1855, and in 1859 Rev William Wales married Hon Louisa Diana Spencer, daughter of the first Baron Churchill and Lady Frances Fitzroy, Lady Frances was daughter of the Duke of Grafton and aunt of Admiral Robert Fitzroy.

Hon Louisa Diana Spencer was the grand-daughter of the Duke of Marlborough, and of the same family of Sir Winston Churchill and Lady Diana Frances Spencer (1961-1997).

Rev William and Hon Louisa died childless and both are buried at Great Houghton, Northamptonshire.

John Wales (1806-1832) entered Christ's Hospital school London in 1811.[91] On leaving school John entered the East India Marine Service but was drowned at sea in 1832,[92] he remained a bachelor.

Marcus Dixon Wales (1807-1824) was educated at Mill Hill School, London,[93] he died aged 17.

Douglas Wales (1808-1873) was educated at Mill Hill School, London.[94] At the age of 16 he entered the Honorable East India Company's service. A naval Captain, he was eventually appointed Harbour Master of Port Louis, Mauritius in 1856.[95] He married Barbe Arnalie Laure de la Volpeliere in 1843, and raised a family of 12.

Douglas Wales died in 1873, at Government House, Malie, Seychelles, and after a distinguished career was given a large splendid funeral. A Union Jack covered the coffin which was borne away by ten of the Government boatmen dressed in uniform, many Mauritius officials attended.[96] Their son Douglas William Wales, (1848-1903) was in the Civil Service, and his eldest sister Mary Susannah Wales married Charles Frederick Edwards, M.R.C.S., Eng. whose son John Douglas Edwards was a Vice-Admiral in the Royal Navy.

It was through these two families that the Russell portraits of William and Mary Wales passed, before being purchased by Christ's Hospital school where they remain.[97]

The surviving children of Douglas eventually inherited the estate of their uncle, Rev William Wales.[98]

George Wales (1809-1829) died aged 19.[99]

SARAH WALES (1768-1811)

Sarah married George Womack at Warmfield. George was a tailor, and brother to her sister Mary's husband. George and Sarah had 7 children, two of whom, Edward and Samuel started a boat building business at Heath boatyard, which lay at the south of Warmfield-cum-Heath parish.

ABIGAIL WALES (1769-1848)

Abigail married Rev Joseph Manners who became a Methodist Minister.[100]

The couple had nine children who were taught to read and write by their mother before they started school. Eventually the family settled at Sheffield in Yorkshire where Abigail and Joseph died. One daughter Mary Wales Manners married Joseph Fenton, who had a cutlery works in Sheffield, and on her mother's death Mary wrote a Memoir.[101] In this narrative Mary wrote of her mother's early life in Warmfield.

WILLIAM WALES' SISTER

SARAH WALES (1739/40-1779)

Sarah Wales was baptized at Kirkthorpe church, and died a spinster, she was buried at Kirkthorpe.

So it was that William Wales, his brother John, and sister Sarah, children of a colliery worker of Warmfield in Yorkshire, lived their lives. While their sister Sarah lived a spinster's life in the small village with their father and mother, the two boys and their respective families followed different paths of diverse fame and fortune.

Endnotes

1 Footnote in Vincent, W., 1800. *The Periplus of the Erythean Sea*. London.

2 Will of William Wales, PRO Probate Records. Ref. PROB 11/1318.

3 Essex Record Office, Bishop of London's Commissary Court, 1827.

4 Will of William Wales, PRO Probate Records. Ref. PROB 11/1318.

5 Guildhall Library, London. Christ's Hospital Manuscript 12806/13/283 Court Minute Books. Vol.XIII. Minute dated 1799.

6 The 1841 Census of England and Wales.

7 Image No 179733. Website of the City of London: collage. cityoflondon.gov.uk/collage/app

8 *The Times*, September 12. 1849; p.7; issue 20279; col B.

9 *Gentleman's Magazine*, 1827; Vol. 142; p.86.

10 The Albin Schram collection of Autograph Letters, S T Coleridge to his brother Revd. George Coleridge. 1791.

11 Trollope, W A, 1834. *A History of the Royal Foundation of Christ's Hospital*. London, William Pickering.

12 Personal communication, The National Portrait Gallery, London.

13 Guildhall Library, London. Christ's Hospital Manuscripts, Presentation Papers of Admissions, 12818 Vol.13. Special Order 156.

14 Matthew, H C G & Harrison, B (Eds), 2004. *Oxford Dictionary of National Biography*. Oxford, Oxford University Press.

15 Blunden, Edmund, 1923. *Christ's Hospital, a retrospective*. London, Christophers. p.126.

16 Trollope, W A, 1834. *A History of the Royal Foundation of Christ's Hospital*. London, William Pickering.

17 Grainger, Elena, 1982. *The Remarkable Reverend Clarke*. Oxford, Oxford University Press.

18   Website: http://www.nla.gov.au/collect/newaq/200406.html

19   Personal communication, Mrs J Elliston.

20   *Gentleman's Magazine.* 1827; Vol. 142; page 86.

21   Burke, John, & Burke, Sir Bernard, (Eds.), 1848. *Patrician.* E. Churton. Vol.6.

22   Pallots Baptism Index for England 1780-1837.

23   Parish Registers of Christ Church and St Leonard, Foster Lane, London. Burials.

24   Guildhall Library, London. Christ's Hospital Manuscripts. Admissions Register Manuscript 12818, Special Order 157.

25   Guildhall Library, London. Christ's Hospital Manuscripts, Court Minute Books, Minute 12806/14. p.132.

26   Matthew, H C G & Harrison, B (Eds), 2004. *Oxford Dictionary of National Biography.* Oxford, Oxford University Press.

27   Website of Cricketworld: http://stats.cricketworld.com/ Players/28/28940/28940.html

28   The 1851 Census of England and Wales

29   Will of Anne Hagley Eyre, PRO Probate Records. Ref. PROB 11/2173.

30   West Norwood Cemetery database, London Borough of Lambeth.

31   Website: http://www.derbyshireuk.net.hathersage.html

32   Rankin, Kathleen, 2007. *Linen Houses of the Bann Valley.* Ulster Historical Foundations.

33   Parish Registers of St Michael, Crooked Lane, London. Baptisms.

34   Parish Registers of St Margaret, Lothbury, London. Burials.

35   Parish Registers of All Saints, Edmonton, London. Baptisms.

36   *London Standard,* Friday, 10th June 1836.

37   In the London Standard of 23rd March 1897 appeared a notice for information on the decendants of Benjamin and George Eyre, sons of William Eyre of Kingsland, Middlesex who had died in 1836 to get in touch with a solicitor in Pontefract, Yorkshire.

38   Parish Registers of St Margaret, Lothbury, London. Burials.

39   *The Western Australian,* 28th August 1937. p.6.

40   *The Perth Gazette & Western Australian Journal,* 7th and 14th November 1835.

41   *Huntingdon and Bedford and Peterborough Gazette,* 22nd March 1834.

42   Guildhall Library, London. Christ's Hospital Manuscript 12818. Children's Registers Vol. II; 1774; p.119.

43   Will of Lancelot Stephens, PRO Probate Records. Ref. Prob 11/692.

44   Will of Lancelott Stephens, PRO Probate Records. Ref. Prob 11/685.

45   Shropshire Archives. Haslewood Collection XD3614/1/1/5, dated 21 October 1740.

46   *Gentleman's Magazine,* 1834, Volume I. p.562.

47   Johnson, R Brimley, 1896. *Christ's Hospital: Recollections of Lamb, Coleridge and Leigh Hunt.* London, George Allen.

48   Trollope, W A, 1834. *A History of the Royal Foundation of Christ's Hospital.* London, William Pickering. p.157.

49   *Hampshire Advertiser.* Saturday 22nd February, 1862.

50   Personal Communication: Jacqueline Cooper, Clavering.

51   ibid.

52   *Huntingdon and Bedford and Peterborough Gazette,* 22nd March 1834.

53   *Leicestershire Mercury,* Saturday 26th September, 1840.

54   Will of Anne Hagley Eyre, PRO Probate Records, Ref. PROB 11/2173.

55   *London Gazette,* 2nd April 1869.

56   Gardiner, Robert Barlow. *Admission Registers of St Paul's School from 1748-1876.* London, G. Bell.

57   These four children would have been Anne Hagley, Mary Judith, John and James Wales.

58   Peter Robb, 2011. *Sex and Sensibility.* Oxford University Press, India.

59 Website: Familysearch.org.

60 British India Office Ecclesiastical Returns – Death and Burial Transcription – Parish Register trsnscripts from the Presidency of Bengal 1713-1948. Archive Ref N-1-6 page 237

61 Personal communication: Jan Shoulders.

62 Peter Robb, 2011. *Sex and Sensibility*. Oxford University Press, India.

63 British India Office Ecclesiastical Returns – Death and Burial Transcription – Parish Register trsnscripts from the Presidency of Bengal, 1713-1948. Archive Ref N-1-6; p. 90.

64 Borthwick Institute of Historical Research, York. Probate records, Prerogative Court of York.

65 ibid.

66 Griffin, John D, 2005. *The Leeds Pottery 1770-1881*. The Leeds Art Collection Fund.

67 Various notices in the *London Gazette*.

68 Griffin, John D, 2005. *The Leeds Pottery 1770-1881*. The Leeds Art Collection Fund.

69 Hall, Marie Boas, 1992. *The Library and Archives of the Royal Society*. London, The Royal Society.

70 Parish Registers of St Mary le Strand, London. Burials.

71 Dawson, Warren Royal, 1958. *The Banks Letters: a calendar of the manuscript of correspondence of Sir Joseph Banks*. London, British Museum.

72 London Land Tax Records, London Metropolitan Archives.

73 A notice from the *Birmingham Gazette*, dated 1st January 1838, stated that the school conducted by the Misses Gilpin will reopen the 8th January at 36 Newhall Street.

74 Griffin, John D, 2005. *The Leeds Pottery 1770-1881*, The Leeds Art Collection Fund.

75 Personal communication, Ron Pullen, Wakefield Family History Society.

76 Personal communication, Jan Shoulders.

77 Mrs Mary Wales Fenton. *Memoir of Mrs Abigail Manners.* (by her daughter). Methodist New Connexion Magazine, October 1848.

78 Peter Robb, 2011. *Sex and Sensibility.* Oxford University Press, India.

79 Public Department Diaries. Bombay Marine. Hon. East India Company.

80 *The Naval Chronicale – Naval History to the present Year 1810.*

81 1810 Jan 15. Captain John Wales, aged 44 years, of the H C Marine on the Bombay Establishment and Marine Surveyor General of India. Year of birth 1766; Archive Ref N-1-8; page 349; Parish register transcripts from the Presidency of Bengal; 1713-1948.

82 Proceedings of the Old Bailey. Ref. t1780115-15.

83 Malden, H E (Ed), 1911. *A History of the County of Surrey.* Victoria County Histories.

84 Guildhall Library, London. Christ's Hospital Manuscript. Presentation Papers Ref. 12818a-1811;p.44.

85 Hampden-Cook, Ernest, 1926. *The Register of Mill Hill School 1807-1926.* London.

86 ibid.

87 Venn, J & J A, 1883-1958. *Alumni Cantabrigiensis.* Cambridge, Cambridge University Press.

88 Personal Communication – Nigel Richardson, Perse School, Cambridge.

89 *Granthan Journal,* 31.8.1889

90 Bulman, David J., 1982. *North Ferriby. A Villagers' History.* North Ferriby, Lockington Publishing Company.

91 Guildhall Library, London. Christ's Hospital Manuscript. Presentation Papers Ref. 12818a-1812; p.33.

92 National Archives PROB 6/228, IR 26/226.

93 Hampden-Cook, Ernest, 1926. *The Register of Mill Hill School 1807-1926.* London.

94 ibid.

95   *The Gentleman's Magazine*, 1856.

96   Funeral report, dated 1st August, 1873, Translated from *La Sentinelle de Maurice*.

97   Wales, Wendy, *A Tale of Two Portraits*. Cook's Log, the Journal of the Captain Cook Society, 2010; vol. 33; No 1; p.18.

98   Probate Registry, York.

99   *The Gentleman's Magazine*, Jan-June 1829. Vol 145; p..286.

100 Stokoe, John (Ed), 1858. *Methodist Records: or Selections from the Journal of…A Lynn…* London, J.B. Cooke.

101 Mrs Mary Wales Fenton. *Memoir of Mrs Abigail Manners*. (by her daughter). Methodist New Connexion Magazine, October 1848.

GENEALOGICAL CHARTS

(Some dates shown are approximate and include years of baptism and burial).

WILLIAM WALES' DESCENDANTS CHART

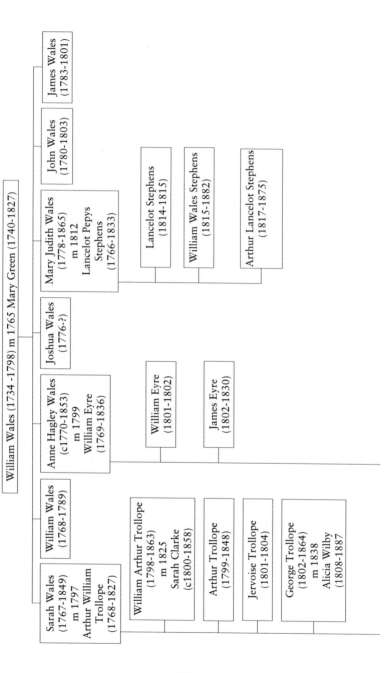

William Wales (1734 -1798) m 1765 Mary Green (1740-1827)

Sarah Wales (1767-1849) m 1797 Arthur William Trollope (1768-1827)

William Wales (1768-1789)

Anne Hagley Wales (c1770-1853) m 1799 William Eyre (1769-1836)

Joshua Wales (1776-?)

Mary Judith Wales (1778-1865) m 1812 Lancelot Pepys Stephens (1766-1833)

John Wales (1780-1803)

James Wales (1783-1801)

William Arthur Trollope (1798-1863) m 1825 Sarah Clarke (c1800-1858)

Arthur Trollope (1799-1848)

Jervoise Trollope (1801-1804)

George Trollope (1802-1864) m 1838 Alicia Wilby (1808-1887)

William Eyre (1801-1802)

James Eyre (1802-1830)

Lancelot Stephens (1814-1815)

William Wales Stephens (1815-1882)

Arthur Lancelot Stephens (1817-1875)

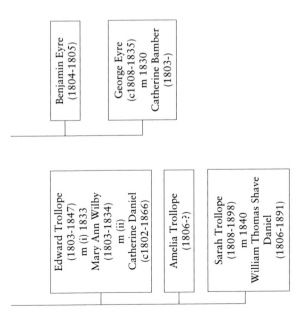

Benjamin Eyre
(1804-1805)

George Eyre
(c1808-1835)
m 1830
Catherine Bamber
(1803-)

Edward Trollope
(1803-1847)
m (i) 1833
Mary Ann Wilby
(1803-1834)
m (ii)
Catherine Daniel
(c1802-1866)

Amelia Trollope
(1806-?)

Sarah Trollope
(1808-1898)
m 1840
William Thomas Shave
Daniel
(1806-1891)

JOHN WALES' DESCENDANTS CHART

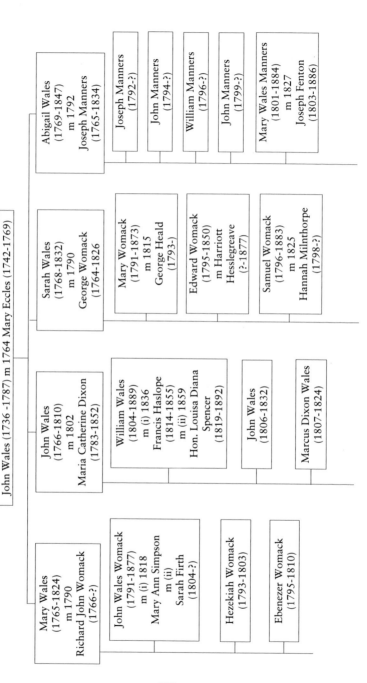

John Wales (1736 -1787) m 1764 Mary Eccles (1742-1769)

Abigail Wales
(1769-1847)
m 1792
Joseph Manners
(1765-1834)

Joseph Manners
(1792-?)

John Manners
(1794-?)

William Manners
(1796-?)

John Manners
(1799-?)

Mary Wales Manners
(1801-1884)
m 1827
Joseph Fenton
(1803-1886)

Sarah Wales
(1768-1832)
m 1790
George Womack
(1764-1826)

Mary Womack
(1791-1873)
m 1815
George Heald
(1793-)

Edward Womack
(1795-1850)
m Harriott
Hesslegreave
(?-1877)

Samuel Womack
(1796-1883)
m 1825
Hannah Milnthorpe
(1798-?)

John Wales
(1766-1810)
m 1802
Maria Catherine Dixon
(1783-1852)

William Wales
(1804-1889)
m (i) 1836
Francis Haslope
(1814-1855)
m (ii) 1859
Hon. Louisa Diana
Spencer
(1819-1892)

John Wales
(1806-1832)

Marcus Dixon Wales
(1807-1824)

Mary Wales
(1765-1824)
m 1790
Richard John Womack
(1766-?)

John Wales Womack
(1791-1877)
m (i) 1818
Mary Ann Simpson
m (ii)
Sarah Firth
(1804-?)

Hezekiah Womack
(1793-1803)

Ebenezer Womack
(1795-1810)

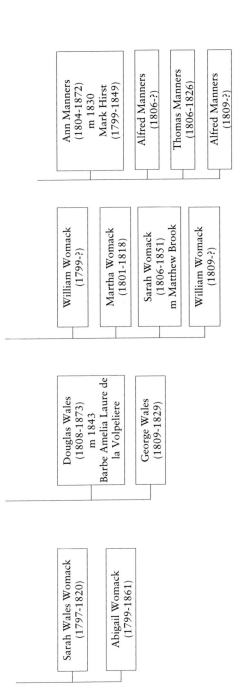

Ann Manners
(1804-1872)
m 1830
Mark Hirst
(1799-1849)

Alfred Manners
(1806-?)

Thomas Manners
(1806-1826)

Alfred Manners
(1809-?)

William Womack
(1799-?)

Martha Womack
(1801-1818)

Sarah Womack
(1806-1851)
m Matthew Brook

William Womack
(1809-?)

Douglas Wales
(1808-1873)
m 1843
Barbe Amelia Laure de
la Volpeliere

George Wales
(1809-1829)

Sarah Wales Womack
(1797-1820)

Abigail Womack
(1799-1861)

GREEN FAMILY CHART

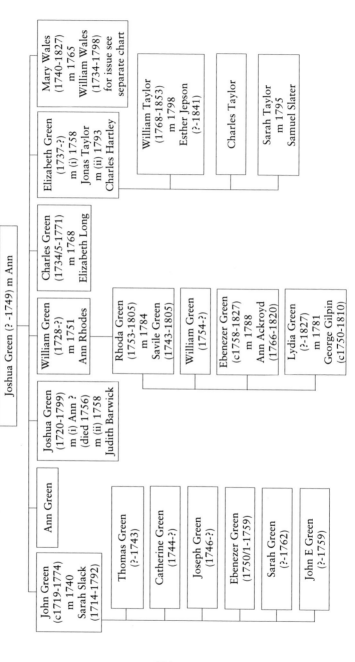

Joshua Green (? -1749) m Ann

John Green (c1719-1774) m 1740 Sarah Slack (1714-1792)

Ann Green

Joshua Green (1720-1799) m (i) Ann ? (died 1756) m (ii) 1758 Judith Barwick

William Green (1728-?) m 1751 Ann Rhodes

Charles Green (1734/5-1771) m 1768 Elizabeth Long

Elizabeth Green (1737-?) m (i) 1758 Jonas Taylor m (ii) 1793 Charles Hartley

Mary Wales (1740-1827) m 1765 William Wales (1734-1798) for issue see separate chart

Children of John Green:

Thomas Green (?-1743)

Catherine Green (1744-?)

Joseph Green (1746-?)

Ebenezer Green (1750/1-1759)

Sarah Green (?-1762)

John E Green (?-1759)

Children of William Green:

Rhoda Green (1753-1805) m 1784 Savile Green (1743-1805)

William Green (1754-?)

Ebenezer Green (c1758-1827) m 1788 Ann Ackroyd (1766-1820)

Lydia Green (?-1827) m 1781 George Gilpin (c1750-1810)

Children of Elizabeth Green:

William Taylor (1768-1853) m 1798 Esther Jepson (?-1841)

Charles Taylor

Sarah Taylor m 1795 Samuel Slater

434

APPENDIX I

The Route from Wakefield to London according to Ogilby's Map

John Ogilby (1600-1676) was born near Dundee. He had enjoyed a varied career, and after the Great Fire of London when he was well into his sixties, Ogilby, together with William Morgan, received a commission from the Lord Mayor of London to survey and draw a map of London. On completion of this survey he set about work on his *Britannia*, an atlas of road maps of England & Wales, which was published the year before he died. The maps are incredibly detailed, as well as place and river names, churches, houses, trees, mills, and inns are illustrated. Where the roads go over bridges, these are noted of either being of stone or wood. Each 1760 yard mile is marked, and further divided into furlongs.

* * *

The road from Wakefield heads over the river Calder, by way of a stone bridge on which is a chapel, the route then enters *Greenheath Moore*, sited at the modern village of Heath, which was originally the heathland to the manor of Warmfield, a village to the left of the road. The map then shows the way entering a lane with arable land on both sides, along the lane is a windmill, and to the right is *a cole mine*.

A further lane leads onto a common, before Pontefract, and eventually on to Ferrybridge twelve miles after Wakefield

Ferrybridge is sited on the modern A1, the Great North Road which heads south to London.

The route from Ferrybridge follows roughly the old A1 road, over the bridge which crosses the river Went, and onto where the map illustrates *Robbin Hoods Well,* a landmark still evident at the side of the A1. Continuing south, through Yorkshire to Bawtry, via Doncaster, the route enters Nottinghamshire, passing Blyth, and through *The Forest of Sherwood* to Newark, where Ogilby illustrates *Gallows* by a square symbol at the roadside. From here the route south follows Ermine Street, the old Roman road.

After Balderton the county of Lincolnshire is entered, and the road heads south to Grantham. Past Kirkstoke is Colsterworth, where the great scientist Sir Isaac Newton (1642-1727) lived at the Elizabethan Manor house of Woolsthorpe. Passing by Witham the way enters the small county of Rutlandshire, through which the road leads to Stamford.

From Stamford, passing between the beautifully illustrated *Burley Hall* (Burley House), and *Wathrop Hall* (Wothorpe Towers). The way via Greetham, Wittering, and Yaxley leads to Alconbury, where the route ceases to follow the A1, and diverts onto the course of the modern B1090 road. through Huntingdon and Caxton, and then the A1198 road, still the route follows the Roman Ermine Street to Kneesworth.

Continuing through Croydon, a toll bar appears on the map, and just south at Royston the rest of the road to London follows the A10 road, still marked on the modern map as the Roman Ermine Street. The road leads from Royston through Chipping and Puckridge to Ware, and enters London, via Hoddesdon and Edmonton to Tottenham High Cross, then along Stamford Hill and Kingsland Road, before heading along Gracechurch Street, to arrive at London Bridge and the river Thames, just 182 miles from Wakefield.

APPENDIX II

Astronomical Observations made by Order of the Royal Society, at Prince of Wales Fort on the North-West Coast of Hudson's Bay by William Wales and Joseph Dymond

1. All the measurements of Venus's diameter; and also all those of the Sun, which are not said to be horizontal, were taken with the micrometer, in the same direction that the last preceding distance of the limbs[2] of Venus and the Sun was measured with.

2. We were obliged to alter the rack-work of the micrometer before we began to measure any distances of the limbs, etc. in order to make it take in the diameter of Venus, off the scale.

3. The heavens at the beginning, and for a considerable time both before and after, were frequently obscured by clouds: but in the intervals, the air was very clear, and the Sun's limb extremely well defined.

4. Soon after Venus was half immerged, a bright crescent, or rim of light, encompassed all that part of her circumference which was off the Sun; thereby rendering her whole periphery visible. This continued very bright until within a few minutes of the internal contact, and then vanished away gradually.

5. We took for the instant of the first internal contact, the time when the least visible thread of light appeared behind the subsequent limb of Venus: but before that

time, Venus's limb seemed within that of the Sun, and his limbs appeared behind hers in two very obtuse points, seeming as if they would run together in a broad stream, like two drops of oil; but which nevertheless did not happen but joined in a very fine thread, at some distance from the exterior limb of Venus. This appearance was much more considerable at the egress than at the ingress; owing, as we apprehend, to the bad state of the air at that time. We took for the instant of internal contact at the egress, the time when the thread of light disappeared before the preceeding limb of the planet, from which time W. W. took notice that he had told about 24" when the limbs of the Sun and Venus were apparently in contact : a circumstance which he did not venture to attend to at the ingress.

6.   We saw nothing like the appearance of an atmosphere around Venus (unless the above-mentioned phenomena may be thought to proceed from thence) either at the beginning, end, or during the time of the transit : nor could we see anything of a satellite; though we looked for it several times.

7.   It may not be improper to add, that the haziness, complained of at the egress, was not owing to any accidental bad quality of the air at that time; it is continually so here to 10° or 12° above the horizon, and often even to 16° or 18°, in what may be called the clearest state of the heavens.

The floor of the Observatory might be above 50 Feet above the level of the Sea at Low-water Mark.

Endnotes

1   Philosophical Transactions of the Royal Society. 1769; Vol. lix.

2   *Limbs* are the apparent outer edge of a sun, planet or moon.

APPENDIX III

Instructions Given to William Wales by the Commissioners of Longitude on his Appointment as Observer on the Voyage of the *Resolution* 1772-1775[1]

Whereas you have agreed (on certain Terms) to go on board one of His Majestys Sloops, named in the Margin, which are now fitting out for a Voyage to remote parts, in Order to make Nautical & Astronomical Observations, and to perform other Services tending to the Improvement of Geography and Navigation, you are hereby required and directed to hold yourself in readiness, to Embark on board one of the said Sloops, when the Necessary Orders shall be given for your reception, and then to proceed in her on the above mentioned Voyage accordingly; And whereas we have Order'd you to be supply'd with the Several Instruments, Books, Maps, Charts & other things specified in the Schedule hereunto annexed which the Astronomer Royal will cause to be deliver'd to you, You are to receive and take into your Charge & Custody the said Instruments, Books, Maps, Charts &c (Giving our Secretary a Receipt for the Same) and to make use of them for the Several purposes to which they are Respectively adapted, taking all possible care of them during the Voyage and When that shall be finished, returning them to us in the best condition you may be able, And, in the performance of the abovementioned Service you are punctually and faithfully to Observe & Execute the following Instructions.

1. You are every day if the Weather will admit,[2] to observe Meridian Altitudes of the Sun for finding the Latitude & also other altitudes of the Sun both in the Morning & Afternoon, at a distance from Noon, with the time between measured by a Watch and the Suns bearing by the 1st Observation[3] in order to determine the Apparent time of the Day and Latitude in case the Sun should be clouded at Noon;[4] You are moreover to Observe distances of the moon from the Sun & fixed Stars with Hadleys Sextants from which you are to compute the Longitude by the Nautical Almanac.

2. You are to Wind up the Watches Every Day, as soon after the times of Noon as you can conveniently, and compare them together and Set down the respective times, and you are to Note also the times of the Watches when the Suns Morning & Afternoon altitudes, or the Distances of the Moon from the Sun and fixed Stars, are Observed; and to compute the Longitude resulting from the Comparison of the Watches and the Apparent time of the day inferred from the Morning & Afternoon Altitudes of the Sun, and as often as you shall have opportunities, you are to Compare one of the said Watches with one of those which may be under the care of the undermentioned Mr Bayley in the other Sloop, and Note down the respective times Shewn by the Said Watches.[5]

3. You are to Observe, or Assist at the Observations of, the Variation of the compass, and to Observe the Variation of the Magnetic dipping Needle from time to time.

4. You are to Note the height of one or more Thermometers placed in the Air & in the Shade early in the Morning and about the hottest time of the day, and to Observe also the height of the Thermometer within the Sloop near the Watches; and to make Remarks on the Southern

Lights if any should appear; And to make Experiments of the Saltness of the Sea and the degree of Cold by letting down the Thermometer at great Depths, as you may have Opportunity.[6]

5. You are to keep a Ship Journal with the Log work'd according to the plain dead reckoning (Leeway & Variation only allowed) Noting therein the length of the Log line & times of running, out of the sand Glasses from time to time;[7] And you are to insert therein also another Account corrected by the last cœlestial Observations & a third deduced from the Watches.

6. You are to teach such of the Officers on board the sloop as may desire it the use of the Astronomical Instruments &[8] the Method of finding the Longitude at sea from Lunar Observations.

7. You are to Settle the position of the head Lands, Islands & Harbours in Latitude and Longitude by the cœlestial Observations and also set down what Longitude the Watches give.

8. Where ever you land you are to make the same observations on shore as you have been directed to make on Ship board, only Observing to take the altitudes with the Astronomical Quadrant instead of the Hadleys Sextants and you are likewise to make the additional observations & to attend to the directions undermention'd—Viz.ᵗ

Whenever you can land safely (should it be for only two or three days) Set up the Astronomical Clock & fix it very firmly to a Massey piece of wood let deep into the ground and fix the Pendulum at the same exact length as it was of when going at the Royal Observatory at Greenwich before the Voyage and take equal Altitudes of the Sun & fixed stars for determining the rate of its going Noting the arc of Vibration of the Pendulum[9] and the Height of the Thermometer within the clock case[10] at the time; this will not only be usefull with respect to the other Astronomical Observations made on Shore, but also when compared with the going of the clock at Greenwich, will shew the Difference of gravity from that at Greenwich, which is a very Curious point in Experimental Philosophy.

Compare the Watches with the Astronomical Clock at Noon & also about the times of the Equal Altitudes.

Observe meridian Altitudes of the Sun and also of fixed Stars some to the North & some to the South for finding the Latitude; Observe also differences of right ascension between the Moon and fixed Stars in the Manner explained by the Astronomer Royal (Philos. Trans: Vol 54. p.348.) in Order to Settle the Moons parallax in right ascension in Various Latitudes.[11]

Make Observations of Eclipses of Jupiters Satellites & Occultations of fixt Stars & Planets by the Moon and any other Observations usefull for settling the Longitude of the place, and you are particularly to exert your best Endeavours to settle the Longitude of the Cape of good Hope with the utmost accuracy, in case you should touch there, by Observations of occultations of fixed Stars by the Moon and Transits of the Moon & proper stars over the meridian with the transit Instrument; And to send to us, from thence a full & particular Acco^t of all your proceedings & Observations.[12]

Observe the height of Barometer once at least every day.

Observe the height of the Tides and the time of high & low water, particularly at the full & change of the Moon and Whether there be any difference & What, between the Night & Day tides.[13]

9.   You are to take particular care that all your coelestial observations, whether made on ship board or on shore, be kept in a clear distinct and regular manner,[14] in a Book wherein the Commander of the Sloop and other Officers may also insert their Observations if they think fit, and that they be written, with all their Circumstances, immediately after they are made or as soon after as they can be conveniently transcribed therein from the loose papers or Memorandum Books in which they may be first Enter'd; which Book is to be always open for the inspection and use of the Commander & other Officers of the Sloop & of Joseph Banks Esq[r] and D[r] Solander who are going on the Voyage in one of the sloops: And you are to send to us, by every safe Conveyance which may Offer, the Results of your several Observations and also the Principal Observations themselves.[15]

10.   You are to co-operate with, and assist M[r] W[m] Bayley (who is under engagements with us to go out in the other of the two sloops abovementioned with Instructions similar to these) in whatever may be for the good of the Service wherein you are jointly imployed, we having given him directions to co-operate with and assist you in like manner. And Lastly,

For your care pains & Expences during the time you shall be employed on the above service; you will be allowed after the rate of Four hundred pounds p Annum to commence from the 25th January last; And for your further encouragement, we have, at your Request Order[ed] the Sum of One hundred & Fifty pounds to be impress'd to you on Account to enable you to fit yourself out, and One hundred and fifty pounds to be paid Annually during your absence or in case of your Death till such time we shall be apprized of it, by half yearly Payments, to your wife for the Subsistence of herself & family which sums, so to be impressed &

paid are to be deducted out of your above mention'd Allowance.

Given under our hands the 7th March 1772

Sandwich	John Smith	
Cha^{S}Hardy	E. Waring	

To	J. West	A. Shepherd
Mr Wm Wales	Nevil Maskelyne	Philip Stephens
	Thos Hornsby	John Smith

By Order of the Commissioners

Jno Ibbetson

Endnotes

1 Beaglehole, J C (Ed), 1969. *The Journals of Captain James Cook on His Voyages of Discovery. II. The Voyage of the Resolution and Adventure 1772-1775*. Cambridge. Published for the Hakluyt Society (Extra Series No. XXXV) at Cambridge University Press. pp.724-728. (following footnotes 2 to 15 are also copied from the above reference)

2 *every day ... admit* not in the Royal Society draft.

3 *with the time ... Observation* not in Royal Society draft.

4 *and Latitude ... Noon* not in Royal Society draft.

5 *and as often ... Watches* not in Royal Society draft.

6 *and to Observe ... Opportunity* not in Royal Society draft.

7 *Noting therein ... time* not in Royal Society draft.

8 *such of the Officers.. Instruments &*: Royal Society draft *the officers on board the ship*.

9 *Noting the arc... Pendulum* not in the Royal Society draft.

10 *within the clock case*: Royal Society draft *in the House*.

11 *Observe also differences ... Latitudes* not in Royal Society draft.

12 *And to send ... Observations* not in Royal Society draft.

13 Royal Society draft here adds: 'Teach the use of the Astronomical Instruments to such of the Officers of the ship as are desirous of being instructed therein'.

14 This clause was perhaps prompted by the confusion of Charles Green's records from the *Endeavour,* on which Maskelyne had already animadverted; see Beaglehole J C (Ed), 1968. *The Journals of Captain James Cook on His Voyages of Discovery. I.The Voyage of* Endeavour *1768-1771.* Cambridge. Published for the Hakluyt Society at Cambridge University Press. pp. cxliv-v.

15 *who are going … themselves* not in Royal Society draft, which also lacks the two concluding paragraphs that follow.

APPENDIX IV

Scientific Instruments & Equipment on *Resolution* 1772-1775[1]

Kendall's watch K1, made on Harrison's principle (John Harrison's prizewinning timekeeper H4)

Mr Arnold's Watch of new construction (box chronometer)

Astronomical clock (by John Shelton) with ruby pallets fitted by Mr Arnold

Alarum clock (by Jno Monk)

Journeyman (or Assistant clock by Jno Monk)

Pocket watch with a second hand (Horizontal stop watch by John Ellicott)

Dolland last improved 3½ ft telescopes with object glass micrometers and moveable wires

(Gregorian reflecting telescopes)

(triple achromatic refractor telescope of 46 in focus and 3¾ in aperture made by Dolland)

Astronomical quadrant of 1 foot radius (made by Bird, for getting very accurate altitudes ashore to find latitude and used as equal altitude instruments to check the clocks)

Common brass Hadley's quadrant

Brass Hadley sextant (two in number, one by Ramsden and one by Peter Dolland with Mr Maskelyne's improvements)

Transit instrument (made by Bird, with achromatic object glass of 3½ ft focus and 3½ in aperture, just carried on one ship during the voyage due to the labour involved in setting it up, a pit 5 ft long and 3 ft deep needed to be dug for this, it was seldom used)

(2 – Knight compasses by Adams)
Magnetic variation compass (by Gregory)
Globe (a pair by Adams)

Marine barometer with spiral tubes by Nairne
2 – common barometers (portable, by Burton)
3 thermometers (by Burton)
2 magnetic dipping needles (one by Nairne to the plan of Rev
    Dr. Mitchell) theodolite (by Burton)
wooden frame with glass roof for observing by reflection – to
    hold quicksilver, or any other fluid, with ground glass roofs
    to keep off the air for the purpose of observing altitudes
    of the sun or stars by reflection with the Hadley's Sextant.
    These were artificial horizons.[2]
Gunter's chain with spare links and rings (by Burton)
(level, by Burton)
Large magnetic steel bar for touching the variation compasses
    and dipping needles
(Log line – the knots on which were 49¼ feet apart to
    correspond to a 30-second glass)
(Apparatus for taking deep-water samples – a thermometer in
    the middle of a strong wooden case)
(Portable wind gauge invented by Dr James Lind, made by
    Nairne)
(Tide gauge, made by Wales with a 12 foot wooden tube 3 in
    square with a small aperture in the bottom through which
    the water was admitted)

Nautical Almanacs for 1772, 1773, 1774 and as much as may
    be printed of 1775
Senex map of the Zodiac
Variation charts

Moveable observatory (bell tents with revolving roofs)[3]
Clock stand[4]

Endnotes

1   Beaglehole, J C (Ed), 1969. *The Journals of Captain James Cook on His Voyages of Discovery. II. The Voyage of Resolution and Adventure 1772-1775,* Cambridge. Cambridge University Press. p.722. With further notes in brackets taken from the article Howse, D.,*Captain Cook's Scientific Instruments* published in The Mariner's Mirror, Vol. 65, 1979, No. 2. p.119-135, reproduced with kind permission of the Society for Nautical Research.

2   Wales was to further describe this particular equipment 20 years later in his publication of 1794 *A Method of Fiinding Longitude at Sea by Time-keepers,* when he even praised Reuben Burrow for his ingeniousness:

"….there are different contrivances for this purpose,; but an oblong trough, filled with quicksilver, and sheltered from the wind, is the only one that can be depended on. I have tried them all; and find that the circular one, with a bubble in the center, though, to appearance, perfect when first made, soon grows useless; the glass which covers the fluid altering its figure, I suppose, from the pressure of the fluid against it. Those which are formed by floating pieces of glass on quicksilver, though filled with the utmost care, are equally unsafe : for the instant the glass comes near any side of the vessel it floats in, it loses its horizontality, And will not recover it: the quicksilver must   therefore be taken out, and put in again: but the trouble attending this operation is the least part of the evil, for when the sun is either rising or falling fast, the observer will not readily discover whether any alteration of this kind has happened or not. The best shelter for the quicksilver, is undoubtedly, a roof formed by two plates of glass; the two sides of each being ground perfectly plane, and parallel to one another: but, to prevent any bad effects from their being otherwise, care must be taken to put the roof on the same way; that is, so that the same side may be toward the observer in the afternoon that was toward him in the morning. Mr Reuben Burrow, who, whatever faults he might have, was certainly a very ingenious man, has recommended a piece of musquetto curtain, stretched in a frame, as a good shelter for the quicksilver. See Asiatic Researches, Vol 1. I have tried this mode of sheltering the quicksilver, and found it answer the purpose very well, when the wind was not very strong, and the   sun was reasonably bright; the sun's limb, however, is not so distinct as it is when the quicksilver is sheltered by glass roof ...."

3   Bayly adapted John Smeaton's portable wooden observatory design for Cook's second and third voyages, replacing the wood with canvas. Smeaton's design was used for the first voyage and other transit of Venus observations including the Hudson's Bay observations of Wales and Dymond. The canvas observatory was described in detail by Wales and Bayly:

"...the framework comprised of eight vertical wooden poles, 5.1 cm in diameter and 1.65m long. Each of these had a spike in one end, which was stuck into the ground. These poles supported a 2.4m diameter circular wooden ring, which came in eight separate sections that were connected by iron plates. Around the outer edge of the wooden ring were small staples, and hooks on the top of the canvas wall covering slotted into these. A second 2.4 m wooden ring sat on top of the "wall ring", and screwed to this were the rafters which met at a crown-piece and supported the thick conical canvas roof. When required, a section of this roof could be removed to expose a triangle of sky. Associated with the observatory was a tripod composed of three 4.7 m long wooden poles, and a rope which ran along one of these was attached to the crown-piece via a hook and eye bolt. This rope was used to raise and rotate the roof when observations were to be carried out. Wales and Bayly stress that the whole of this Observatory, except the three (tripod) poles ... when taken down and packed up properly, is contained in a chest six feet and nine inches long, and about twenty inches square... Another admirable feature of this type of observatory was that it could be quickly and easily erected or dismantled, whenever necessary " (Orchiston, Wayne, 1998. *Nautical Astronomy in New Zealand. The Voyages of James Cook*. Wellington, Carter Observatory Board. p.61.)

4   Designed by John Smeaton and comprising an iron block and
     frame to which the clock was bolted in the Observatory. (see
     Howse D. & Hutchinson B., 1969. *The Clocks and Watches
     of Capt James Cook*. London, The Antiquarian Horological
     Society. p.71).

APPENDIX V

The Works of William Wales
(Being a comprehensive List of the published Works, edited or written, wholly or in part, by William Wales)

1760: Wales, W. *An Ode, in two parts, humbly inscribed to the Rt Hon W Pitt*. London.

1766: Wales, W. & Green, J. (ed). *Miscellanea Scientifica Curiosa*, Periodical Publications, London.

1769: Wales, W. and Dymond, J. *Astronomical Observations made by Order of the Royal Society, at Prince of Wales's Fort, on the north-west coast of Hudson's Bay*. Philosophical Transactions of the Royal Society lix,: pp 467-488.

1770: Wales, W. *Journal of a Voyage, made by Order of the Royal Society, to Churchill River, on the north-west Coast of Hudson's Bay; of Thirteen Months Residence in that Country; and of the Voyage back to England; in the years 1768 and 1769*. Philosophical Transactions of the Royal Society Vol. lx for the year 1770: pp100-136, London.

1770: Wales, W. and Dymond, Joseph. *Observations on the State of the Air, Winds, Weather, etc. made at the Prince of Wales's Fort, on the North-West Coast of Hudson's Bay, in the Years 1768 and 1769*. Philosophical Transactions of the Royal Society vol. lx,: pp 137-78.

1772: Wales, W. *General Observations made at Hudson's Bay.* London: 4to. Volume prepared from the Hudson's Bay reports in the Philosophical Transactions of the Royal Society.

1772: Wales, W. *The Two Books of Apollonius concerning Determinate Sections. As they had been Restored by Willebrordus Snellius, by John Lawson, to which are added, the same two Books by William Wales.* London: 4to, pp xi+40, 5 folding plates.

1772-74: Wales, W. *Journal of William Wales.* Selections were published in Beaglehole, J C (Ed) *The Journals of Captain James Cook on His Voyages of Discovery II. The Voyages of the Resolution and Adventure 1772-1775.* Cambridge University Press, pp 776-869. (first published in 1961). The manuscript Journal is held in the Mitchell Library, Sydney, MSS Safe PH 18/4.

1772-75: Wales, W. *Journal of a Voyage made by Order of the Commissioners of Longitude, On Board of his Majesty's Sloop Resolution.* The Admiralty Copy titled *Log of the Resolution,* is held in the Records of the Board of Longitude.

1777: Wales, W. and Bayly W. *The Original Astronomical Observations Made in the Course of a Voyage Towards the South Pole, and round the World in His Majesty's Ships the Resolution and Adventure, in the years MDCCLXXII, MDCCLXXIII, MDCCLXXIV, and MDCCLXXV,* London: Ed. W. Wales. pp. lv. 385. pl 4. J. Nourse; J. Mount & T. Page: W & A Strahan.

1778: Wales, W. *Observations on the Solar Eclipse which happened June 24, 1778.* Philosophical Transactions of the Royal Society Vol. 68. pp 1013-1018.

1778: Wales, W. *Remarks on Mr Forster's Account of Captain Cook's last Voyage round the World, in the Years 1772, 1773, 1774 and 1775.* London: Printed for J. Nourse, opposite Catherine Street, Strand.

1780: Robertson, J. *The Elements of Navigation, containing the Theory and Practice, with necessary Tables and Compendiums for Finding the Latitude and Longitude at Sea to which is added a treatise of Marine Fortification.* Fourth edition, with additions and revised by William Wales. London.

1781: Wales, W. *An Inquiry into the Present State of Population in England and Wales, and the proportion which the present Number of Inhabitants bears to the number at former periods.* London, C. Nourse.

1781: Mr Eden, Mr Wales and Mr Hewlett *Uncertainty of the present Population of this Kingdom, deduced from a candid review of the accounts lately given of it.* London.

1781: Wales, W. *Hints relating to the Use which may be made of the Tables of Natural and Logarithmic Sines, Tangents, etc in the numerical resolution of affected Equations.* pp. 23. 1 plate, 4o. Also published in, Philosophical Transactions of the Royal Society Vol. 71, No 3. Pp 454-478.

1781: Maskelyne, N. (ed). *Requisite Tables.* 2nd Edition. Included Tables by Wales for finding Latitude by two altitudes of the Sun. 10,000 copies were printed and sold initially for 12s each. This work included an Explanation written by William Wales.

1784: Long, Roger (1680-1770). Astronomy: in five books. Cambridge, 2 vols., 1742-1785 (xvi, 728 pages, 97 plates, 4to. (This work was completed by William Wales before its eventual publication).

1784: Wales, W. *A Defence (against P.C. Le Monnier) of the Arguments advanced in the Introduction to tables. To which is added A treatise of marine fortification.* (in Vol 1). The fifth edition, with additions, carefully revised and corrected by William Wales. London: Publisher C. Nourse.

1785: *Captain Cook's Last Voyage against the existence of Cape Circumcision.* London. Pamphlet, Beddie number 1553.

1786: Robertson, J. *The elements of Navigation; containing the theory and practice. With the necessary tables. To which is added A treatise of marine fortification.* (in Vol 1). The fifth edition, with additions, carefully revised and corrected by William Wales. London: Publisher C. Nourse.

1788: Wales, William. *Astronomical Observations, Made in the Voyages Which were Undertaken by Order of His Present Majesty, for Making discoveries in the Southern Hemisphere, and Successively Performed by Commodore Byron, Captain Wallis, Captain Carteret, and Captain Cook, in the Dolphin, Tamer, Swallow and Endeavour.* London, Published by Order of the Commissioners of Longitude.

1788: Wales, W. Footnote describing the life of Charles Green. In Kippis, A. *The Life of Captain James Cook.* London.

1794: Wales, W. *The Method of finding the Longitude at Sea by Timekeepers; to which are added, The Tables of Equations to equal Altitudes, more extensive and accurate than any hitherto published.* London.

(These tables first appeared in the 1773 Nautical Almanac, and again in the 1774 Almanac.)

1796: Robertson, J. *The Elements of Navigation containing the Theory and Practice with the necessary Tables and*

Compendiums for finding the Latitude and Longitude at Sea, to which is added a Treatise of Marine Fortification. London. F. Wingrave. Sixth Edition

1797: Wales, W. *Achronical Rising of the Pleiades*, a dissertation appended to *Voyage of Nearchus; from the Indus to the Euphrates* the original Journal preserved by Arrian, which is part of the work *The Periplus of the Erythrean Sea* by William Vincent, DD. Published London 1800. London.

1802: Wales, W. *Tables requisite to be used with the Nautical Ephemeris*. The Third Edition improved. London: Commissioners of Longitude.

Twenty two pen-and-ink charts drawn by Wales in the manuscript of his Journal on Cook's Second Voyage, and preceded by a note on methods of constructing them.[1] The following are illustrated in Beaglehole's work:

Porto Praya[2]; Marquesa Islands[3]; Matavai Bay[4]; New Hebrides[5]

Endnotes

1   Beaglehole, J C (Ed), 1969. *The Journals of Captain James Cook on His Voyages of Discovery. II. The Voyage of Resolution and Adventure 1772-1775*, Cambridge. Cambridge University Press. p.clxii.

2   ibid., 28. Fig.13.

3   ibid., 370. Fig. 56.

4   ibid., 382. Fig. 58.

5   ibid., *facing page* 449, Fig 65.

APPENDIX VI

Notes on Remunerations Received by William Wales

Computing for the Nautical Almanac:-

from 1765 paid for each 12 month's calculations of the Nautical Almanac – £70.[1]
from 1767 this rose to £75.[2]
from 1781 to £80; rising to become £100 from 1789.[3]

Actual Nautical Almanac calculations completed by William Wales were:[4]

For the Almanac of		
	1767	6 months
	1768	6 months
	1769	9 months
	1770	3 months
	1772	1 month
	1773	7 months
	1774	8 months
	1796	2 months
	1797	1 month

Hudson's Bay Expedition 1768/9 from the Royal Society

£300 per annum, plus expenses[5]

June 1778. Fee from the Hudson's Bay Company paid for recommending Inland Surveyors to the Company.

£5.5.0[6]

Summary of Board of Longitude remunerations:[7]

26th May 1770	Tables of equal altitude for Nautical Almanac – reward	10.10.00
7th July 1777	Computation of observations from Cook's voyage	150.00.00
7th July 1777	Cost of paid assistant for above	23.09.00
15th July 1780	Requisite Tables – Second Edition – paid as a Reward for his are and trouble in collecting, preparing and revising for the Press a complete set of Tables to be used with the Nautical Almanacs.	150.00.00
1st March 1788	Editing *Astronomical observations in the Southern Hemisphere*	167.00.00
1st March 1788	Paid as further compensation for the above.	43.00.00
1st June 1799	3rd edition Requisite Tables (paid to executors)	300.00.00

Further rewards from the Board of Longitude:[8]

5th December 179	Examining John Williams' tables	10.10.00
	Carriage of instruments	25.12.05[9]

Paid as Secretary to the Board of Longitude:[10]

1796. three quarterly payments of £20	60.0.0.	
1797, four quarterly payments of £20	80.0.0.	
1798, four quarterly payments of £20	**80.0.0.**	220.00.00

1772-1775 Paid in total for Cook's Second Voyage as astronomer [11]   1433.08.11

The figure represents £400 per annum for a total of 3 years and 213 days at sea.

Also paid to Wales for this voyage was £50 for completing drawings and calculations while on shore.

Of the above figure Mrs Mary Wales was paid Half a Year's Allowance of £75, to the 24th July 1772, and in House of Commons Journals is described as 'for the better Support of herself and Family during her Husband's Absence'. It was further noted that this was to be deducted for the Allowance that would be paid to him. This allowance was then paid to Mary Wales each half year during her husband's absence.[12]

Christ's Hospital remunerations:[13]
Yearly payment of £20 for instructing 12 boys in the art of navigation being on the foundation of Henry Stone Esq to fit them for sea service. Order of Court the 23rd December 1714.

1776-1784 Eight years and 9 months at £20 per annum	£175.00.00
1785 3 months at £5 and 9 months at £25 per annum	23.15.00
1786-1798 Thirteen years at £25 per annum	325.00.00
John Stock Foundation, 1781	43.15.00
1785-1793 8 years and nine months at £5 per annum	

In 1777 Wales' salary as Master of the RMS was £100 per annum[14]

This then rose at the Committee of Almoners meeting on 8th February 1785,[15] when William Wales, Mathematical Master petitioned the Committee to consider his salary increase, and it was resolved to pay Mr Wales:

£140 per annum as Master of the Royal Foundation
(previously £100)
£20 from Mr Stones foundation, then this was later raised to
£25
£5 from John Stock
A total of £170 per annum from Christmas last.

Endnotes

1. Croarken, Dr M, *Providing Longitude for all: the eighteenth century computers of the Nautical Almanac.* (Sept 2002), Journal of Maritime Research.

2. Howse, D, 1989. *Nevil Maskelyne – the seaman's astronomer.* Cambridge University Press.

3. ibid.

4. Personal communication, Dr Mary Croarken.

5. Beaglehole, J C, 1974. *The Life of Captain James Cook.* London, Adam & Charles Black. p.103.

6. Hearne, Samuel & Tyrell, Joseph Burr, 1934. *Journals of Samuel Hearne and Philip Turnor.* Toronto, Champlain Society.

7. Howse, Derek, November 1998. *Britain's Board of Longitude: The Finances, 1714-1828.* Mariner's Mirror, Vol. 84, No. 4. pp 400-417.

8. Personal communication, Dr Mary Croarken.

9. ibid.

10. Board of Longitude Papers. 14/02, 79.

11. Personal communication, Dr Mary Croarken.

12. Journals of the House of Commons, Vol. 34. From an Account of Money issued by the Treasurer of the Navy, in Pursuance of providing an award for discovering Longitude, improving Lunar Tables and encouraging discoveries and improvements useful to Navigation, dated 19th April 1773.

13. Guildhall Library, London. Christ's Hospital Manuscripts, Treasurer's Ledgers, 12823, Vols. 6,7,8.

14. Guildhall Library, London. Accounts of Christ's Hospital

School Vol 21-22 Manuscripts Mss12,819.

15 Guildhall Library, London. Christ's Hospital Manuscript, Court Minute Books, 12806/12 pp.423/4.

APPENDIX VII

Points Raised by William Wales with Georg Forster after Captain Cook's Second Voyage

From the Work: *Remarks on Mr Forster's Account of Captain Cook's Last Voyage Round the World, in the Years 1772, 1773, 1774, and 1775.* by William Wales, Published by J Nourse in 1778, London

1.   11th July 1772. While waiting to leave Portsmouth *Resolution* broke from her moorings. Johann Forster claimed that he was the first person to see this, and had told Mr Gilbert the master who was on deck with him that the ship was in danger, when this had been immediately rectified, he added that thereafter the incident was treated by the crew as a sign that the voyage would be successful. On the contrary, Wales had been told by Mr Gilbert that he was already dealing with this situation when Dr Forster arrived on the deck, and the incident had never been treated as an omen by the crew of a successful voyage.

2.   13th August 1772. Forster implied that neither the Captain nor the Astronomers made any attempt to make astronomical observations on the island in the bay of Porto Praya. Wales explained that it was their business here merely to survey the bay, and a very accurate survey by Cook and Wales of the bay was the result.

3. 14th August 1772. It was implied by Forster that the whole crew were characters of iron-hearted insensibility, and wanton barbarism, when monkeys were taken onto the ship at St Jago. In fact the Captain was not immediately aware of this, and when he did find out he ordered them to be removed at once for the sake of the Company's health.

4. 21st August 1772. When a swallow was found around the ship on leaving St Jago, Forster thought it probable that some unfeeling person had lured it into his cabin and fed it to a favourite cat. According to Wales there was absolutely no foundation for this to have been the case.

5. 5th September 1772. On taking sea temperatures at different depths Forster had criticized Wales on his methods, when in fact the experiments had been carried out accurately.

6. 10th December 1772. Forster had calculated at length the amount of ice contained in a large island, but the method adopted had been made on unscientific principles according to Wales.

7. 25th December 1772. Wales recorded that Forster's criticism of the noise and state of drunkenness of the sailors on Christmas day only reflected the way he viewed such occasions.

8. 9th January 1773. Dr Forster was of the opinion that the water obtained from snow and ice, when drunk, caused soreness and swellings in the throat and neck, however in Wales' experience, such water which was consumed at Hudson's Bay did not show the same symptoms, and so far as he was able to ascertain, it had not caused such illness on *Resolution*.

9. 16th May 1773. Wales remarked on Forster's observations of the water spouts, when he described

their bases as bright when illuminated by the sun, Wales pointed out that the sun had not been shining when the spouts were observed. Forster also wrote of hailstones and lightning at this time, but neither was witnessed by either Wales nor anyone else he had spoken to who had seen the event.

10. 18th May 1773. Wales told that although they had been at different latitudes, Forster had implied that Adventure Bay in Van Diemen's Land was the same bay named Fredric Henry's Bay by Tasman.

11. Forster had, according to Wales, unnecessarily commented at length on the seamen's connections with the women of New Zealand.

12. On describing the journey from New Zealand to Otaheite, Forster implied that it had been tedious and disagreeable, and claimed on arrival to be in a lower latitude than 30 degrees, due to having observed some tropical bird which he claimed had been a sure sign. Wales commented that this observation exceeded everything he had ever known, apart from Don Quixote's method of knowing when he had crossed the equator.[1]

13. 13th August 1773. Forster had agreed with Dalrymple's findings, that Otaheite was the same island which Quiros called *Sagittaria*. Wales wrote at length to illustrate that Dalrymple's theory was wrong, having examined the geography of Otaheite it could not have been the land described by Quiros as *Sagittaria*.

14. 18th August 1773. Forster wrote that he had witnessed muskets being fired at a native who had stolen knives from Captain Cook's cabin. Wales had witnessed the same event, and maintained that the muskets were fired 'high above' the head of the man, and not 'at' him.

15. Wales commented on the many inconsistencies he had found in Forster's work, whereby he often contradicted himself by making reflecting comments, the purpose of which appeared to lead to ill-natured remarks.

16. 25th August 1773. It was implied by Forster that when the Tahitians attacked *Dolphin,* the reason originated from an earlier assault on them by Europeans, but Wales assured that there had never been opportunity for the Europeans to carry out such an outrage.

17. 2nd/3rd September 1773. Wales criticized Forster's judgements when writing of a number of events of both a nautical and geographical nature, and often made errors when relating to matters of that kind.

18. 9th September 1773. When Forster described William Hodges' drawing of *Tinamai,* the daughter of chief *Oreo* of Raiatea as a "tolerable idea of a Taheitean boy," Wales remonstrated by concluding that this lady must have been greatly favoured by Forster enough to cause this outburst of expression, for it could only be love which turns every fault into a beauty, and such admiration could seldom forgive anything which detracts from that ideal.

19. 2nd October 1773. William Hodges was further censured by Forster when he accused Hodges of misplacing some of his drawings made when they landed at Eaoowhe, causing Hodges' later illustrations of the native people to be copied from Forster's descriptions of them rather than the artist's own sketches. Hodges denied ever having lost such drawings.

20. 6th October 1773. Wales wrote of Forster's total disregard of the truth when he described the scene of a jacket being stolen from one of the jolly boats. He claimed that he had witnessed how shots were fired at the thief without the Captain's orders, and several

people on shore had been wounded, but these, although innocent, were not the least offended by the incident. Wales had been in the boat at the time, and witnessed the whole incident when he explains the Captain had not been in the boat, and that not one of the people watching from shore had been hit, only the thief had been hit and then only very slightly wounded.

21. 6th October 1773. According to Wales there followed a misrepresentation more unjust than that immediately above, when Forster wrote of a thief entering the Master's cabin, his escape and eventual capture, which Wales had witnessed and proceeded to write in full his own account of the event into these *Remarks,* showed that Forster's interpretation of the incident was strewn with inattention to detail.

22. The eagerness by the seamen to trade for curiosities at places visited on the voyage was ridiculed by Forster, even though according to Wales, Forster and his son had frequently purchased them from their cabin windows, even when this practice had been strictly forbidden. Wales went on to tell of a second reason for the seamen's eagerness to purchase items, being that they could then sell them on to Dr Forster, who had not managed to purchase such himself.

23. During the storm encountered off New Zealand Forster complained that the sailors had uttered horrible curses and oaths, which he had implied had only added to the horrors of the event. Wales in defence of the sailors' behavour, wrote that as the Doctor swore so dreadfully at times himself, they would never dream that their words could have ever caused him the least concern.

24. 1st November 1773. Wales corrected Forster's positioning of the bay, in which *Resolution* anchored in Cook's Straits, which lay on the east side of *Cape Terawitte,* not the west side as Forster had indicated.

25. 3rd November 1773. Forster had indicated that he had not hesitated in permitting the Earl of Sandwich to have an engraving made of the Forsters' drawing of a flax plant, but as Wales pointed out, he was being paid a large amount of money for making these drawings for the person making the request.

26. 22nd November 1773. While moored off New Zealand, Forster commented that perhaps the discord between neighbouring natives had been caused by "Our people" greedily asking for more valuable goods to be traded, resulting in robberies among neighbours in order to satisfy the needs of the ship's company. But as Wales once more asserted, the people who showed the most eagerness to obtain these goods were the Forsters themselves.

27. Note was made by Wales of the Dr Forster's treatment of the memory of the late Dr Hawkesworth, by taking revenge at every opportunity.

28. 12th March 1774. Forster discussed reasons why previous navigators failed to find Easter Island, and concluded that they did not have the use of chronometers to find their longitude, nor Mayer's tables. But as Wales pointed out, in most cases they were certainly not looking for it.

29. 12th March 1774. In mentioning the above, Dr Forster had furtively mentioned the incident when Arnold's watch had stopped immediately after leaving New Zealand. This had annoyed Wales, as Forster had written that "the watch was stopped" and had broadcast that this had been the case on reaching London, intentionally to blame Wales and Cook. Thus here Wales took the opportunity to explain the whole affair, together with relating correspondence.

30. 15th March 1774. Wales wrote of Dr Forster's inaccuracy when describing the statues at Easter Island as 'carved from the same red *tufa stone* which covers the whole of the island', when in fact it was only the large cylindrical stones on the heads of the images which were made of the red stone, the rest of the stone used was a light grey stone.

31. 15th March 1774. Dr Forster maintained that he had seen no calabashes at Easter Island, yet according to Wales there were several, both seen growing, and acting as utensils.

32. 8th April 1774. Wales wrote again of a truly cruel misrepresentation of events by Dr Forster when he told of the shooting of a thief on board during their stay at the Marquesas.

33. 11th April 1774. Dr Forster remarked on the the natives of the Marquesa Islands not being able to pronounce the name of their own country so well as he. Wales disputes Forster's authority, and tells of Forster's imperfect pronounciation of the English language, when he didn't pronounce the word England the same as the English did.

34. 17th April 1774. Wales told that the gentlemen who had been on shore at *Teoukea* had described the natives as very fierce and savage, totally disagreeing with the way Dr Forster had described them.

35. 17th April 1774. Wales disputed Dr Forster's description of the coral islands, when he explained that the richest and lowest parts of them were "generally to leeward".

36. 22nd April 1774. Among all Wales' remarks which condemn the writings of Dr Forster, there appeared one which he agreed with, and praised Forster on describing the general character of the women of Otaheite, which had in his opinion been misinterpreted by the writers of former voyages, including Dr Hawkesworth.

37. 28th April 1774. Wales disagreed with Dr Forster's interpretation of the natives of Otaheite's stories on cannibalism.

38. Once more Wales referred to the Forster's over exposure of the entertaining stories gleaned from the amorous transactions of the sailors, and he concluded by relating that they would remind the authors, "he who is without sin, should cast the first stone".

39. 2nd May 1774. Dr Forster had written of the marriage of Mahine, and implied that a midshipman had been present who had not been able to recall the ceremony, and so it had been regrettable that no intelligent observer had been present to learn more of these customs of the island. Wales who had witnessed part of the ceremony then went on to describe it in detail, he further added that he saw no-one else there from the ship other than some common sailors.

40. 2nd May 1774. With regard to Omai, the boy from Otaheite who had returned to England with Cook on his first voyage, Dr Forster criticises those responsible for him, and that they did not teach him the trade of carpenter or smith while in England. But then as Wales pointed out, Omai would have had no iron to work on when he returned home.

41. 6th May 1774. Wales wrote of his disgust when Dr Forster related that some of the women on board in Otaheite had told of the king's sister allowing some of her servants into her bed, and suggests that if a foreigner had told of a European royal lady admitting one of her domestic attendants into her bed, it would be treated deservedly with contempt.

42. 8th May 1774. When Dr Forster wrote of the stealing of a sentry's musket, he implied that it was Otoo who told the sergeant. Wales explained that everyone knew about this incident long before Otoo appeared.

43. 20th May 1774. Regarding the walk into the countryside at Uaheine, according to Wales, Dr Forster described this in a manner which could be misinterpreted, when he wrote of the conduct of the officers.

44. Wales disputed Dr Forster claiming that the society of Aree-oe were married in the same manner as Oediddee had been.

45. 3rd June 1774. At Uliatea Dr Forster told of a man who he had met named Tootavai, from whom he claimed he had learnt the whole of the culture of the Society Islands. Wales disputed this, and insisted that Captain Cook and the Doctor had had much trouble interpreting the information, and had to call in a midshipman to help.

46. 3rd June 1774. Wales questioned why Dr Forster had written "with great justness indeed" when he told of the natives of Otaheite being bad physiologists, on suggesting Dr Forster and Captain Cook were brothers. In fact Forster had written *physiognomists* rather than *physiologists*.

47. 4th June 1774. Wales commented on the prevalence of venereal disease among the crew, and generally agreed with Dr Forster that it appeared to have been endemic in Tahiti and the Society Islands long before Wallis's expedition.

48. 25th June 1774. On Forster erroneously describing *Resolution's* passage through reefs near Annamocka, Wales advised that had the ship gone the way Dr Forster indicated, very fatal consequences would have resulted.

49. 27th June 1774. According to Wales, Dr Forster misinterpreted the facts when Mr Patten had been left on the shore at Annamocka, and Wales proceeded to give a true account of the matter.

50. 27th June 1774. Wales wrote at length on the many errors evident in Dr Forster's account of events following the theft of Lieutenant Clerke's musket, and that each error had been aimed at injuring the character of the people involved.

51. The description by Dr Forster of the geography of Annamocka and other places was, according to Wales, "exuberant beyond expression" and not true representation of the places.

52. 3rd July 1774. Although Dr Forster described Turtle Island as about seven miles long, Wales maintained it's length was between two and three miles.

53. 3rd July 1774. Dr Forster had indicated that the master was under his direction when he had gone out to sound, and here it is stressed by Wales that this was typical of the behavour of the Doctor when on board, that he continually treated the officers with disrespect and meddled in their affairs, which had led to unease throughout the whole of the voyage.

54. 24th July 1774. Wales advised those looking for a reef which had been described by Dr Forster as being off the south point of Three-hill Island, that in fact it lay off the north-west point.

55. 24th July 1774. Wales defended Cook after Dr Forster implied that his navigation had relied on good fortune and a degree of rashness, Wales described Cook as "one of the ablest and most experienced navigators that this, or former ages had produced".

56. 24th July 1774. When Dr Forster described a monument as 150 yards, Wales corrected him, by assuring this was in fact 150 feet in height.

57. 1st August 1774. Dr Forster's account of the affair at Erramanga was described by Wales as "the most single piece of misrepresentation and detraction that ever

dropped from a pen". In an attempt to put matters right, he quoted Cook's account of events at length, and went on to explain Hodges interpretation of the transaction after Forster inferred he had invented it.

58. 10th August 1774. When Dr Forster recorded that the natives of Tanna were cannibals, Wales stated that this was without foundation.

59. 10th August 1774. Wales was totally opposed to the theories of Dr Forster on the history of social communication between neighbouring islands, and their resulting language similarities.

60. 16th August 1774. Dr Forster wrote of the pigeon which had fed on nutmeg at Tanna, and that he had presented one of these creatures to Her Majesty. Wales made it clear that as no live pigeon was carried from Tanna to England during the voyage, then Forster must have meant a pigeon from the East India islands.

61. 18th August 1774. Wales discussed the unscientific method used by Dr Forster when attempting to determine the temperature of water in certain hot-springs.

62. 19th August 1774. Of the matter of the shooting dead of a native at Tanna by a centinel who was under Cook's orders, Wales was at pains to explain that having spoken to Mr Whitehouse, who witnessed the killing, that the centinel had acted in self defence, and therefore he was not guilty of murder, as Dr Forster inferred.

63. 26th August 1774. Wales asked why Dr Forster had written of his doubts that St Philip & James's Bay, as named by Cook, was the bay described by Quiros, when the maps and the descriptions compared exactly.

64. 1st September 1774. On reading Dr Forster's remarks at the end of the chapter, when *Resolution* left the New Hebrides, Wales again sprang to the defence of Captain

Cook's character, after Forster implied that Cook had put the lives of the crew at risk.

65. 11th September 1774. Wales sprang to his own defence, and that of other members of the Ship's company who were involved in scientific experiments and observations, when Forster claimed that during the voyage he was refused access to a lot of the results. Wales personally had been much concerned of Forster's persistence in asking him for information, and after he became suspicious that Forster may not be allowed to write up the official account of the voyage on his return, Wales had then refused him any details of his work.

66. 13th September 1774. When Dr Forster described New Calendonia as a country of much drought, Wales remarked that as it had rained during their visit, Forster had no reason to arrive at that conclusion.

67. 13th September 1774. Once again Wales had been forced to remark on yet another attack by Dr Forster on the poor mariners, which had been without justification.

68. 13th September 1774. Dr Forster wrote of his experience of being in a boat with Cook and Wales, who had witnessed the natives gesturing that they had enemies who were cannibals. Wales maintained that on that occasion he had no recollection of such intelligence, and could only assume that the Doctor was mistaken.

69. 25th October 1774. Wales abhorred Dr Forster's views on his passion for revenge, which he claimed was fixed in everyone to guard against instrusion from others, and Wales suggested that perhaps the Doctor offered this in defence of his own behaviour during the voyage.

70. 2nd November 1774. In New Zealand Dr Forster recorded that when a party was sent out to make brooms, they had robbed tools from one of the native huts, he added that a similar event occurred during

the *Endeavour's* voyage, in both cases Forster wrote of many of the party carrying out the stealing, but as Wales corrected, in both cases only one of the party had been found to be guilty.

71. At this point although Wales admitted that he had been thus far resolute not to recriminate, he felt it necessary after the Doctor's pains to present himself as such a 'paragon of humanity', to acquaint the reader with the fact that on two occasions during the voyage, the Doctor had twice to be kept within limits, once by Captain Cook, and once by Lt Clerke, after he had been found guilty of attacks on natives.

72. 10ᵗʰ November 1774. When Dr Forster wrote with apparent authority, claiming that he and his son had made observations to determined the angle at which the ship inclined, Wales wrote that not once did either Dr Forster or his son make experiments of this kind.

73. 23ʳᵈ December 1774. When William Hodges had illustrated a bird, in his drawing of Christmas Sound, Dr Forster had written that it was more like the *Rukh* of Arabian tales than the hawk which they had seen on Tierra del Fuego. Wales comments on the sarcasm of the Doctor's manner of writing, and concludes that he is sure Hodges' work was not intended to rival that of Georg Forster.

74. 25ᵗʰ December 1774. Dr Forster clearly disagreed with the philosophers' views from the *Endeavour* voyage, on the happiness of the people of Tierra del Fuego. Wales reminded him however that he had the same views as the philosophers when at Otaheite – and suggested that Forster therefore changed sides with his arguments as he pleased.

75. 21/22ⁿᵈ December 1774. Wales wrote that little confidence could be placed in Dr Forster's account,

when he had told of an incident at Christmas Sound, when a marine went ashore and had not been missed for two days. On the contrary, Wales assured that this man had been working with him on shore on one of the days, and had returned to the boat that night.

76. 1st January 1775. At Staten Land, Dr Forster had not gone on shore due to Mr Pickersgill having orders not to stay – however Mr Gilbert had had permission to set Wales on shore where he liked, and Wales made the most of this opportunity by staying and giving a full account of his findings – although he admits not as copious an account as Forster would have given.

77. Again Wales found it necessary to warn the reader of Dr Forster's incorrect descriptions of the geography of coastlines, and indicated that if they were taken notice of by future navigators, then they could be in danger, resulting in fatal consequences.

78. 14th January 1775. Dr Forster read in Guyots Accounts of 1756 of the position of South Georgia, which he confirmed was the 'same as his observations'. Wales' own observations however differed by some 40 miles.

79. 25th January 1775. A thorough account was given by Dr Forster of the island of South Georgia, and an explanation as to why it wasn't habitable. Wales called on his experience of Hudson's Bay, and argued that in like conditions, the islands northward of that place were inhabited.

80. 2nd February 1775. Wales went to some lengths to clarify how ice is formed near land, and how it couldn't possibly be formed in the middle of an ocean, after Dr Forster claimed that because of Mr Nairne's experiment, it was no longer certain that a southern continent existed, but as Wales explained, Mr Nairne's experiments had nothing to do with the question of whether or not there

was a southern continent, he merely proved that it was possible for small amounts of salt water to freeze at sea, providing there was something solid for it to attach itself to.

81. 22nd February 1775. When Dr Forster stated that some officers thought the islands of ice were land, which they observed on 14th December, 1774, Forster had also thought them to be land, as Wales reminds him.

82. 7th April 1775. Wales commented on Dr Forster's language when he spoke of the keeper of the Prince of Orange's menajerie at the Hague, whom he described as guilty of 'gross ignorance and canine malice'. This had effected a public apology from Georg Forster in the *Monthly Review,* according to the footnote on page 829.

83. 15th May 1775. Again Wales found it necessary to correct Dr Forster's description of coastlines, when he described the shoreline of St Helena as the south-eastern, Wales assured that this should have been the north-western.

84. 29th May 1775. Wales once again defended the sailors, when they had been subjected to Dr Forster's opinions of them. This time Forster had stressed that even they showed pity when viewing the wreck of a vessel.

85. 11th June 1775. Further to the item above, Wales was shocked when he read that Dr Forster accused the sailors of killing many of his animals, which were collected at the Cape of Good Hope, 'slily and enviously. Wales queried how this could have been, when they showed signs of 'drooping' days before they died, and the ones in Forster's cabin, of which the sailors had no access, died first.

86. 14th July 1775. Dr Forster noted that Wales had observed from the garden of the consul's house, without

permission of the Portuguese, on Fayal Island. Wales assured the Doctor, and the public, that he had asked and obtained permission without the least objection

Endnotes

1   In *Don Quixote,* Quixote tells Sancho that he will know they have passed the equator when he can no longer reach down and feel a flea on his leg.

APPENDIX VIII

Geographical Features
named after William Wales

SOUTH ISLAND, NEW ZEALAND

Mount Wales[1]– (Location 45°38'S – Longitude 166°40'E); height 974 metres. Mountain on Resolution Island, in the Fiordland National Park, north of Dusky Sound in New Zealand.

Named by Captain Cook after William Wales, May 1773.

Wales Point[2] – (Location 45°48'S – 166°35'E) is a coastal feature in Dusky Sound, Fiordland National Park, New Zealand, between Pickersgill Harbour and Cascade Cove.

Named by Captain Cook after William Wales, March 1773.

Another associated place is **Astronomers Point** (Location 45°46'S – 166°34'E) which is shown immediately north of where the Resolution lay in Pickersgill Harbour, marked on a chart drawn by Henry Roberts in 1773. Roberts was 15 years old and a pupil of William Hodges.[3]

ALBERTA/BRITISH COLUMBIA CANADA

Wales Peak[4] – (Location: 52°11'05N – 117°39'15W); height 3109 metres, or 10201 ft, it is located on the continental divide, at the head of the creek flowing northeast into the upper Athabasca and Columbia rivers.

Named by Alfred J Ostheimer in 1927 after William Wales, English mathematician and astronomer, who visited Hudson's Bay in 1769, and sailed with Captain Cook on his second voyage as co-navigator.

First ascended in 1927 by J De Laittre, W R MacLaurin, guided by J Weber.

Wales Glacier – lies to the east and south-east of the above 'Wales Peak'.

BRITISH COLUMBIA, CANADA

Wales Point[5] – (Location 54°42'00 N – 130°29'00 W) is a Cape in British Columbia, Canada, at the West point of the entrance to Portland Inlet, which Vancouver lumps with Observatory Inlet.

Named by George Vancouver in August 1793. In his Journal he notes "The west point of Observatory Inlet I distinguished by calling it Point Wales, after my much-esteemed friend, Mr Wales, of Christ's Hospital; to whose kind instruction in the early part of my life, I am indebted for that information which has enabled me to traverse and delineate these lonely regions".[6]

Other places associated with the above are:-

Observatory Inlet, Wales Harbor, and Wales Passage

Wales Island[7] – (Location: 54°45'00N – 130°29'00W)[8] British Columbia, Canada. Island at the entrance to the Portland Canal.

Endnotes

1   Robson, John, 2004. *The Captain Cook Encyclopædia.* London, Chatham Publishing.

2   ibid.

3   Begg, A Charles & Begg, Neil C, 1966. *Dusky Bay.* Christchurch. Whitcombe & Tombs Ltd.

4   Website of Peakfinder: http://www.peakfinder.com

5   Robson, John, 2004. *The Captain Cook Encyclopædia.* London, Chatham Publishing.

6   Kaye Lamb, K, 1984. *Voyage of George Vancouver.* London, Hakluyt Society.

7   Robson, John, 2004. *The Captain Cook Encyclopædia.* London, Chatham Publishing.

8   Website of Natural Resources, Canada: http://geonames2.nrcan.gc.ca

INDEX

492

Stephens, Philip, Secretary to the Admiralty, 61, 119, 249, 313, 444

Stephens, William Wales (ww's grandson), 362, 404, 410

Stock, John, benefactor of Christ's Hospital, 287

Stone, Sir Henry, Governer of Christ's Hospital, 287

Stow's, John, Survey of London, 22

Stuart, James, architect and artist, 294

Swallow, HMS, 111

Swiney, Rev, vicar of Warmfield, 104

Symmer, Robert, experiments with static electricity, 155

Tahiti, 101, 108, 111, 112, 114, 115, 179, 180, 181, 185, 188, 197, 203, 214, 215, 216, 241, 321, 352, 469

Tamar, HMS, 111

Tannock, James, RA, artist, 401

Tasman, Abel Janszoon, explorer, 189, 191, 221, 463

Taylor, Isaac, marine on *Resolution*, 180

Taylor, Johnas, husband of Elizabeth Green, ww's sister-in-law, 64

Taylor, Professor EGR, author of mathematical history, 385

Taylor, William, son of Elizabeth Green, ww's sister-in-law, 64, 302, 416

Tent observatory, (Illustration, 278)

Terra Australis Incognita, 111

Thetis, EIC ship, 412

Thompson, D'Arcy Wentworth, pupil at Christ's Hospital, 265

Thompson, David, HBC explorer, 84, 99, 296, 297

Thomson, James, poet, 171

Thring, Edward, of Uppingham School, 419

Tolkein, J R R, author, 395

Tom's Coffee House, 407

transit of the planet Mercury, 1769, 115

transit of Venus observations at Tahiti, 115

transit of Venus, 1769 results, 108

transits of Venus, 137

Triestine Society, 333

Trinity House, 274, 291, 294, 390

Trollope family, 400, 402

Trollope, Amelia (ww's granddaughter, 404

Trollope, Arthur (ww's grandson), 403

Trollope, Arthur William (ww's son-in-law), 276, 336, 367, 372, 384, 387, 388, 399, 400, 402, 404, 406, 409

Trollope, Edward (ww's grandson), 399, 403

Trollope, George (ww's grandson), 400, 403

Trollope, Jervoise, (ww's grandson), 403

Trollope, Sarah (ww's daughter), 55, 64, 65, 72, 76, 102, 130, 274, 294, 358, 372, 384, 387, 388, 399

Trollope, Sarah (ww's granddaughter), 399, 404

Trollope, William Arthur (ww's grandson), 298, 373, 401, (Portrait Illustration, 282)

Turner, John, of Portsea, 365

Turnor, Philip, Hudson's Bay surveyor, 296, 297

Vancouver, George, sailed on Cook's second and third voyages, 144, 149, 153, 200, 321, 355, 356, 357, 365, 383, 419, 478

variation compass, 84, 447

Venus, transits of, 35, 36, 37, 59, 61, 62, 63, 69, 70, 72, 85, 92, 94, 95, 96, 107, 108, 112, 115, 117, 119, 125, 131, 137, 139, 144, 180, 184, 215, 248, 274, 293, 298, 319, 326, 367, 397, 437

493